LINTON C. FREEMAN . . .

received his Ph.D. in Sociology in 1957 from Northwestern University. He has since served as Assistant Professor and Associate Professor of Sociology at Syracuse University, and as Visiting Lecturer at Northwestern University. Since 1963 he has been Chairman of the Systems Research Committee at Syracuse University where he has been involved in interdisciplinary research in behavioral science.

Dr. Freeman has published some twenty papers in the journals of sociology, psychology, anthropology, and statistics, and has produced several research monographs.

Elementary Applied Statistics:

for Students in Behavioral Science

Elementary Applied Statistics:

For Students in Behavioral Science

LINTON C. FREEMAN *Syracuse University*

John Wiley & Sons, Inc. *New York · London · Sydney*

Library of Congress Catalog Card Number: 65-14256
Printed in the United States of America

Preface

This book is for students. It is not a reference book. It is not a technical essay in statistics. It is simply a textbook designed to provide behavioral science students with a general overview of statistical applications.

In organization this book departs from the standard. Many authors are concerned chiefly with mathematical derivation; others stress computation. Here the emphasis is on understanding the reasoning underlying statistical usage.

This textbook is organized around two main themes: (1) the nature of the problem under study and (2) the form of the data at hand. No attempt is made to survey all the available statistical techniques, but a range of techniques is included. These techniques are introduced only as they contribute to an understanding of the logic of statistical analysis.

Much emphasis is placed on the logic of statistical relationships. Science is seen here as the study of relationships among variables. This basic idea is probably the main contribution of the field of statistics to its various fields of application. I hope that the student who completes this book will find it natural to think about the problems in his field in these terms.

There are many people to whom I owe a debt of gratitude. Many of my former teachers have contributed to this book. Among these the contributions of Douglas S. Yamamura, Harry V. Ball, Donald T. Campbell, Douglas M. More, and Robert F. Winch were outstanding. Many of my colleagues have read part or all of the manuscript. Without the helpful suggestions of Morris H. Sunshine, Abdel M. Zikery, Thomas J. Fararo, Robert McGinnis, and Richard J. Hill I would still be trying to prepare the manuscript. Finally, I wish to thank the many students who worried patiently through earlier drafts of this book. Outstanding among these is my wife, Sue Freeman, who has cheerfully served as a guinea pig for every word of text, not once, but time after time. To her I gratefully dedicate this book.

I am indebted to the Literary Executor of the late Sir Ronald A. Fisher, F.R.S., Cambridge; to Dr. Frank Yates, F.R.S., Rothamsted, and Oliver and Boyd, Ltd., Edinburgh, for permission to reprint Table V from their book, *Statistical Tables for Biological, Agriculture and Medical Research.*

LINTON C. FREEMAN

Syracuse, New York
February 1965

Contents

Elementary Applied Statistics:

for Students in Behavioral Science

Section A

Backgrounds for the Study of Statistics

We are all the victims of statistics.

Anyone who reads a paper or a magazine, who listens to the radio or watches television, who looks at billboards or who talks with his friends and neighbors—in short, everybody—is exposed to statistics.

Mello Weeds, we are told, contain 21% less nicotine and 86% less tar. The value of the dollar today is less than half its real worth. Americans have a higher ratio of bathtubs per person than any other people. Atomic explosions cause bad weather, cigarettes cause cancer, and depressions cause falling hemlines. The average doctor has 3.3 children, and 92 out of every 100 voters favor Brown for senator. These and other bits of statistical fact and fancy clutter our airwaves and bylines daily. Thus, if we are to live in this world, we must work out a way of dealing with the load of statistical sense and nonsense which is dumped daily in our laps.

There seem to be three possible techniques for dealing with this problem: (1) we can close our eyes and our ears and try to ignore it all; (2) we can throw open our senses, throw away our sense, and believe the statistics which come our way, even when they contain contradictions as they so often seem to; or (3) we can learn a little bit about statistical analysis—about how to think statistically—and try to make reasonable judgments in handling the statistics we encounter.

This is a book with a bias. It assumes that the best way to deal with statistics is to know a little about statistics. It has as its basic purpose an attempt to communicate that small bit of information about statistical thinking which will aid the reader in making reasonable judgments about the statistics he encounters. This, then, is the basic purpose of the book—

to enable the reader to think better in a world where statistical arguments are rife. This, however, is not its sole purpose. For this book is designed primarily for students of social science. And although the everyday person is often exposed to statistical data, the social science student is almost overwhelmed. From the first course in sociology or economics through the last graduate seminar, there is nothing but statistics. The literature of sociology, psychology, and economics and increasingly that of anthropology and political science is filled with charts and graphs and tables. Even the textual materials include such statistical terms as variable, correlation, average, and significance. And the conclusions are more and more often based on statistical reasoning. So, if the student is ever going to understand the social science literature, it behooves him to pick up a little statistics—if only in self-defense.

This book is designed to help the student of social science deal with the statistics of his science. It assumes no knowledge of mathematics beyond high school algebra nor does it attempt to instruct the student in mathematical statistics. Rather, it is concerned with introducing the non-mathematical reader to thinking about statistics and to statistical thinking. The emphasis here is on *understanding* statistics. Much reliance therefore is placed on communicating statistical ideas in a language with which the student can be assumed to be conversant—plain English. Symbols and numbers are kept to a minimum and they are used as shorthand representations and examples of concepts which are discussed in ordinary English.

Like most fields of study, statistics has sense in it; this book attempts, through its organization, to underline that sense. An attempt is made to fit each problem studied into a logical and coherent plan. The organization of each chapter and the organization of the chapters as a whole reflect this plan. If the student first learns this plan of organization, then keeps it in mind and fits each subsequent chapter into its proper place, he will have no trouble at all in "making sense" of statistics.

The chapters in this first section are designed to introduce the field of statistics. The subject matter and applications of statistics will be described and the plan of this book will be outlined. In addition, a brief review of symbols and mathematical rules is included. The student who thoroughly understands these first chapters will find no difficulty in coping with the rest of the book.

I The Subject Matter of Statistics

The field of statistics can perhaps be best understood as a special language. And like any language, it allows us to think about things and to communicate our thoughts to others. It is not special in the sense that it will allow us to think or talk of anything different from what we can in our ordinary speech. It is special, however, in that it encourages us to talk in a more precise manner than we could in another language. It is this emphasis on precision that is the strength of statistics. If rigorous thought and precise communication are our aims, statistics is the language for us.

Like other languages, the language of statistics includes words and rules of grammar; these are the tools of a language. Statistics, however, is a limited language with a limited set of tools. In statistics we can talk only about the characteristics of things we can observe. Before the techniques of statistics can answer the questions put to them, they must be provided with data—with the raw materials of observation.

Some statistics require data of one sort, some another, but all statistics need data that are based on observations. This chapter will be concerned with an examination of the observational data required by all statistics and with the various kinds of observational data which are used by the several different statistics. Three forms of data will be discussed: nominal scales, ordinal scales, and interval scales. However, before we can examine specific types of data we must consider some of the general characteristics of all data that are useful for statistical analysis.

Variables

In any scientific study it is necessary that we observe and record some characteristic or characteristics of the world of our experience. We deal with things we see or touch or smell or hear; these things are all observable. But observability alone is not enough; they must also be capable of differing. If some observable characteristic of an object changes when it is observed again and again, or if it differs between one object and another, it is said to *vary*. In the language of the statistician it is called a *variable*. A variable, then, is an observable characteristic of something which is capable of taking several values or of being expressed in several different categories. Thus weight is a variable, for all objects do not weigh the same amount and a single object may change its weight from time to time. And age is a variable, and college grades, and strength and sex and speed and size and anything you can name which is (1) characteristic of objects or persons, (2) observable, and (3) differs from observation to observation. These, then, are the raw materials of statistical analysis. They are the data that constitute the subject matter of statistics.

Scales

If the data of a variable are to be put to use in a statistical analysis, they must be recorded in some systematic fashion. Each variable must be defined operationally; that is, it must be described in terms of the steps which are required in recording its changing values. Such a definition requires both a description of the characteristics to be observed and specification of the categories among which variation will be recorded. Statisticians often call this procedure of operationally defining variables *scaling*; the resulting descriptions are called *scales*.

In many, perhaps most, cases the scale of a variable will be dictated by common usage. Thus, in our society, the variable age is usually scaled in years, counting the first anniversary of birth as 1, the second as 2, and so on. Except for very young children, such a count is made in years, rounding not to the nearest whole year, but rather to the last anniversary passed. Thus a man who tells you he is 21, may have been born 21 years and 2 days earlier or perhaps 21 years and 362 days. We are already provided, therefore, with a standardized operational definition of age and a means of scaling that variable.

It is important to remember that the scale used to record a variable is not a part of the variable itself. The values taken by a variable are a part of its operational definition. Although some variables have generally accepted sets of values or categories, others, particularly in social science, have no well-established scales of measurement. These variables require that the investigator himself determine the categories among which they may be expected to vary. In studying a variable like social class, for example, one investigator might devise a scale which would yield three classes, say, upper, middle, and lower, but another investigator might specify four classes: upper, middle, working, and lower. Then, too, some variables, like popularity, might require that we start fairly fresh, without much precedent of common usage to go by, and work out an entirely new scale. A person's popularity might be scaled according to the frequency of his contacts with others, or by asking his associates their opinions of him, or in any number of ways. The important thing is to work out a rigorous way of defining a variable operationally before trying to launch into statistical analysis.

Constructing scales, then, is the outcome of operationally defining variables. And scales are necessary to provide data in any statistical study. However, scales are not all alike. They vary from extremely simple affairs consisting only of two unordered categories to quite complex devices including a long series of equally spaced classes starting from a real zero point. We shall discuss three of the most important types of scales.

Nominal Scales. The simplest scale consists of nothing but a set of categories. The basic operation of scaling consists of classifying observations into categories. Any two observations may be equal (in terms of the variable in question) and they are therefore classified into the same category, or they may be unequal, which leads to their classification into different categories. The categories therefore must be mutually exclusive and collectively exhaustive. That is to say, each observation can be classified only into *one* category of the set and each can *always* be classified into some one of them. Sex, for example, is such a nominal scale; all people can be classified into the category male or the category female, and no one may be classified as both.

Usually the classes in a nominal scale are named as they are in the preceding example. Sometimes, however, they are assigned numbers. Assignment of numbers to players in various positions in college football is an example of this practice. Some teams, for example, assign numbers 1 through 29 to quarterbacks, 30 through 39 to fullbacks, 40 to 49 to halfbacks, and so on. These numbers do not imply order; they are simply names which designate categories. Thus an end who wears number 87 is not any "better" or "higher" than a quarterback who wears 27. Eighty-seven merely indicates that its bearer plays a different position from the man who wears 27.

This example illustrates an important characteristic of nominal scales: although numbers may be used to designate classes, these numbers have very few of the usual attributes of numbers. They may not be added; two halfbacks with numbers in the forties do not equal one end with a number in the eighties. In fact, they permit no arithmetic operations at all. These numbers are merely labels for categories. Different labels designate different categories. The original labels may be exchanged for any other set providing that each is replaced by one and only one new label. They may be names (halfback, fullback, and so on) or numbers (40's, 30's, and so on) or even letters, but in any case no order is implied. These scales do not allow us to "measure" variation in any strict sense. Instead, variation is labeled—categories are named along with criteria for classifying observed cases into one or another category.

Many of the variables studied by behavioral scientists are of this nominal or classificatory type. A human ecologist may be interested in regions—say, Northern, Southern, Eastern, Western—and an anthropologist may be concerned with types of descent systems—matrilineal, patrilineal, bilateral—or a family sociologist with marital status—single, married, widowed, divorced. Each of these variables represents scaling at its simplest form where characteristics of objects are merely categorized into various classes.

In each of these examples, and in all nominal scales, observation leads to the classification of each case into one and only one of an unordered set of classes. There may be any number of classes from two on up, but every time they must be mutually exclusive and together they must permit of the classification of any observable case. Because of this emphasis on classification alone, nominal scales are often called just *classifications*.

Many statistical writers use the word qualitative to describe nominal scales. They distinguish between these unordered or qualitative scales and scales which are ordered or quantitative. Essentially, however, this is just a distinction between two levels of strength or complexity of scale types. As we shall see, quantitative scales take more into account; they are simply more complex schemes for classifying observed data.

Ordinal Scales. Like nominal scales, ordinal scales are made up of sets of mutually exclusive classes. Ordinal scales, however, possess one additional attribute: the classes form an ordered series. Whereas nominal scales only classify, ordinal scales classify *and order* the classes.

Suppose we are interested in scaling the variable "hardness" for three substances, say diamonds, glass, and wood. We may use "scratchability" as our criterion, and we should then attempt to scratch each substance with each of the others. We will probably find that the diamonds will scratch the glass and the wood and that they will be scratched by neither of these substances. And the glass will scratch the wood and the wood will scratch neither. Relative to hardness, then, we are able to establish a hierarchy—a rank ordering—in which the diamonds rank hardest, the glass less hard, and the wood least hard. In this example we should establish three ordered classes ranging from hardest to least hard.

Ordinal scales, then, establish an ordered series of classes. These classes may be named as in the preceding example (hardest, less hard, least hard), or they may be assigned numbers, which is the more common approach. Thus, diamonds rank 3 in hardness, glass 2, and wood 1.[1] These numbers express the important attribute of order in such scales; they allow us to talk in such terms as "harder than," "higher than," or "more than." However, they do not imply how much harder, higher, or more. Diamonds are harder than glass, but on the basis of such a scale, we do not know how much harder they are. And we do not know whether diamonds are as much harder than glass as glass is harder than wood. Rank 3 is higher than either rank 2 or rank 1 in hardness, but we cannot assume that it is twice as hard as 2 or three times as hard as 1 or anything of that sort. Ordinal scales permit discussion of "moreness" or "lessness," but they make no assumptions as to how much more or less.

Since ordinal scales include a record of order, the labels assigned to their categories must preserve that order. Any labels may be used (new ones may be substituted for old) as long as the original order is preserved. This was done when we substituted the numbers 3, 2, 1 for the labels hardest, less hard, least hard, in the preceding scale. But we may, with equal legitimacy, name our categories 9, 4, and 1 or even 1285, 103, and 18. Because the magnitude of the differences among these values has no significance, any new values may be substituted as long as the order is not changed. This procedure is called an *ordinal* or *monotonic transformation.*

Pairs of observations on an ordinal scale, like those on a nominal scale, may be equal (that is, they may belong to the same class or category) or they may be unequal and therefore belong to different classes. If two observations represent different categories in an ordinal scale, either the first must be greater than the second or the second greater than the first. At no point may their order be ambiguous.

Anything which can be recorded in an ordinal scale can, of course, be simplified and treated as if it were not ordered. When we are not concerned with order, we can simply ignore it and treat ordinal data as if they were nominal. However, if we simplify our ordinal scale into a nominal form, we are often neglecting to use the information supplied by the index. So, in general, it is not wise to simplify a scale, for in doing so we are throwing information away.

Social class as measured by sociologists is an ordinal scale. It enables one to rank persons—to speak in such terms as "higher than" or "lower

[1] Very often the highest rank is assigned the lowest number 1, and other classes, in descending order, are number 2, 3, and so on, so that the lowest class has the highest number. In order to eliminate this contradiction, we shall adopt the procedure suggested by Cureton (n.d.) and assign the lowest number to the lowest rank. Then each successively higher rank will be assigned the next higher number.

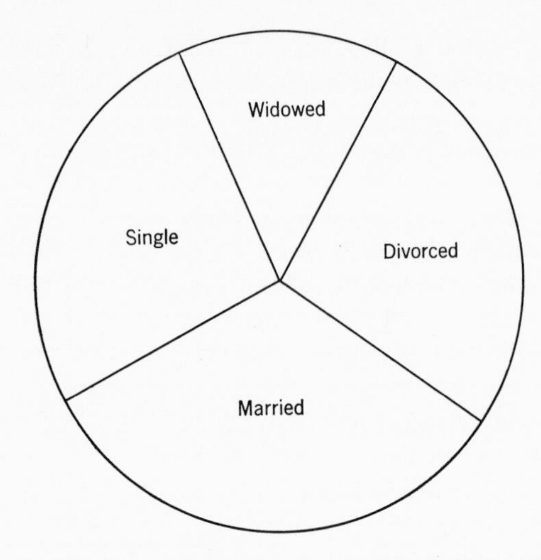

Fig. 1.1. A pictorial representation of a nominal scale—marital status.

than," but never to answer how much higher. And attitude tests usually produce ordinal scales. We can talk of "more pro-" or "more anti-," but again the order is the end result; and we are usually unable to determine degrees of difference.

In conclusion, then, although nominal scales classify, ordinal scales classify and order. The ordinal scale provides us with a ranked series of mutually exclusive classes. These are often called simply *ranks*.

Hardest 3
Less hard 2
Least hard 1

Fig. 1.2. A pictorial representation of an ordinal scale—hardness.

Interval Scales. Interval scales have all the qualities of ordinal scales plus one more. Not only do they provide an ordered series of classes, but the intervals between any two pairs of adjacent classes are equal. In this case the distance between 1 and 2 is the same as that between 8 and 9, 112 and 113, or between any two adjacent classes. Temperature as it is usually measured is an interval scale. The one degree between 70° and 71° is the same as the one between 89° and 90°. This enables us not only to compare individual cases, but to talk about how many units more or greater one case is than another. We are not restricted to reporting merely that today is colder than yesterday as we would be if we used an ordinal scale; we can say that it is 13° colder. Here, then, we have an ordered series of ranks plus equal intervals; an interval scale or simply a *measure*.

To construct an interval scale it is necessary to establish some standard unit of measurement. For any two observations that are not equal, the degree of their difference must be expressible in terms of the standard unit.

The units of measurement may, of course, be changed. A constant may be added to the number for each observation or each may be multiplied by a constant. Changes of this sort will affect neither the order nor the relative magnitude of differences in such scales; they are called *linear transformations*.

Interval scales are less common than the simpler forms in behavioral science data. However, we do deal with such variables as number of children and frequency of interaction that can be expressed as interval scales. Three children is the same increase over two as two is over one. And seven interactions is the same frequency less than eight as four is less than five. Some of these are even more complex forms of scales, but here they are all grouped together under the classification of interval scale.

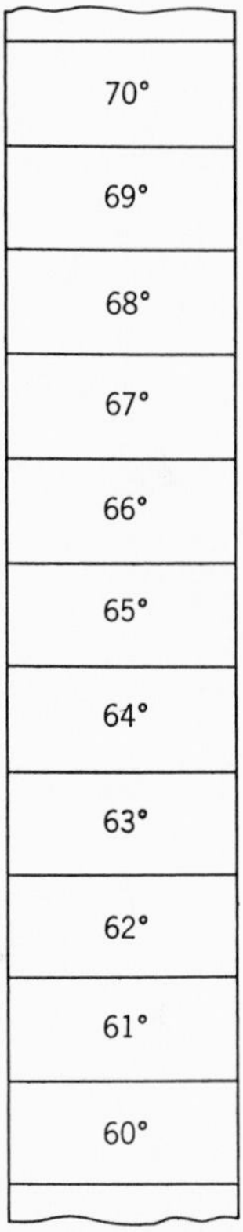

Fig. 1.3. A pictorial representation of an interval scale—temperature.

We can also always simplify interval scales. A variable like height, for example, need not be recorded in the interval scale of feet and inches. It may be defined in terms of a pair of ranks; say everyone over 5 ft. 5 in. would be ranked as 2 (tall) and everyone below that figure as 1 (not so tall). Or to simplify further, even the notion of order may be dropped and the two categories can be treated merely as nominal categories.

This consideration points up the essential distinction among our three types of scales. Nominal scales classify—they can be visualized as sets of categories, each with a different name, which together exhaust the possibilities (Fig. 1.1). In ordinal scales, however, categories within the scale are ordered (Fig. 1.2). And the classes within interval scales are both ordered and equal in size (Fig. 1.3).

These distinctions are important in choosing statistics for the analysis of data.

2 The Uses of Statistics

The field of statistics has a long, but unearned, reputation for producing lies. It is altogether too easy to find a pair of items like the following:

Advertisement of the Sunny Dells Development Association, September 1, 1963.

Sunny Dells is a good place to live. The average family income in our town is $11,400 a year.

Pamphlet distributed by a reform political candidate, September 5, 1963.

Our taxes must go down if our town is to survive. Present rates are excessive when we stop to consider that the average family in Sunny Dells earns only $6800 per year.

Clearly, there is something wrong here. The typical family in Sunny Dells obviously cannot earn both $11,400 and $6800 a year. Can it be that one or both of these averages has lied?

The truth is not that statistics lie, but that liars use statistics. In a fact-minded culture like ours, the statistical argument has great appeal. The "average" can be determined by any of a half-dozen different procedures, and sometimes these will provide quite different results. The not too honest purveyor of statistics can take advantage of this situation and provide the consumer with an average which is not necessarily appropriate to the problem but one which is best designed to make his point. It is up to the consumer of statistics, therefore, to learn enough about the range of techniques that are available and their proper use to protect himself from this kind of statistical hard sell. A person who has a reasonably good grasp of the field of statistics will seldom be misled by the inappropriate use of a statistical technique.

The honest user of statistics must always keep one fact in mind: in some instances the use of one statistical procedure is appropriate; in others it is not. The choice of a statistic in a particular situation must be based on two considerations: (1) the nature of the available data and (2) the type of problem at hand. Chapter 1 discussed the kinds of data we might reasonably expect to encounter. This chapter will be concerned with the types of problems to which statistical analysis may be applied.

Three Jobs for Statistics

Hundreds of statistical techniques are available to the contemporary scientist or statistician. Of these, probably no more than twenty or thirty are used regularly in social science, but even twenty or thirty distinct techniques can be quite a confusing array unless they can be understood in terms of their uses.

Fortunately, for the user of statistics, most of the procedures we find can be roughly classified in terms of just a few basic applications. Social scientists generally confine their applications of statistics to three: (1) summarizing observations on a single variable, (2) describing association between variables, and (3) making inferences. Other applications may occasionally be found, but these three are the only ones that occur commonly in social science. They will be discussed in this chapter.

In general, people seem to be both neat and lazy. We express our inclination toward neatness by filing away everything we observe in a more or less orderly fashion in our minds or in our books. And the laziness shows when the filing system is examined, for instead of filing complete statements of our experiences, most of us are content with brief (and often not too accurate) summaries of the things that we know.

One of the primary activities of the social scientist, or of any person for that matter, is reporting things he has observed. "This is a hot day," we say, or "My class is small this year." Here, in each instance, we are describing one characteristic of one object. In the first instance, a day is the object, and its temperature is the characteristic. In the second, a group of students is the object, and their number the characteristic.

Usually, however, we are not concerned with describing a single case. Rather, we want to describe some characteristic of several objects. We might say something like, "Saturday and Sunday were both hot," or even, "Saturday, Sunday, Monday, Tuesday, Wednesday, Thursday, and Friday were all hot." Obviously, however, as soon as we try to deal with more than a few cases such a description becomes extremely cumbersome. Thus, instead of long-winded enumerations of all the days that seemed warm, we usually report merely that, "The week-end was hot," or "The whole week was a scorcher." We use a linguistic shortcut to summarize our experience.

In each of these examples we have used ordinary English to describe or summarize something we have observed. If our powers of observation are adequate, and if we have some facility with the language, we can communicate reasonably well in this fashion. A good deal of ambiguity, however, still remains. This is where statistical procedures come in handy. If we use statistical language, our communication can be less ambiguous. We can adopt scaling procedures and instead of saying "This is a hot day," we should say, "The temperature is 107° in the shade." And instead of "My class is small this year," we may report that "My class contains three students." Here the mode of expression suggested by statistical scaling obviously yields more precise statements and leads therefore to more effective communication.

When our observations are many, statistical techniques may be used to summarize them. Ideally, such a summary should be brief, and yet it should reflect, as much as possible, the sense of the original observations. An adequate summary should enable us to record and to communicate our observations.

There are many statistics which may be used to summarize observations. Among the most useful are those that belong to a set we call *averages*. There are many kinds of averages, but they are alike in that they all attempt to determine a typical observation to represent the entire distribution. So instead of "Last week was hot," we may say, "The average temperature was 88° last week." The latter statement is much more precise than the former.

If we calculate an average to summarize a particular set of observations, we are always left with the question of how satisfactorily it accomplishes that summary. The use of an average suggests a need for further information that will reveal just how typical this typical observation is. Statistics of this latter type are called *indexes of variation*; they help us to make judgments about the adequacy of our averages. We can, for example, think about two very different temperature patterns, each with an average of 88°. One week, let us say, fluctuates between 68° and 108°. The other week remains around 88°; it varies no more than 2° one way or the other. An index of variation is used to summarize this pattern of change or difference. Together, an average and an index of variation provide a summary of a set of observations.

Many more examples can be given, but these should illustrate the point. The language of statistics is more precise than other languages; it allows us to make more accurate reports and summaries of the characteristics of things we observe.

Describing the Relationship between Two Variables

A second aspect of communication involves the description of relationships or association. One of the primary aims of the social scientist is to reduce the apparent complexity of man's social life. If we look around us, we see that men differ in their attitudes, their values, even their conceptions of what is true and what is false. Sometimes they congregate in large cities, and sometimes they go off by themselves and live as hermits. They vote differently, earn different amounts of money by different means, and spend it in different ways. They worship different gods and follow different leaders. Some men conform to all the rules of their fellow men and others seem always unwilling or unable to restrain themselves. Men are strong or weak, kind or unkind, open or withdrawn; the range of behavior men exhibit seems almost limitless.

The social scientist, however, need not be intimidated by this seemingly endless range of variation. For he has found that the behavior of his fellows—like the behavior of stars or atoms or falling bodies—is not completely random and unpredictable. It is usually possible to specify conditions under which at least part of this variation disappears. When such conditions have been specified, a relationship has been established.

Among Eskimos, for example, persons differ with respect to their occupations. However, within the various age-sex statuses, the differences disappear almost completely. Mature men hunt, mature women prepare hides, and so on. Thus the variable, occupation, does not vary when the variable, status, is taken into account. The two variables are related; they are related in such a way that knowledge of one implies knowledge of the other, and our world is—in one degree—less complex.

Any description of relatedness between observable characteristics may be viewed as a matter of guessing. When we say that in Chicago the season and temperature are related, we are asserting that if we know the value taken by one of these variables, we can guess the value of the other more accurately than we can without such knowledge. If we are told that the temperature in Chicago is 92° on a certain day, we guess that the day occurred in summer. And if we are asked to guess the temperature of a winter day, we pick a figure in the twenties or thirties. Clearly, this relationship is not perfect; occasionally in January the thermometer has reached 68° and sometimes in August it has dropped to 37°. But such occasions have been rare; in general, the relationship holds.

There may be a very large relationship or a very small one, but if we can guess one variable from another at all, we have a useful knowledge. There is a very small relationship between smoking and lung cancer. Yet this relationship, small as it is, may be helpful in finally discovering the causes and cure of cancer.

From this discussion it is clear that we can describe and discuss relationships between variables in everyday English. However, as in describing a single variable, the lack of precision in our language places unnecessary restrictions on our discourse. Whereas in English we must say that this and that are highly related (or not so highly related), in statistical language we can affix a precise number to their relationship. This number tells us the exact degree of their relatedness—precisely how much a knowledge of one variable helps us in guessing the other. Using this statistical tool, called the *coefficient of association*, we can describe relationships in a rigorous fashion. So again, precision is our reward for using statistical language.

Inference

Thus far, our discussion has been confined to the role of statistics in helping us to describe and summarize things we have experienced. However, statistics can be useful also in generalizing from past experience, in making predictions about the cases we have yet to see.

Every day each of us makes a series of decisions based on generalizations of relationships we have perceived in the past. When we leave home in the morning, we may look at the sky and decide whether to wear a raincoat. We know that one attribute of the weather (whether the sky is overcast or not) has in the past, often been related to another attribute (whether it rains or not), and we assume that this relationship will continue to hold. We do not then just arbitrarily decide to take or leave our raincoats (we do not toss a coin); instead we judge in terms of a generalization of our past observations of the relationship between overcast skies and rain. Similarly, our decision to go to college may be based on our prior knowledge of the relationship between amount of education and potential earning as it has applied to others. Here we predict that the same rule will apply to us. And our desire to avoid a course in statistics may result from our earlier perception that the amount of mathematics in a course is generally related to its difficulty.

In this manner we use our knowledge of a past relationship between things as a guide for future behavior. Whenever we have been able to guess one characteristic of something on the basis of our knowledge of another, we assume that the relationship will continue to hold. In effect, we look at a few cases and generalize from these to the cases we have yet to see. This procedure seems to serve as a useful general guide for behavior.

Clearly, however, some generalizations are better than others. That is, some of our predictions stand up in light of further observations, whereas others do not. Our grandmothers, for example, thought that the emotional experiences, good and bad, of a pregnant woman would be reflected in the physical and emotional makeup of her child. Generalizations of this sort are probably built on the occurrence of a chance case or two and they persist without further followup. Although this generalization is patently false, our common folklore is still full of such nonsense. We try to avoid generalizing on the basis of too few cases, and we try to make sure that the cases are typical. But our ordinary linguistic tools let us down. How few cases are too few? And how can we tell if those we have observed are truly typical of the whole set?

Again, statistical procedures are helpful. The procedures of statistics include some which are called *statistics of inference*; these are designed to help us answer the questions we have raised. Common sense tells us that the more cases we observe the more probable are our generalizations. These statistics tell us how sure we should be on the basis of any given number of cases. So again precision is the reward of the user of statistics.

Statisticians distinguish two types of statistics of inference: *estimates* and *tests of significance*. Estimates refer to direct generalizations of observations. The average income of college graduates, for example, is an estimate based on studies of some, but not all, college graduates. Tests of significance, however, are concerned with comparing our observations with some hypothetical state of affairs. We may guess, for example, that there is a relationship between education and income in America. It would be prohibitively expensive to try to study the whole population of Americans, but we could take a sample of that population. Suppose that for the cases in our sample we did find some relationship between education and income. A critic may argue that the observed relationship is peculiar to our sample—that if we had studied the whole population of Americans, no such relationship would have been indicated. A test of significance would enable us to determine the precise probability that such was the case. It would allow us to determine the likelihood of getting an apparent relationship in our sample if there were none in the population.

In both cases the basic problem is one of generalizing from observed data to the larger population of cases from which the observations were drawn.

3 How to Work with Numbers and Letters

Introductory statistics has a reputation for being a difficult course. It requires that the student be able to juggle numbers around—to add and subtract, for example—and that he do it according to a set of rules expressed in an abstract symbolic formula. Many students view this prospect with something less than eager anticipation. The fact is, however, that the skills required are really quite simple and for the most part generally known.

No great mathematical sophistication is necessary for an understanding of elementary statistics. Numbers and the rules for their treatment, however, cannot be avoided entirely if one is going to grasp the fundamental principles of the field. This does not mean that the student will have to master college mathematics, but it does suggest that he must be familiar with simple arithmetic and high school algebra.

Most of us already know what we need to know. The mathematical skills required are those we use each day in paying our bills and counting our change. If the student will relax and attempt to follow the mathematical examples in this book by referring to the nonmathematical text materials, he should have no trouble. The basic arithmetic and symbolic skills that are required will be reviewed in this chapter.

Symbols in Statistics

No one has any trouble when he picks up a cookbook and reads something like the following:

To boil an egg, gently place one egg into a pot containing enough boiling water to cover. Boil slowly for three to five minutes.

On the other hand, many of us are brought up short when we pick up a textbook and read a formula like this

$$\bar{X} = \frac{\sum_{i=1}^{N} X_i}{N}$$

Our reaction is unreasonable. The symbols in the formula are nothing but shorthand for the following statement:

> To compute the average (arithmetic mean) of several scores, add all the scores together and divide their sum by the number of scores summed.

Both the cookbook and text assume that you want to know how something is done, and both provide instructions for doing it. The statistical instructions are usually given in shorthand; this saves space and clarifies possible confusion for long, complicated instructions, but essentially they are the same thing as those in the cookbook. Even cookbooks use symbols (like T for tablespoon, t for teaspoon, and C for cup) whenever recipes are long. And they provide lists of ingredients in a sort of code summary for complicated cooking. Thus basically, except for the greater brevity of instructions in statistics books, cookbooks and statistics textbooks do the same thing: both provide instructions for making a desired product whether it be a cake or a chi-square.

For our purposes we can limit our discussion to five types of statistical symbols with which we are dealing.

Variables. First there are *variables*—the symbols which refer to the observable *raw materials* of statistical study. This book will confine its discourse to two such variable symbols X and Y. If a problem is concerned with, say, describing the heights of sixth graders in Des Moines, the symbol X may be used to refer to the variable height.

A subscript is a small symbol, a letter or number, placed slightly below and to the right of a variable symbol. Thus X_1 refers to the height of an individual sixth grader in our example, X_2 is the height of another, and so on. Letters may be used instead of numbers; we can designate their heights as X_a and X_b, but if we have more than 26 observations, we will run out of letters. Typically, we use numbers (X_1, X_2, and so on) to designate particular observations and a letter (X_i) to discuss the score of some unspecified individual. In our example, then, X_1 is the height of the first child, X_2 of the second, and X_i refers to the height of any unspecified child.

The symbol Y will be used along with X whenever a problem involves two variables. If, for example, we are interested in the relationship between height (X) and weight (Y) for our sixth graders, both symbols are used.

Operators. The second major class of statistical symbols is made up of *operators*. These are the symbols we already know. They are the *instructions* which tell us what to do with our raw materials. This book will use the usual set: $+$, to add; $-$, to subtract; $\times$ or a centered dot $\cdot$ or no symbol at all, to multiply; /, $\div$, or the usual fraction symbol ——, to divide; the exponent ^{2} to square; and the radical sign $\sqrt{}$, to extract the square root.

One symbol that may be new to many students will be used a great deal: the Greek letter $\sum$ (sigma) which means to summate or add. $\sum$ is a shorthand symbol used when several things are to be added. If we want to add ten scores, we can always write

$$X_1 + X_2 + X_3 + X_4 + X_5 + X_6 + X_7 + X_8 + X_9 + X_{10}$$

or the same expression can be shortened to

$$X_1 + X_2 + \cdots + X_{10}$$

which means the same thing. The three dots ($\cdots$) simply mean "and so on."

This same instruction, however, may be put in still another way.

$$\sum_{i=1}^{10} X_i$$

When $\sum$ is used, it instructs you to add up everything that follows (X_i) starting with the case specified below the $\sum$ symbol ($i = 1$) and ending with the case specified above (10). This example may be read: add up ($\sum$) all the observations (X_i) ranging from the first ($i = 1$) through the tenth (10). If we want only the sum of observations 3 and 4 ($X_3 + X_4$), we can write

$$\sum_{i=3}^{4} X_i$$

and if we wish to indicate that all of some unspecified number of cases should be added together, we can use N to symbolize the unspecified number of cases and write

$$\sum_{i=1}^{N} X_i$$

This says: sum all the observations from the first to the Nth; it is a general instruction for the addition of all cases regardless of their number. When this general instruction is intended, and when the range of values to be summed is obvious, it is customary to omit the notation of limits and write

$$\sum X_i$$

or even

$$\sum X$$

This indicates that the summation is to extend over all the cases under consideration.

Constants. The third kind of symbols are called *constants.* They are quantities which remain the same for the whole problem or even for several problems. X_1 and X_2 are constants in any particular problem since X_1 is the score of the first case, and X_2 the score of the second, and so on. Then, too, N is a constant, for it symbolizes the number of cases being considered in any particular problem. The most important class of constants for us will be numbers 1, 2, 3, 4, and so on. Their meaning remains stable no matter what the problem.

Statistics. Symbols of the fourth kind refer to the *results* of your labors—they are *statistics*—the products of statistical manipulation. There are a great number of statistics, but in this book we shall examine only a few. They will be discussed in the following chapters. One example, however, has already been given: $\bar{X}$ is the average or arithmetic mean, it is the result of a statistical computation.

Connectives. The only other symbols we shall see are *connectives*; they are shorthand for such phrases as "and you will get" or "is equal to." The following ones will be used:

$a = b$	*a* is equal to *b*.
$a < b$	*a* is less than *b*.
$a > b$	*a* is greater than *b*.
$a \leqslant b$	*a* is less than or equal to *b*.
$a \geqslant b$	*a* is greater than or equal to *b*.

They are the symbols that connect the product of your effort (a statistic) with the operations you make on your raw materials.

If we return to our earlier example, perhaps we can see it in a new light.

$$\bar{X} = \frac{\sum_{i=1}^{N} X_i}{N}$$

Here

$\bar{X}$ is a statistic, the average or arithmetic mean, a product of statistical manipulation;

$=$ states that the mean is determined by performing the operations specified on the right of the expression;

X_i stands for any unspecified score, the observations under investigation;

$\sum_{i=1}^{N}$ instructs us to add all those scores from the first to the last;

—— instructs us to divide; and

N is the symbol for the number of cases studied.

It should be clear by now that Wallis and Roberts are right when they suggest that understanding

> ...the meaning of such a "mathematical" expression does not actually require any knowledge of mathematics; all that it requires is knowledge of the meaning of the symbols.[1]

The table provided in Appendix A summarizes all the statistical symbols contained in this book. With the help of this table and these rules, the most complicated statistical formula should be simple to decipher and use.

A Brief Review of Arithmetic

Most students will have very little trouble with the mathematics found in this book. Occasionally, however, you may run into a problem that requires a skill you just do not remember. This review section is included to help you overcome such problems. The mathematics is, as you will see, very simple, but perhaps this brief review will help you past a forgetful moment.

Order of Operations. When a formula requires you to perform a series of arithmetic operations, it is necessary that they be done in the proper order. Thus, although $\sum X_i^2$ and $(\sum X_i)^2$ both require summing and squaring, their order and hence your results will differ. Some commonly accepted rules for ordering operations are listed.

1. *Numbers may be added in any order.* For example, $4 + 2 + 6 = 6 + 2 + 4 = 4 + 6 + 2 = 6 + 4 + 2 = 2 + 4 + 6 = 2 + 6 + 4 = 12$.
2. *Numbers may be multiplied in any order.* Thus $10 \times 1 \times 3 = 10 \times 3 \times 1 = 1 \times 10 \times 3$ and so on.
3. *When a problem requires several different kinds of operations, multiplication and division are performed first, then addition and subtraction.* For example, $3 \times 2 + 3 + 8 \div 2 = 13$. That is, $3 \times 2 = 6$ and $8 \div 2 = 4$; then $6 + 3 + 4 = 13$.
4. *When several terms are enclosed in parentheses, collected above or below a dividing bar, or under a radical sign, they are treated as a single number.* Thus

$$3(8 - 2) = 3 \times 6 = 18$$

and

$$\frac{4 + 2}{4 - 1} = \frac{6}{3} = 2$$

and

$$\sqrt{6 - 2} = \sqrt{4} = 2$$

[1] W. A. Wallis and H. V. Roberts, *Statistics: A New Approach*, Glencoe, Illinois: The Free Press, 1956, p. 113.

In the illustration just given involving $\sum X_i^2$ and $(\sum X_i)^2$, $\sum X_i^2$ tells you to square each score (X_i^2) and then add them up ($X_1^2 + X_2^2 + X_3^2 +$ etc.). The parentheses, however, change the order of operations, so $(\sum X_i)^2$, requires that you add the scores ($X_1 + X_2 + X_3 +$ etc.) and then square their sum. The importance of this distinction can be seen if we take an example. Suppose you have the scores of three students—call them 1, 2, and 3—on an arithmetic test. Let us say

$$X_1 = 2$$
$$X_2 = 3$$
$$X_3 = 9$$

Then

$$\sum X_i^2 = X_1^2 + X_2^2 + X_3^2 = 4 + 9 + 81 = 94$$

But

$$(\sum X_i)^2 = (X_1 + X_2 + X_3)^2 = (2 + 3 + 9)^2 = 196$$

Signed Numbers. In order to understand the meaning of a negative number we can think of a thermometer. If the temperature on a winter day is 10° above zero and it drops 15° at nightfall, it is then 5° below zero or $-5°$. In speaking of a change in temperature we can separate two components, the amount or magnitude of change and its direction. If the temperature is 0 and it rises to 5° or falls to $-5°$, it has changed the same amount. However, the direction of change is indicated by the sign, + for a rising value and − for a falling one. The magnitude of any number, ignoring its sign, is called its *absolute value*; it is expressed symbolically by enclosing the number in vertical lines. Thus $|5|$ means either $+5$ or -5 without regard to its sign. Often, however, we are interested in the algebraic value of a number; here we are concerned with its magnitude and with its direction, plus or minus.

Manipulation of signed numbers is called algebraic; it is summarized in the following rules:

1. *To add numbers with the same sign, sum and assign the common sign to the total.* Thus

$$(+2) + (+2) + (+3) = 7$$

or

$$2 + 2 + 3 = 7$$

And

$$(-5) + (-4) + (-1) = -10$$

2. *To add numbers with unlike signs, add the positive and the negative numbers separately, compute the absolute value of the difference between them, and use the sign of the larger number.* For example,

$$(+2) + (-4) + (-3) + (+1) = -4$$

Since

$$(+2) + (+1) = +3$$

and

$$(-4) + (-3) = -7$$

so

$$\begin{array}{r} |7| \\ -\underline{|3|} \\ 4 \end{array}$$

but since the largest sum (-7) is negative, we must use its sign and the answer is -4.

3. *To subtract one signed number from another, change the sign of the number to be subtracted and add.* Here

$$\begin{aligned}(-3) - (-2) &= \\ (-3) + (+2) &= -1\end{aligned}$$

or

$$\begin{aligned}(-2) - (+10) &= \\ (-2) + (-10) &= -12\end{aligned}$$

4. *The result of multiplying or dividing two numbers of unlike signs is always negative.* For example,

$$(-7)(2) = -14$$

$$\frac{16}{-2} = -8$$

Square Roots. Most people remember having learned to extract square roots during grade school. If not, it will not be necessary to relearn grade school procedure; it is possible to read any roots needed from a table. Table A in the Appendix is a short square root table. To use it, simply look down the first column until you find the number N for which the square root is needed. The corresponding root is listed in the column headed $\sqrt{N}$.

Care must be taken in reading the roots of numbers too large or too small for this table. The table shows, for example, that the number 3 has as its root 1.7321. The root of 30 is 5.4772, and the root of 300 is 17.3205. But how about 3000 or .3?

The solution to this problem is in the tabled values. Note that 3 and 300 have essentially the same root; it differs only in the location of the decimal point. But 30, on the other hand, has an entirely different root. Any sequence of digits has two such roots. Which of the two is appropriate in a given case depends on the location of the decimal point. If the digits are paired off to the left and the right of the decimal, the proper root may be selected. The square roots for various numbers that contain the digit 3 are shown in Table 3.1.

Table 3.1

N	Paired	First Pair	$\sqrt{N}$
3000	30 00.	30	54.772
300	03 00.	03	17.321
30	30.	30	5.4772
3	03.	03	1.7321
.3	.30	30	.54772
.03	.03	03	.17321

Whenever the first pair is 30, the root is 54772, and whenever it is 03, the root is 17321. The placement of the decimal point is governed by the following rule:

The decimal point in $\sqrt{N}$ is moved one place for every two places it is moved in N.

Rules for the Use of $\sum$. It is sometimes useful to know certain rules for the use of $\sum$, the summation symbol. For example,

$$\sum_{i=1}^{N}(X_i + Y_i) = \sum_{i=1}^{N} X_i + \sum_{i=1}^{N} Y_i$$

which says that the summation of the sum of the two variables (X and Y) is equal to the sum of their summations. It makes no difference whether you add each X_i to each Y_i and then sum their total from 1 to N or sum all the X_i's and all the Y_i's and add their sums; the result is the same.

Suppose, for example, that we have five observations of X and five of Y. Let

$$\begin{array}{ll} X_1 = 4 & Y_1 = 7 \\ X_2 = 2 & Y_2 = 8 \\ X_3 = 9 & Y_3 = 1 \\ X_4 = 3 & Y_4 = 5 \\ X_5 = 1 & Y_5 = 2 \end{array}$$

Then $N = 5$ and

$$\sum_{i=1}^{5} X_i = 4 + 2 + 9 + 3 + 1 = 19$$

and

$$\sum_{i=1}^{5} Y_i = 7 + 8 + 1 + 5 + 2 = 23$$

and

$$\sum_{i=1}^{5} X_i + \sum_{i=1}^{5} Y_i = 19 + 23 = 42$$

But

$$\sum_{i=1}^{5} (X_i + Y_i) = (4 + 7) + (2 + 8) + (9 + 1) + (3 + 5) + (1 + 2) = 42$$

The result is indeed the same.

Another rule is expressed in the following equation:

$$\sum_{i=1}^{N} kX_i = k \sum_{i=1}^{N} X_i$$

A constant k may be moved across the summation sign. That is to say, if we are instructed to multiply each of a series of numbers by a constant

$$kX_1 + kX_2 + \cdots + kX_N$$

we can simply sum our numbers and multiply that sum by the constant; the result is the same.

Let us take the same five values of X_i and let $k = 5$. Then

$$\sum_{i=1}^{5} kX_i = (5)(4) + (5)(2) + (5)(9) + (5)(3) + (5)(1) = 95$$

and since we have already established that

$$\sum_{i=1}^{5} X_i = 19$$

$$k \sum_{i=1}^{5} X_i = (5)(19) = 95$$

A third useful rule is the following:

$$\sum_{i=1}^{N} k = kN$$

The summation of a constant is equal to the product of that constant and the number of times it is summed.

Let $k = 4$ and $N = 5$; then

$$\sum_{i=1}^{5} k = 4 + 4 + 4 + 4 + 4 = 20$$

and

$$kN = (4)(5) = 20$$

Rounding Numbers. At one point or another in the process of statistical computing, numbers are typically expressed in decimal form. In such cases, the problem of how many figures to retain in computing and reporting results is evident. Numerous rules for rounding have been proposed. The fact is, however, that very little is known about the effects of applying various rounding procedures. The best general solution to the problem of rounding numbers is to keep as many numbers as can be conveniently handled. In calculating, retain one or two more decimal places than are required in the answer. Then rounding to the desired number of places should be the last step in the calculation.

In the process of rounding numbers, the following three conventions are useful.

1. *If the first of the digits to be dropped is less than* 5, *drop them with no change in the preceding number.*
2. *If the digit or digits to be dropped are greater than* 5 (*that is, if the first digit to be dropped is* 6 *or larger or if the first digit is* 5 *followed by digits other than* 0), *raise the preceding number by* 1.
3. *If the digit to be dropped is exactly* 5 (*followed by nothing but zeros*), *raise the preceding number by* 1 *if it is odd and leave it alone if it is even.*

This last convention is purely arbitrary, but it introduces no special problems. The application of these rounding procedures is illustrated in Table 3.2.

Table 3.2

Result of Computation	Rounded Result
4.59	4.6
.324	.32
9841.500	9842.0
28.500	28.0
6.0501	6.1
21.5002	22.0

Ratios, Proportions, and Percentages. Ratios, proportions, and percentages are useful for reporting data. The ratio depends on the fact that data are never meaningful in and of themselves—that they derive their meaning only in the context of comparison with other data. The ratio is simply a technique for stressing the intended comparison.

Suppose we discovered that the number of males in a certain small community was 34. Our response to such a gem of information may well be, "So what?" But if we were told that the ratio of men to women was 34/2, our response would be of a very different sort; we may well start thinking about army camps or frontier communities where males traditionally predominate to a very great extent.

A ratio may be expressed as a pair of numbers like the one in the illustration just given or the implied division may be completed:

$$\frac{34}{2} = 17$$

When the division is made, the resulting single number is still an implicit pair of numbers. Thus

$$\frac{34}{2} = \frac{17}{1}$$

All single number ratios are ratios-to-one. They may be interpreted as the number of items in the first class to each item in the second. In this case there are 17 males to each female in our hypothetical community. The general formula for any ratio is

$$\text{ratio} = \frac{f_a}{f_b}$$

where f_a = frequency in a class or category,
f_b = the frequency in another category.

One kind of ratio that is especially important is called the *proportion*. A proportion is simply a ratio of the frequency in a given class to the total frequency.

$$\text{proportion} = \frac{f_a}{N}$$

where f_a = frequency in a class,
N = the sum of all frequencies in all classes.

Thus, for the data on sex just listed, the proportion of males is 34/36 = .994. This may be interpreted as suggesting that .94 of each case is male—a somewhat strained idea!

In view of the obvious difficulty of putting most proportions into words, they are commonly modified by multiplication by a constant. The typical constant is 100 and the name for such a modified proportion is a percentage.

Thus

$$\text{percentage} = 100 \cdot \text{proportion}$$

For this example this suggests that 94.4 out of every hundred cases are males. The decimal may be a little unwieldy, but this is certainly an easier idea to express than the raw proportion.

In actual practice it is customary to jump back and forth between proportions and percentages without stressing the multiplication or division involved. This will be the practice of this book. Often .94 will be read as 94% with no further comment. None, I hope, will be necessary.

This completes our discussion of arithmetic procedures. Much more could be said on details and specific devices, but this general review should serve to remind the reader of some of the more useful rules and procedures. Occasionally, a student comes along who just cannot or will not remember even the basic skills of arithmetic. If these students are truly to understand the statistics presented in this book, they must do a little extra work and refresh their mathematical memories. They would do well to run through a text in high school algebra, the review sections in a college algebra text, or best of all, a review book like Helen M. Walker, *Mathematics Essential for Elementary Statistics* (1951).

This chapter has attempted to introduce the student to the symbolism of statistics. A system for classifying and understanding symbols has been presented, and the necessary mathematical skills have been reviewed. From here on we shall stop talking about learning statistics and start learning to talk about statistics.

The remainder of this book is divided into three sections. Each section is devoted to one of the three main tasks of statistics outlined in Chapter 2. Section B is concerned with summarizing observations on variables, Section C with describing association, and Section D with statistical inference. The chapters within each section are devoted to the various forms of data introduced in Chapter 1. This plan of organization is designed to stress the importance of using appropriate statistical methods. Each method is considered in terms of the problem to which it may be addressed and the type of data for which it is suitable.

Section B

Summarizing Distributions on a Single Variable

Statistical procedures can help us to describe and summarize our experience in three ways: (1) the use of such procedures can aid us in making careful observations by emphasizing the need for some system in looking at the world; (2) the procedures of statistics can help us in describing our observations by providing a language for neat, precise communication of what we see; and (3) they can provide us with techniques for constructing accurate summaries of our experience. In the language of statistics, these are called (1) scaling, (2) enumeration, and (3) summary, respectively. Scaling was the concern of Chapter 1; the remaining two topics will be covered in Section B. In this introduction we shall take up the topic of enumeration, and problems of summary will be examined in Chapters 4, 5, and 6.

Enumeration

The nature of scales and the various types of scales were defined in Chapter 1. Just as the procedures of scaling were concerned with the problem of care in observation, enumeration procedures are concerned with the problem of care in reporting observations. It is just as easy to make slipshod statements about what we see as it is to look at things in a sloppy and unplanned way. Statistical enumeration procedures are designed to help us to be rigorous in our reports—to report just what we observe, no more and no less.

Distributions. In the broadest sense statistical enumeration is simply the process of recording and reporting actual observations. When we have constructed a scale and we go out and apply it to our observations—when we have collected actual data according to the rules dictated by the scale—the resulting set of scaled observations is called a *distribution*. We may, for example, enumerate a class of ten schoolchildren according to the nominal scale of sex; this could result in the following distribution of sex:

male	female	female	male	female
female	female	male	male	female

The distribution would consist of nothing but a list of ten class names in no particular order, each denoting the classification of one person.

If we have data on the ordinal scale of final grades for these students, we may enumerate their grades and produce this distribution:

C	*C*	*A*	*C*	*B*
D	*C*	*A*	*B*	*B*

and if we have data on the interval scale of age, our enumeration may produce a distribution like this:

9 9 9 8 9 9 10 9 10 9

In each of these cases all the recorded data are revealed by the enumeration. But in each case, an unordered list is rather cumbersome and difficult to grasp. If our aim is effective communication, such unordered lists are of questionable value. In most situations, particularly as the number of cases becomes large, it is better to list our observations in an ordered distribution or *array*. Thus, if we rearrange our lists for the same three sets of observations, we obtain the following arrays.

SEX

	male	male	male	male	
female	female	female	female	female	female

FINAL GRADE

A *A* *B* *B* *B* *C* *C* *C* *C* *D*

AGE

10 10 9 9 9 9 9 9 9 8

Lists of this sort are, of course, a good deal easier to comprehend at a glance.

Usually there is a still more effective way to list a whole set of observations—a *frequency distribution*. To use a frequency distribution we merely list the appropriate categories in the scale in question and tabulate the frequency of occurrence for each.

For our three lists we obtain the following three frequency distributions.

Sex	Frequency
Male	4
Female	6

Final Grade	Frequency
A	2
B	3
C	4
D	1

Age	Frequency
10	2
9	7
8	1

Obviously, such frequency counts accomplish much in the way of aiding communication. These final distributions are brief and explicit, and they reveal at a glance all the information contained in the original unordered lists.

One condition under which even such frequency distributions can become unwieldy occurs when the number of observed classes is greater than 10 or so. Suppose, for example, we observe 100 residents of a small town and record their ages to the nearest year. In such a situation we may expect to observe cases ranging over 80 or 90 years. Even a frequency distribution of such range would tend to go on and on. But in this instance communication can be improved by combining categories and listing the frequencies for *class intervals* (Table B.1).

Table B.1

Age	Frequency
80 or more	3
70–79	6
60–69	7
50–59	10
40–49	12
30–39	12
20–29	15
10–19	10
Under 10	25

This is a relatively effective way of presenting data which are described in a large number of classes. It is wise to remember, however, that the use of class intervals involves the sacrifice of some data. From Table B.1, for example, we know that seven people range somewhere between 60 and 69 years of age. But we do not know whether they all cluster down around 60, up around 69, or whether they tend to be grouped around the midpoint of the class interval.

Sometimes the use of class intervals is necessitated by the concepts employed. Social psychologists, for example, are sometimes concerned with a concept such as "personal isolation." One way of examining a person's isolation may be in terms of whether or not he was living with other members of his own family group. For adults, then, it may be possible to construct a rough index of personal isolation in terms of marital status. We can collect data on marital status using the usual categories: single, married, widowed, and divorced, and form an index by combining single, widowed, and divorced into an "isolated" class and treat married as "nonisolated." In such cases, where concepts dictate the combination of classes, such combinations are perfectly acceptable.

Then, too, when we have difficulty in classifying cases precisely, combining classes is sometimes a way out. Most people, for example, are not eager to reveal their exact incomes to strangers. In an interview setting, therefore, it might be wise to present them with a request to classify themselves with a $2000.00 interval rather than to demand an exact figure. In such a case, grouping classes would be an expedient to permit the gathering of data. Often such situations arise where it is necessary to sacrifice precise measurement for accurate classification.

Graphic Presentation. Frequency distributions are often expressed graphically either by *histograms* or *frequency polygons*. A histogram is

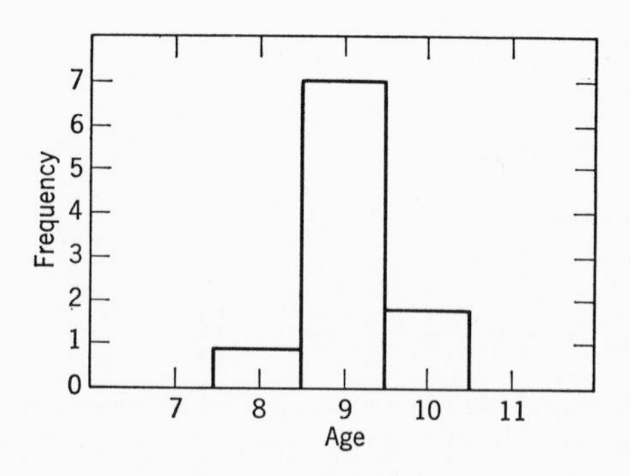

Fig. B.1. A histogram.

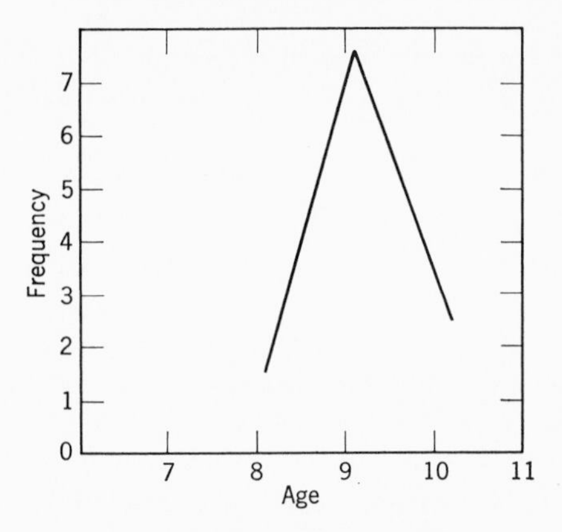

Fig. B.2. Frequency polygon.

simply a bar graph that presents a pictorial view of a distribution. The age distribution of schoolchildren just considered, for example, can be expressed by the graph in Fig. B.1. Such a histogram contains all the information reported in the original frequency distribution.

This same information may also be expressed by means of a frequency polygon (Fig. B.2). Here dots are placed where the tops of the bars would be if a histogram were drawn. Then the dots are joined by drawing straight lines. Such graphic methods are often useful in communicating the results of observation. Furthermore, they permit the classification and comparison of various distributions in terms of their shapes.

Frequency Curves. It is convenient to think of some variables as continuously distributed. Thus, although number of children (1 or 2 or 3, but never 2.57) is a series of discrete steps, weight (125, 125.1, 125.01, 125.001, and so on) may be viewed as continuous. The sequence of

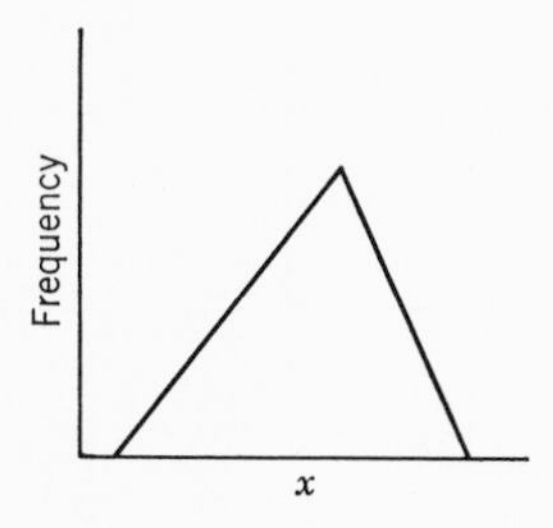

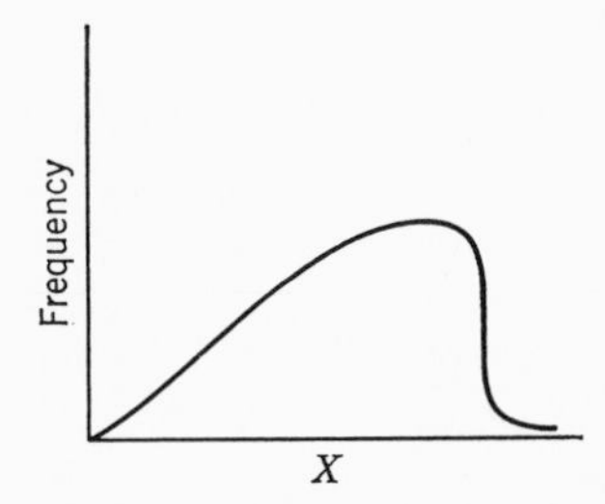

Fig. B.3. Unimodal curves.

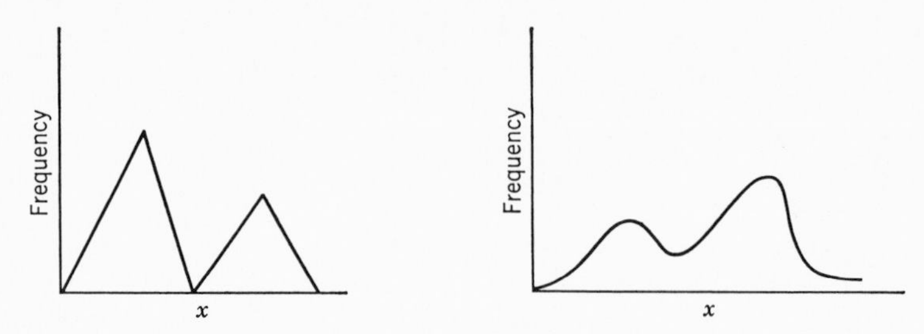

Fig. B.4. Bimodal curves.

decimal places can, in theory, be extended indefinitely so that there are no steps or breaks between 125 and 126.

In practice, of course, we can never record continuous values. We must stop extending our decimals somewhere when we are making actual measurements; we reach the limit of precision of our measuring instruments. We can, however, conceive of continuity for certain variables (like height or weight) and this allows us to talk about frequency curves.

A frequency curve is the limiting case of a frequency polygon for a continuous distribution. When the size of the intervals of measurement becomes infinitesimally small, and when the number of intervals and the number of cases both become infinitely large, the plot of the frequency distribution is a curve.

In practice, we sometimes have a continuously distributed variable, many small intervals of measurement, and a large number of observations. In such cases, we think of the frequency polygon that pictures our observations as an approximation to the curve we may get with an infinite number of continuous observations. Such curves may take any form or shape whatsoever. Certain elements of form, however, may be used to describe and compare recurring patterns.

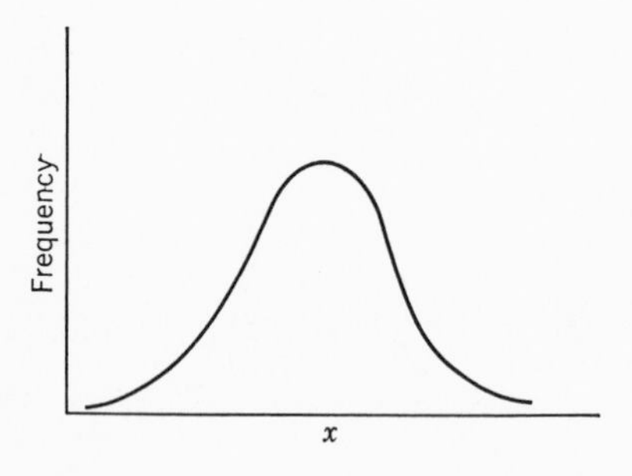

Fig. B.5. A relatively high curve.

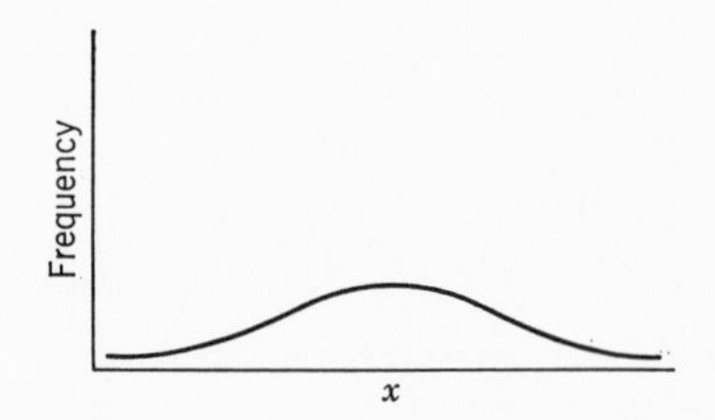

Fig. B.6. A relatively flat curve.

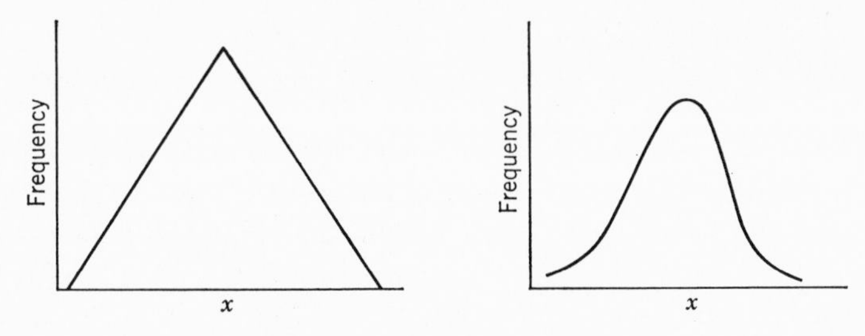

Fig. B.7. Symmetrical curves.

A frequency curve, for example, can be described in terms of the number and height of its *peaks* or points of high frequency. Curves with one prominent peak are called *unimodal*, as shown in Fig. B.3. Two peaked curves are *bimodal*; they have two points of relatively high frequency (Fig. B.4).

Of course, other curves may have three or more high points and still others no high points at all. Thus distributions may be compared in terms of the number of peaks they present in their frequency polygons.

The height or *peakedness* of a curve is another element of interest. Some distributions show a relatively high degree of peakedness (see Fig. B.5). Others, as shown in Fig. B.6, are relatively flat. Comparisons in terms of height can therefore be made.

Still another element of interest is balance or symmetry. Some curves are symmetrical; if they were cut out and folded in the center, one side would cover the other exactly (Fig. B.7). Others, however, are asymmetrical or skewed—their sides do not balance (Fig. B.8).

Furthermore, frequency curves may be classified in terms of their smoothness, the number of inflections or bends they exhibit, or the over-all picture they present to the eye. Certain general shapes are simple enough or common enough to have earned special names. The rectangular

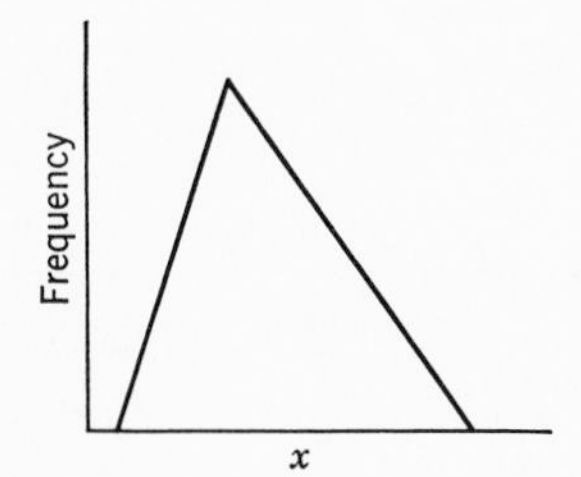

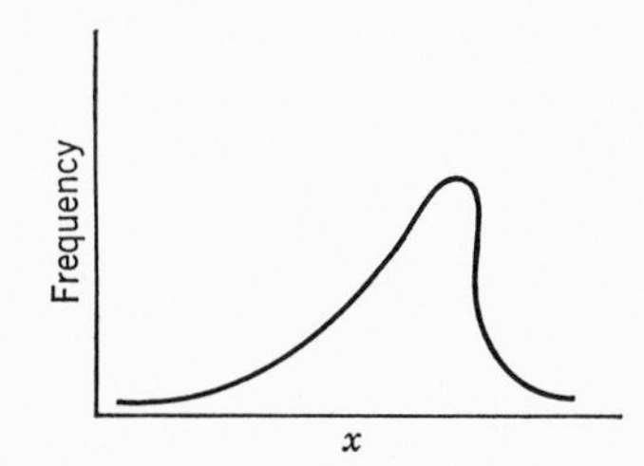

Fig. B.8. Skewed curves.

distribution, for example, in Fig. B.9 is an extremely simple type. It is found whenever all classes in the variable under consideration have identical frequencies. Similarly, some distributions are U-shaped and some are J-shaped. They are pictured just as their names imply. But the most important distribution for most statistical work is the bell-shaped or *normal* distribution (Fig. B.10). This normal curve is important because the observed distributions of a great many variables approximate it quite closely. Then, too, it has wide utility in problems of sampling and statistical inference.

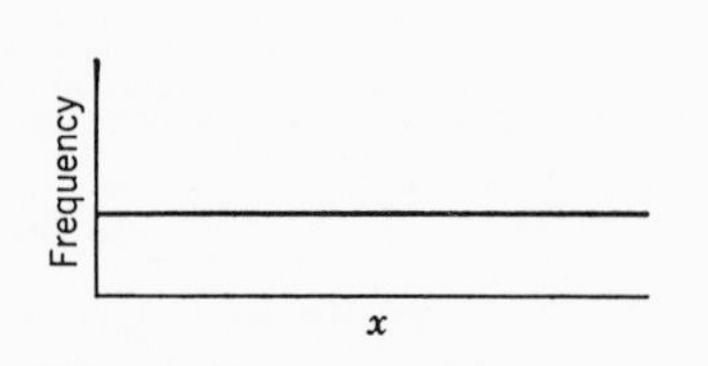

Fig. B.9. Rectangular distribution.

It is a mistake to believe that all, or almost all, observed variables are normally distributed. A great many, however, are. Physical characteristics like height and weight, psychological characteristics like I.Q., and errors of observation all tend to be normal in form. No particular set of observations is *exactly* bell-shaped, but the distributions of such variables approach the normal form quite closely as the number of observations becomes large and the size of intervals of measurement becomes small.

The curve of the normal distribution may be described exactly by means of a rather complicated equation. This equation gives the height of the curve (the *ordinate*) for any particular value of the variable in question. Such a curve has the following properties:

1. It is unimodal—it has one peak—and its greatest frequency is in the center.
2. Its two sides are symmetrical about the center.
3. Its frequencies become smaller and smaller—it approaches closer and closer to the horizontal axis—as it goes out from the center in both directions. But theoretically it never reaches the axis.
4. It has a standard curvature and "peakedness" which are described by its equation and expressed in tables of the normal curve.

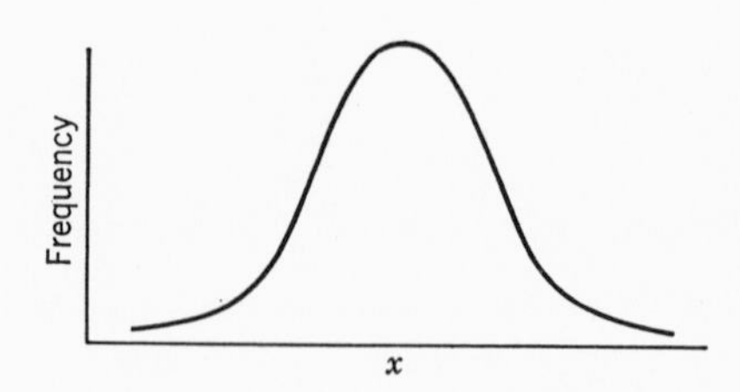

Fig. B.10. Normal distribution.

Here we have only touched on the properties of the normal curve. We shall return to this topic later in the book.

Summarization

It is often inconvenient or impossible to try to record or remember every observation in a distribution. Therefore we need some way to summarize our observations. Statistical procedures can provide us with more accurate means of doing this summarizing than our ordinary language can. The next three chapters will examine statistical summary techniques appropriate for various kinds of data.

4 Summarizing Distributions on Nominal Scales

When we have recorded a large number of observations on a nominally scaled variable, some simple summary of the whole distribution is often useful. In such cases the *mode* is the usual summary statistic. The adequacy of the mode as a summary may be evaluated by means of v, *the variation ratio*. These two statistics will be examined in this chapter.

The Mode

Function. The mode is one kind of average; it expresses the typical observation in a nominal distribution. By using the mode we are able to characterize an entire nominal distribution by means of a single class name or number.

Rationale. In order to understand the mode we need to define only our use of the word "typical" in this context. Suppose we were to poll the adult residents of a small town concerning their marital status. We might obtain the following results.

Marital Status	f
Single	12
Married	225
Widowed	53
Divorced	10

One way to define the typical marital status among these townspeople is to pick the class which has the largest representation—the mode. The mode, then, is the name (or number) of the class possessing the largest frequency in a distribution. It is a "best guess" of the characteristic in question in that if you were asked to guess the marital status of an unspecified person in the town, you would guess the largest class; that way you would have the least chance of being wrong. "Married" is the mode for this distribution.

Procedure. The procedure for determining the mode is exactly that shown in the preceding section. Determine the frequency of observations classified into each category in a nominal scale and select the category with the largest frequency; that is the mode. If two classes are tied for the largest frequency, there are two modes. With three ties there are three modes and so on, but if all the classes are tied, the distribution has no mode.

Example

In 1953 and 1954 Peterson, Andrews, Spain, and Greenberg observed the daily activities of 94 physicians in general practice in North Carolina.[1] Each physician was observed for about three and one-half days while he worked in his office, the hospital, and on house calls. Each was rated on some 200 items designed to evaluate his approach to general practice.

One item required the observer to classify the manner in which each physician handled emotional problems in his patients. The results of these observations are tabulated in Table 4.1.

Table 4.1. *Distribution of Methods Used by 94 Physicians in Dealing with Emotional Problems of Their Patients*

Category of Method	*f*
No general recognition of problems	27
Recognition of problems, but poor treatment or no treatment undertaken	51
Recognition of problems and competent treatment undertaken	16
Total	94

If we want a single over-all summary of the approach to emotional problems taken by these physicians, we might use the mode. The modal response is the category "Recognition of problems, but poor treatment or no treatment at all." To put it more formally,

Mode = recognition of problems, but poor treatment or no treatment at all.

This is our summary; it is the best guess or typical case of response to emotional problems among these physicians.

[1] Osler L. Peterson, Leon P. Andrews, Robert S. Spain, and Bernard G. Greenberg, "An Analytical Study of North Carolina General Practice 1953–1954," *The Journal of Medical Education*, **31** (December, 1956), Part 2, 1–165.

Summary of Procedure. To determine the mode in any distribution:

1. Determine the frequency in each of the classes in the scale.
2. Select the class with the largest frequency; this is the mode.

Other Statistics. There are no other statistics that do the same job as the mode.

Variation Ratio

The variation ratio v is as straightforward and direct as the mode. It is both simple to compute and easy to understand.

Function. Any distribution of observations has two characteristics: (1) an average or typical observation and (2) more or less variation or difference among the observations. For distributions on nominal scales the mode is the typical observation. However, by itself, the mode is not a satisfactory summary. It leaves us with a question of just how typical an observation it is. This is where v is of value. v is an index of the amount of variation or the range of difference among the cases in a distribution of nominal scale classifications.

Rationale. The easiest way to grasp the meaning of v is to go back to the idea of guessing. The mode is the best guess, and v is simply the proportion of wrong guesses. Consider the data on marital status introduced earlier:

Marital Status	f
Single	12
Married	225
Widowed	53
Divorced	10

If we are told to guess the marital status of an unspecified person in the distribution, we will, of course, guess "Married"—the mode. If we repeat the operation and guess the mode for each and every individual in the distribution, we will be wrong 75 out of the total 300 cases. The proportion of incorrect guesses then is

$$\frac{75}{300} = .25$$

This is v, the proportion of nonmodal cases. The smaller v is, the more satisfactory the mode is as a summary of the distribution. The larger v is, the less satisfactory the mode.

The importance of v may be understood by considering another example. Suppose we are concerned with sex as a variable. And suppose we have two distributions, one from an engineering college and one from a liberal arts college. The following, let us say, are our observed distributions:

Engineering College		Liberal Arts College	
Sex	f	Sex	f
Male	482	Male	1004
Female	18	Female	996

In both these cases the modal sex is male. These two modes, however, summarize quite different distributions. Although the engineering college is overwhelmingly male, in the liberal arts college males predominate only slightly. This can be made explicit by computing v in each case.

For the engineering college,

$$\frac{18}{500} = .036$$

For the liberal arts college,

$$\frac{996}{2000} = .498$$

The mode therefore is a far better summary of the sex of these engineering students than it is of these liberal arts students.

Procedure. The variation ratio may be calculated by the procedure just described, but, in general, it is simpler to use the following formula:

$$v = 1 - \frac{f_{\text{modal}}}{N} \tag{4.1}$$

where f_{modal} = the frequency in the modal class,
N = the total number of cases in all classes.

Here, in effect, we are subtracting the proportion of correct guesses from unity to determine the proportion of incorrect guesses. This is easier because it saves us the trouble of adding up all the incorrect guesses.

The computation and interpretation of v are straightforward. The only problem that can arise is when a distribution has more than one mode. Here, v is calculated on the basis of any one of the modal classes. If we are called on to guess, we shall have to guess one of the modes (it would make no difference which one) and the cases falling in the others will have to be counted as errors along with the nonmodal cases.

Example

Sommer has investigated the ways in which pairs of people arrange themselves when they sit down together at a table for eight.[2] Sommer was concerned with the degree to which people seated themselves in face-to-face, side-by-side, or corner-to-corner positions when they sat down to talk. His data are recorded in Table 4.3.

Table 4.3. *Arrangements of People Interacting*

Arrangement	f
Face-to-face	5
Side-by-side	16
Corner-to-corner	30
Total	51

The mode for this distribution is corner-to-corner. v may be calculated by applying Formula 4.1.

$$
\begin{aligned}
v &= 1 - \frac{f_{\text{modal}}}{N} \\
&= 1 - \frac{30}{51} \\
&= 1 - .59 \\
&= .41
\end{aligned}
$$

Thus 41% of these couples seated themselves in nonmodal fashion.

Summary of Procedure. To compute v the following steps are necessary.

1. Calculate the total number of cases and the frequency in the modal category (or in any one modal category if there is more than one mode).
2. Compute v using Formula 4.1.

Other Statistics. A number of other statistics might be used in order to obtain the information recorded in the variation ratio. Most of these are equivalent to or derivable from v. Only two differ enough to deserve special mention here.

UNCERTAINTY MEASURE. The statistic $\hat{H}$ is a measure of uncertainty. It is based on information theory and has therefore some advantage over v

[2] Robert Sommer, "Studies in Personal Space," *Sociometry*, **22** (September, 1959), 247–260.

as a generalizing and comparative statistic. $\hat{H}$, however, is recorded in a binary (two-valued) number system which makes it relatively difficult to interpret. See Senders (1958) for a discussion of $\hat{H}$.

MUELLER AND SCHUESSLER'S INDEX OF QUALITATIVE VARIATION. The index of qualitative variation employs a different approach to assessing variability than the variation ratio. Instead of calculating a simple proportion of nonmodal cases, Mueller and Schuessler are concerned with providing an over-all index of heterogeneity for a set of nominally scaled observations. This statistic is discussed by Mueller and Schuessler (1961).

I.Q.V., along with $\hat{H}$, has essentially the same purpose as v. All are designed as indexes of variation for nominal scales. Choice among them may be dictated by the problem at hand, but it is often largely a matter of personal taste.

5 Summarizing Distributions on Ordinal Scales

When data are collected on an ordinal scale, the mode and variation ratio are not wholly satisfactory as summaries of observed distributions. Ranks embody more information than nominal classifications—they include a record of the order among the cases in the distribution. But since neither the mode nor v is sensitive to order, we need some new summaries, ones that will preserve some record of the original arrangement of our observations.

When our data are ordinal, then, we may use the *median* as an average and the *decile range* as the index of variation. This chapter will be concerned with these statistics.

The Median

Function. The median is a kind of average that is appropriate for ordinal data. By recording a rank to represent an entire distribution, the median enables us to summarize that distribution in a single number.

Rationale. Since ordinal data are not merely categorized but arranged in *ordered* categories, the middle of the arrangement has great importance as a summary. The middle of a distribution is called the *median.* It is

Table 5.1. *Final Examination Results of Two Groups of Students Taught by Different Methods*

Method 1		Method 2	
Betty	A	John	B
Bill	A	Joan	C
Bart	B	James	D
Brett	B	Jean	F
Barbara	C	Joyce	F

the case around which the others are distributed, so it is typical in the sense that it represents neither extreme but the central tendency of the whole array.

Consider, for example, the distribution of class grades in Table 5.1.

In a case like this it is obvious that, as a whole, the students taught by Method 1 performed better than those instructed by Method 2. The median, however, can provide us with a means of direct comparison. The middle grade in the first array is B, and that in the second is D. These two medians summarize the relative standings of their respective distributions, and show that, for these students at least, Method 1 is superior.

In the general case, the median describes the central tendency of an ordinal distribution. Thus it captures the general tendency of the distributions towards relatively high or relatively low rankings.

Procedure. The median has been described as the middle case. This may be put more precisely by the following definition.

The median of an ordinal scale is any point which neither exceeds nor is exceeded in rank by more than 50% of the total observations.

If the distribution contains an odd number of observations, applying the rule will lead to the selection of the middle case. If, however, there is an even number of observations, complications may arise.

First, let us examine the procedure for computing the median when the number of cases is odd. Suppose we were able to rank seven students in social class background.

Student	Rank
A	4
B	3
C	3
D	3
E	2
F	1
G	1

The seven students are arrayed in order from the highest to the lowest with several ties. In this distribution the middle case is the fourth from the top (or from the bottom)—the case with three persons ranking above and three ranking below it. That case is represented by student *D* whose rank was 3; so the median rank is 3. This rank neither exceeds nor is exceeded by more than half the other ranks.

Let us suppose now that there were only six students.

Student	Rank
A	4
B	3
C	3
D	3
E	2
F	1

In this situation, with an even number of ranks, there is no middle case. The middle of the distribution is located between student *C* and student *D*. Since both these students ranked 3, however, the middle of the distribution must be 3. Rank 3, then, is the median; it is the only rank that neither exceeds nor is exceeded by more than half the observations in other ranks.

Suppose, however, the six students were ranked in the following way.

Student	Rank
A	4
B	3
C	3
D	2
E	1
F	1

Now the middle of the distribution must fall between student *C*, who ranks 3, and student *D*, who ranks 2. Both these ranks, 2 and 3, satisfy the criterion of neither exceeding nor being exceeded by more than half the other ranks; both then are eligible to be the median. In such cases convention dictates that we locate the median halfway between the two middle ranks, at $2\frac{1}{2}$. If we remember that the $\frac{1}{2}$ in this case refers solely to position or order and not to amount of difference, the custom is satisfactory. But we must never lose sight of this fact. A value of $2\frac{1}{2}$ indicates only that the median is located between rank 2 and rank 3; it does not imply an actual halfway location as it would if we were dealing with interval data.

In summary, to determine the median of a distribution the cases must be ordered in an array from the highest to the lowest rank. If the number of cases is odd, the median is the rank of the middle case. If the number is even, the median is located on the basis of the two middle cases; when these cases are tied, the median takes their rank; when they differ, the median is ranked halfway between the two.

Example

As part of a larger study of political power Mac Rae and Price scaled thirty-four United States Senators with respect to their votes on issues involving foreign aid.[1] Each Senator was ranked in terms of the degree of internationalism shown in his voting for each year from 1946 through 1954. In 1946, for example, there were nine roll call votes in the Senate on issues of foreign aid. The votes of these Senators on these issues showed a consistent pattern, so Mac Rae and Price were able to rank the Senators from those opposing all foreign aid to those supporting it in every case. Table 5.2 shows the rankings for 1946.

Table 5.2. *Ranks of 34 United States Senators on the Amount of Internationalism Shown in Their Votes in 1946*

Senator	Rank	Senator	Rank
Hayden	8	Kilgore	7
Smith (New Jersey)	8	Hickenlooper	7
Wiley	8	Eastland	7
Ferguson	8	Bridges	7
Knowland	8	Cordon	6
Murray	8	Byrd	5
Morse	8	Russell	4
Fulbright	8	McCarran	4
Saltonstall	8	McClellan	3
Magnuson	7	Butler (Nebraska)	2
Chavez	7	Capehart	2
George	7	Johnston	1
Maybank	7	Ellender	1
Green	7	Millikin	1
Hill	7	Johnson (Colorado)	1
Aiken	7	Langer	1
Hoey	7	Young	1

Now if we wished to summarize these ranks in a single number we could use the median. Here we have an even number of cases (34), so the median must be determined by using the two middle cases (17 and 18). The seventeenth case from the top is Senator Hoey, the eighteenth, Senator Kilgore; since both of these men rank 7, the median internationalism rank among these 34 Senators is 7. This is our summary: it is the typical rank

[1] Duncan Mac Rae, Jr., and Hugh D. Price, "Scale Positions and Power in the Senate," *Behavioral Science*, **4** (July, 1959), 212–218.

in internationalism for these Senators in 1946. Any Senator ranking higher than 7 may be described as relatively internationalist, whereas a Senator ranking below 7 may be called relatively noninternationalist.

Summary of Procedure. To determine the median for any ordinal distribution:

1. Arrange the ranks in order from the highest to the lowest.
2. Determine whether N, the number of cases, is odd or even.
   (*a*) If N is odd, the middle case is the median.
   (*b*) If N is even, the two middle cases must be used.
      i. If they are tied, the median takes their rank.
      ii. If they differ, the median is located halfway between them.

Other Statistics. There are no other statistics that do the same job as the median. The mode may be used for ordinal data, but since it is not sensitive to order, it may fail to capture the tendency of the whole distribution to be either high or low.

The Decile Range

The decile range is one of a large number of measures of variability which can be used for ordinal data.

Function. The function of d, the decile range, parallels that of v, the variation ratio. When the median is used to summarize a set of observations, d reveals the scatter or the variation of the whole range of observations—it shows how well the median represents all the individual cases. The median and d, taken together, are needed for a satisfactory summary of a set of ordered scores.

Rationale. The median is one of a whole set of measures of location that are defined in terms of cumulative frequencies. In general, such measures are called *quantiles*, and certain special types have special names like quartiles, deciles, and centiles or percentiles. All these quantiles are points which are determined by dividing a distribution into segments in terms of proportions of cases falling below them. The first quartile, for example, is the rank below which one-quarter of the cases fall, and the first decile is the point below which one-tenth of the cases fall. In this light, the median is the point below which one-half of the cases fall; it is the same as the second quartile, the fifth decile, or the fiftieth centile.

Since quantiles are measures of position, if we take the difference between any two of them we have a simple and direct index of variation.[2] Eighty percent of the cases, for example, fall between the first and the ninth deciles; 10% are below the first decile, and 10% above the ninth. If the number of ranks falling between the first and ninth deciles is large, the variation is great; if the number is small, there is little variation.

Compare in Table 5.3 the two distributions over the same set of ranks.

Table 5.3

Distribution *A* Ranks	Distribution *B* Ranks
9	6
8	6
7	6
6	5
5	5
5	5
4	5
3	4
2	4
1	4

In both distributions the median is 5. The ranges, however, from the first to the ninth deciles differ greatly.

In the first distribution we can locate the first decile by finding the point below which 10% of the cases fall. Since $N = 10$, one case constitutes 10%; so the first decile falls between rank 1 and rank 2—its value is 1.5. Ninety percent or nine cases fall below rank 9; so the ninth decile is between 8 and 9 or 8.5. The range between 8.5 and 1.5 is 7, the decile range for distribution *A*.

In distribution *B* the first decile is 4, the ninth is 6, and the range is $6 - 4 = 2$. Clearly, then, the first distribution involves more variation than the second. The middle 80% of distribution *A* ranges across 7 ranks, whereas that for the second distribution covers only 2 ranks. When we know both the median and the decile range, we have a summary not only of the location (high or low) but of the spread or variation in a distribution.

Procedure. The procedure for computing the decile range is simply an extension of the computing technique for the median. It is necessary to

[2] Strictly speaking, subtraction is not appropriate for ranks. The difference between two quantiles is a measure of the number of *ranks* between two points in the frequency distribution. Thus it may be used as an index of variation only for comparisons on the *same set of ranks*.

locate two ranks: d_1 the rank below which 10% of the cases fall, and d_9 the rank below which 90% of the cases fall. To find d_1 we must multiply the total number of cases, N, by .1 in order to determine the number of cases in the lowest 10%. Then when we arrange the cases in order, we can locate d_1, the dividing line, the point below which the lowest 10% of the cases fall.

Suppose we had the distribution of ranks with $N = 31$ as in Table 5.4.

Table 5.4

12	9	6	4
12	8	6	4
11	8	6	3
11	8	6	3
10	7	5	2
10	7	5	2
10	7	5	1
9	7	5	

Then $.1N$ equals 3.1; that is, 3.1 cases are in the lowest 10%. Since there are more than three cases in the 10% with which we are concerned, d_1 must fall within the fourth case from the bottom; d_1, then, equals 3. As a general rule, when the number of cases by $.1N$ is not a whole number, d_1 is the rank of the next case. If, however, $.1N$ produces a whole number, d_1 is a rank halfway between the rank of the top case in the lowest 10%

Table 5.5

	12	8	6	
	12	8	5	
	11	7	5	
	11	7	5	
	10	7	5	
Set 1	10	7	4	
	10	6	4	$d_1 = 3.5$
	9	6	3	
	9	6	2	
	8	6	1	

and the next rank. Thus, when $N = 30$, $.1N = 3$, and d_1 is the rank halfway between the third and the fourth cases. Tables 5.5 and 5.6 are two examples where $N = 30$.

Table 5.6

	12	8	6	
	12	8	5	
	11	7	5	
	11	7	5	
Set 2	10	7	4	
	10	7	3	
	10	6	3	$d_1 = 3$
	9	6	3	
	9	6	2	
	8	6	1	

To compute d_9 we could determine $.9N$ and count up from the bottom of the distribution. But since d_9 and d_1 are symmetrical and since

$$.9N = N - .1N$$

we can simply use the same number, $.1N$, and count *down* from the top of the array. Thus for the three specimen distributions above $d_9 = 11$.

To determine d, then, we subtract d_1 from d_9, this gives the range which includes the middle 80% of the cases. Symbolically, we can write it as follows:

$$d = d_9 - d_1 \tag{5.1}$$

where d_9 = the rank below which 90% of the cases fall,
d_1 = the rank below which 10% of the cases fall.

Example

As a part of a study of social class in France and America, Rogoff compared the responses of Frenchmen and Americans to a multiple-choice question on class affiliation.[3] Each subject was given a series of four ranked classes (upper, middle, working, and lower) and asked to indicate his own affiliation. Her results for those individuals who classified themselves are shown in Table 5.7.

The median rank for both Frenchmen and Americans is 2, working class. There, however, the similarity ends. If we compute d for each of these distributions, the difference becomes apparent.

[3] Natalie Rogoff, "Social Stratification in France and in the United States," *American Journal of Sociology*, **58** (January, 1953), 347–357.

Table 5.7. Responses to Multiple-Choice Question on Class Affiliation in France and the United States

France			United States		
Class and Rank		Number of Respondents	Class and Rank		Number of Respondents
Bourgeois	4	227	Upper	4	33
Middle	3	665	Middle	3	472
Working	2	798	Working	2	559
Peasant	1	426	Lower	1	11
Total		2116	Total		1075

For the French, $.1N$ equals 211.6. The first decile, then, is the 212th case from the bottom. But since the first 426 cases all rank 1, d_1 must equal 1. When we count down 212 cases from the top to locate d_9, we find that since the top 227 cases are tied at rank 4, d_9 must be 4. For the French, therefore,

$$\begin{aligned} d &= d_9 - d_1 \\ &= 4 - 1 \\ &= 3 \end{aligned}$$

The middle 80% of the self-ratings vary over a range of 3 ranks.

Now for the Americans, $.1N = 107.5$. That means that d_1 is the rank of the 108th case from the bottom—in this distribution, 2. And d_9 is the 108th case from the top—rank 3. For the Americans, then

$$\begin{aligned} d &= d_9 - d_1 \\ &= 3 - 2 \\ &= 1 \end{aligned}$$

The middle 80% of the cases range over only one rank.

If we compare the French and American distributions, we find that although the medians are the same, the decile ranges differ. The Americans in this sample are a good deal more homogeneous in their self-classifications than are the Frenchmen.

Summary of Procedure. To compute the decile range it is necessary to determine two points: d_1 the first decile, and d_9, the ninth decile. These may be determined in the following way:

1. Arrange the ranks in an array from the highest to the lowest.
2. Calculate $.1N$, the number of cases in 10% of the distribution.
   (*a*) If $.1N$ is a whole number, count up $.1N$ ranks from the bottom of the distribution. d_1 is the rank halfway between the $.1N$th

case and the one above it. To locate d_9 count down $.1N$ cases from the top and d_9 is the rank halfway between the $.1N$th case from the top and the one below it.

(*b*) But if $.1N$ is not a whole number, round it to the next larger whole number. Then d_1 is the rank of the case of that number from the bottom and d_9 is the rank of the case of that number from the top.

3. Compute d according to Formula 5.1.

Other Statistics. A great many other statistics may be used for the same purpose as d. Some of the more common ones are the following.

THE RANGE. The range is the difference between the highest and lowest observation. As such, it is a measure of variability. See Wallis and Roberts (1956) for a discussion of the range.

OTHER INTERQUANTILE RANGES. Several other interquantile ranges have been used as measures of variability. Perhaps the most common is the semi-interquartile range, which is half the difference between the first and third quartiles. Wallis and Roberts (1956) have an excellent discussion of these various measures of variation. In general, however, d is at least as satisfactory as any interquantile range.

6 Summarizing Distributions on Interval Scales

Either the mode or the median may be used to summarize an interval distribution, and either the variation ratio or the interdecile range can be used as an index of dispersion. In general, however, we can do a better job of summarizing interval data by using the *mean* and the *standard deviation.* It is these two statistics with which this chapter will be concerned.

The Mean

Function. The mean is a one-number summary of a distribution of interval scores. Like the mode and the median it is a kind of average; in fact, when people say "the average" they are generally talking about the mean. And like any average, the mean provides a single score which is designed to represent an entire distribution.

Rationale. One good way to understand the mean is in terms of an analogy to a point of balance or center of gravity. Suppose we have an old-fashioned teeter-totter or seesaw and some children each weighing exactly the same amount. Let us go further and imagine that these children are pliable youngsters and that when we load them where we want them they will stay put.

Let us now load the children on the seesaw and consider whether it will balance or not. Obviously, as we load children on one end or the other, the balance will depend on two factors: (1) the relative weights of the children and (2) their respective distances from the fulcrum or point of suspension. Since our children, however, all have equal weights, the balance depends only on their distance from the fulcrum. It is clear, for example, that if we had four of the children arranged as in Fig. 6.1, the seesaw would balance (each square represents one child). In this illustration the fact that there are two children on each side of the fulcrum is not the critical factor for balance; it is their respective distances on each side that counts. There is a child one unit to the left of the fulcrum (-1) and

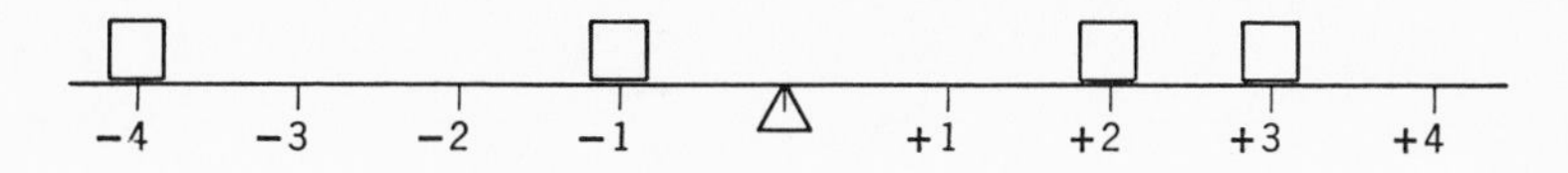

Fig. 6.1

one child who is four units to the left (−4). The total distance to the left therefore is (−1) + (−4) = (−5). On the right side there is a child at (+2) and one at (+3). These sum to (+5) and the seesaw balances. The seesaw will balance whenever the sum of the distances of the children to the left of the fulcrum is equal to the sum of the distances of those to the right. So as long as we can move the fulcrum we can always balance the seesaw.

The mean of a distribution of interval scores is exactly like the fulcrum of our seesaw. It is the point of balance around which a set of scores is distributed such that the scores above are balanced by those below. As an example consider the heights of the following seven schoolchildren:

	Inches
Arthur	66
Adam	63
Alice	59
Abel	61
Anthony	63
Arlene	62
Adele	60

Now if we imagine that these scores can be arranged on a seesaw, we can try to locate the point of balance. Obviously, the fulcrum cannot be located down near 59 in. or up near 66 in. since that would rule out any possibility of balance. It must be somewhere near the center, say 61 in., 62 in., or 63 in. Let us try 61 in., which is shown in Fig. 6.2. Here the seesaw refuses to balance. There are only three (2 + 1) units of distance (or deviations) on the minus side and ten (1 + 2 + 2 + 5) on the plus side. At 62 in., however, balance is restored (Fig. 6.3). There is a total

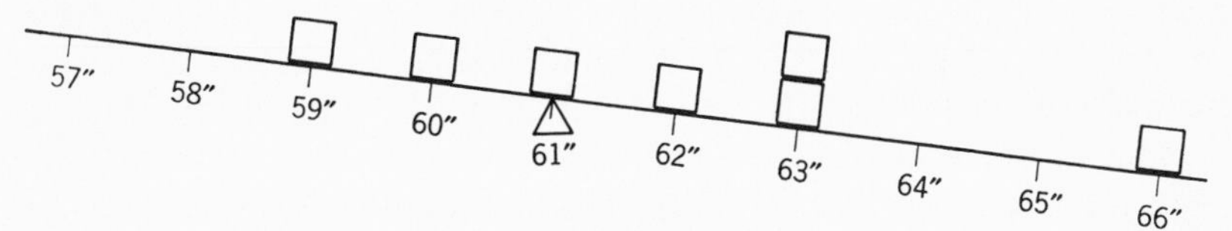

Fig. 6.2

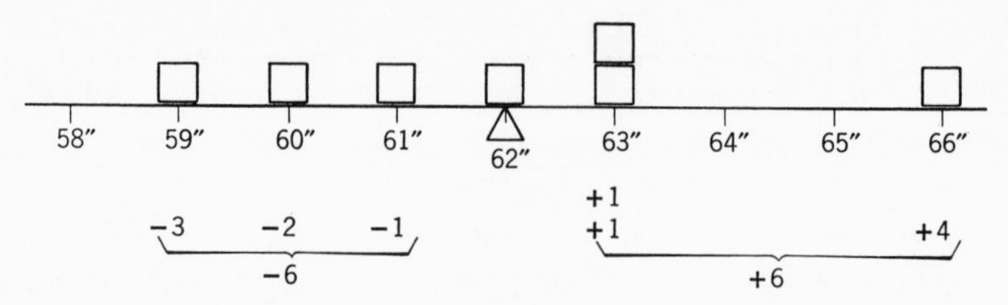

Fig. 6.3

of six (3 + 2 + 1) minus deviations and six (1 + 1 + 4) plus deviations. The mean height for these children, then, is 62 in.; that is the balance point for this distribution of seven heights. As such, it summarizes the weight (the tendency to be high or low) for the whole distribution.

Procedure. It is always possible to work out the mean in the trial-and-error fashion already described. All of us remember, however, from grade school days, a much more direct and simple method of computation. To find the mean of a set of scores simply add them together and divide their sum by the number of scores in the set. We can simplify even more by shortening that expression into symbols.

$$\bar{X} = \frac{\sum_{i=1}^{N} X_i}{N} \tag{6.1}$$

where $\bar{X}$ is the mean,

X_i represents a score,

$\sum_{i=1}^{N}$ instructs you to add from $i = 1$ to N,

N is the number of cases.

In other words, add up all the scores from the first to the Nth,

$$\sum_{i=1}^{N} X_i = X_1 + X_2 + \cdots + X_N$$

Then divide their sum by the number of cases:

$$\frac{\sum_{i=1}^{N} X_i}{N}$$

and you have the mean

$$\bar{X} = \frac{\sum_{i=1}^{N} X_i}{N}$$

We can apply this procedure to our earlier example involving the heights of seven children.

$$\sum_{i=1}^{N} X = 66 + 63 + 59 + 61 + 63 + 62 + 60 = 434$$

$$N = 7$$

$$\bar{X} = \frac{\sum_{i=1}^{N} X_i}{N} = \frac{434}{7} = 62$$

We get the same result we obtained earlier by trial and error.

Example

Merriam and the author have reported the results of a study in which they attempted to distinguish between two styles of cult music on the

Table 6.1. *Proportions of Minor Thirds Found in Two Samples of Twenty Songs Each*

Rada Type	Ketu Type
.529	.211
.281	.327
.412	.204
.541	.115
.574	.199
.399	.278
.416	.023
.350	.100
.203	.484
.471	.121
.359	.363
.394	.108
.550	.081
.332	.136
.423	.280
.440	.411
.385	.170
.440	.189
.414	.152
.249	.220

basis of a statistical study of their musical form.[1] They took samples of 20 songs each from the Ketu cult of Brazil and the Rada cult of Trinidad. Counts were made of the proportions of various intervals (musical distances between adjacent notes) which were used in each song. Results of the count for the use of minor thirds are reported in Table 6.1. When we look at the figures in Table 6.1, we can make comparisons between the proportions of minor thirds used in Rada and Ketu music. The first Rada song, for example, employed a larger proportion of minor thirds than the first Ketu song, and the second Ketu song used more than the second Rada one. If we really want to compare these two samples for the entire twenty songs, we must calculate their respective means. For the Rada type,

$$\bar{X} = \frac{\sum_{i=1}^{N} X_i}{N}$$

$$= \frac{.529 + .281 + .412 + .541 + .574 + .399 + .416 + .350 + .203 + .471 + .359 + .394 + .550 + .332 + .423 + .440 + .385 + .440 + .414 + .249}{20}$$

$$= \frac{8.162}{20}$$

$$= .4081$$

And for the Ketu type,

$$\bar{X} = \frac{\sum_{i=1}^{N} X_i}{N}$$

$$= \frac{.211 + .327 + .204 + .115 + .199 + .278 + .023 + .100 + .484 + .121 + .363 + .108 + .136 + .280 + .411 + .170 + .189 + .152 + .220}{20}$$

$$= \frac{4.172}{20}$$

$$= .2086$$

Thus it is clear that for the forty songs in question the Rada use a greater proportion of minor thirds than do the Ketu. Since Rada used an average of .4081 minor thirds and the Ketu only .2086, we can distinguish between these musical styles on the basis of their use of minor thirds.

[1] Linton C. Freeman and Alan P. Merriam, "Statistical Classification in Anthropology: An Application to Ethnomusicology," *American Anthropologist*, **58** (June, 1956), 464–472.

Summary of Procedure. For any data distributed on an interval scale the mean may be calculated by applying Formula 6.1.

Other Statistics. Several other procedures may be applied in addition to or instead of the mean. They will now be discussed.

THE MODE. The mode may be used for interval data, but it is crude and insensitive to order, and its location may be the result of the width and location of intervals. See Wallis and Roberts (1956) for further discussion on this application of the mode.

THE MEDIAN. In general, the mean is superior to the median as a summary of interval scores. One instance, however, when the median is better occurs when the distribution is strongly asymmetrical or skewed one way or the other. Income generally produces such a skewed distribution; a few cases have extremely high incomes, but most tend to bunch up at the bottom. Then the mean, which as a balance point is sensitive to the extremeness of extreme cases, will be high, but the median—always the middle—will be lower and therefore more typical of the spirit of the entire distribution. When this occurs, it is probably wise to use the median as a summary. See Huff (1954) for an elaboration of this problem.

THE HARMONIC MEAN. The harmonic mean is limited to special applications in the economics of price. See Croxton and Cowden (1939) for an extensive discussion of this statistic.

OTHER MEANS. There are several other measures of central tendency, but since they contribute very little to meaningful summarization of data, they will not be discussed here. The only one of interest in this context is the *quadratic mean*

$$\bar{X}_{\text{quad}} = \sqrt{\frac{\sum X^2}{N}}$$

which is the square root of the mean of the squares of the observations. This is important only in that the standard deviation is a special case of the quadratic mean. It will be discussed in the following section.

Standard Deviation

Most beginning students seem to feel that the standard deviation s has less intuitive appeal than any other statistic they come up against. It certainly seems to make less sense than the mean deviation (see the end of this chapter), but it has several advantages which make it preferable to any other statistic as an index of dispersion. (1) If successive samples are drawn from the same population, s will tend to vary less from sample to sample—it is more stable than other indexes of variation; (2) the standard deviation permits algebraic manipulation; and (3) it provides a basis for several of the more advanced statistical procedures. Given these advantages it is not surprising that we almost never see any other statistic used as an index of variation for interval data.

Function. The standard deviation is an index of dispersion or variation that may be used for data in the form of interval scale scores. It reveals how widely the scores in a distribution vary around the mean; thus it is an index of the value of the mean as a summary of the distribution. The mean and the standard deviation, together, provide a summary of the location and the spread in a set of scores.

Rationale. One way to summarize the variation or spread of a distribution is to calculate some sort of average of the distances of each of the scores from the mean. We cannot, however, use the ordinary mean as our average. For, as we saw earlier, the mean is the balance point in a distribution, and the sum of the deviations or distances of all of the other scores from the mean must always be zero. For example, Table 6.2 shows a distribution of observations of the number of children playing in a small park each afternoon for a week.

Table 6.2

Day	Number of Children
Sunday	5
Monday	3
Tuesday	4
Wednesday	4
Thursday	2
Friday	4
Saturday	6
Total	28

The average number of children playing on an afternoon of the week in question is

$$\bar{X} = \frac{\sum_{i=1}^{N} X_i}{N} = \frac{28}{7} = 4$$

But if we calculate the sum of the deviations of each of the observations from the mean, we shall get zero as our answer (Table 6.3). And the mean of these deviations is, of course, also zero. Since the mean of any distribution is always the point of balance, the sum of the deviations of the other scores from the mean must always be zero.

Table 6.3

Day	Number of Children	Average Number	Deviation
	X_i	$\bar{X}$	$X_i - \bar{X}$
Sunday	5	4	1
Monday	3	4	−1
Tuesday	4	4	0
Wednesday	4	4	0
Thursday	2	4	−2
Friday	4	4	0
Saturday	6	4	2
Total	28	28	0

Here is where the quadratic mean is of value. If each deviation is squared, they all become positive and therefore they no longer total to zero. Then we can add up the squares and divide by the number of cases, as we do with an ordinary mean, and next extract the square root in order to convert back to our original units of measurement. Symbolically, this results in the following formula:

$$s = \sqrt{\frac{\sum_{i=1}^{N} x_i^2}{N}}$$

where s = the standard deviation,
$x_i = X_i - \bar{X}$, the deviation of each score from the mean,
N = the number of cases.

Let us see how this works for our data on children's play habits (Table 6.4).

Table 6.4

Day	No. of Children	Average Number	Deviation	Squared Deviation
	X_i	$\bar{X}$	x_i	x_i^2
Sunday	5	4	1	1
Monday	3	4	−1	1
Tuesday	4	4	0	0
Wednesday	4	4	0	0
Thursday	2	4	−2	4
Friday	4	4	0	0
Saturday	6	4	2	4
Total	28	28	0	10

$$s = \sqrt{\frac{\sum_{i=1}^{N} x_i^2}{N}}$$
$$= \sqrt{\frac{10}{7}}$$
$$= \sqrt{1.428}$$
$$= 1.19$$

Thus the standard deviation is 1.19 children.

That leaves us with a problem of interpretation. What does the standard deviation mean? Clearly, it is not a point of balance like an ordinary mean, but, on the other hand, it is a kind of average. The standard deviation has the following characteristics.

1. It is always a positive number.
2. It measures variability in the same units as those of the original observations.
3. *No matter how the original observations are distributed* the mean plus or minus two standard deviations ($\bar{X} \pm 2s$) will include at least 75% of the observations.
4. *No matter how the original observations are distributed* the mean plus or minus three standard deviations ($\bar{X} \pm 3s$) will include 89% or more.

This list of four characteristics of s provides us with some basis for interpretation. Simply, we can view s as an index of variation; as variation increases, s increases.

Under certain circumstances we can make even more elegant interpretations of the standard deviation. These interpretations are based on the fact that many interval scale distributions are roughly normal. The normal curve and the standard deviation are related in such a way that as our observations approach the shape of a normal curve they tend to become completely determinate from knowledge of the mean and the standard deviation. Thus, if our observed distribution is smooth, unimodal, and if the mode falls within one standard deviation of the mean, $\bar{X} \pm s$ will include at least 56% of the cases, $\bar{X} \pm 2s$ will include at least 89%, and $\bar{X} \pm 3s$ will include 95% or more. Furthermore, when the distribution of our observations is shaped like the smooth bell of the normal curve, we can determine precisely the proportion of cases above and below any given deviation score. For normal (or nearly normal) distributions, $\bar{X} \pm s$ will include 68.26% of the cases, $\bar{X} \pm 2s$ will include 95.54%, and $\bar{X} \pm 3s$ will include 99.73%. Note that in this case the standard deviation may be used to specify the exact proportion of cases included in any range instead of setting some minimum level as it did in the non-normal situations. Thus from a knowledge of s and of the deviation from the mean for any particular score we can determine the proportion of cases falling above and below that score—its exact standing in the distribution. Let

$$z_i = \frac{x_i}{s}$$

The standard score z_i is the distance of any score from the mean of the distribution *expressed in standard deviation units*; it is the number of standard deviations from the mean of any specified score. Table B in the Appendix lists the proportion of cases falling between a z-score and the mean, and the proportion of cases falling above that z-score. This table can be used to determine the standing of any particular score.

Suppose, for example, we measure the I.Q.'s of a class of students and obtain the following results in a normal distribution:

$$\bar{X} = 120$$
$$s = 10$$

Now let us take a particular student whose I.Q. score is 125. For this student,

$$x = X - \bar{X} = 125 - 120 = 5$$
$$z = \frac{x}{s} = \frac{5}{10} = .5$$

Table B shows that when $z = .5$, the proportion is .1915 or 19.15% between z and the mean, and .3085 or 30.85% in the tail. This student's I.Q. therefore is higher than 69.15% (50% + 19.15%) of his classmates and lower than 30.85%. Table B, then, provides us with a reproduction of any normal distribution. When we know both $\bar{X}$ and s in the normal case, we have a complete enumeration of an entire distribution.

Procedure. The procedure described in the formula may be used to compute s. If we put it in symbolic form, the formula becomes

$$s = \sqrt{\frac{\sum_{i=1}^{N}(X_i - \bar{X})^2}{N}} \tag{6.2}$$

where X_i = an observed score,
$\bar{X}$ = the arithmetic mean,
N = the number of cases.

Example

Fava collected information in order to compare the role of women in various academic professions.[2] In her report she has compared the percentages of women who earned doctoral degrees in various fields over the years from 1949 to 1958. Her data for sociology and psychology are reported in Table 6.5.

Table 6.5. Percentages of Those Earning Doctoral Degrees in Sociology and Psychology, 1949–1958, Who Are Women

Year Conferred	Field	
	Sociology	Psychology
1949	8	17
1950	18	15
1951	14	13
1952	14	14
1953	8	14
1954	15	11
1955	12	12
1956	17	14
1957	12	16
1958	19	15

The average percentage of women earning doctoral degrees in sociology for the period in question and the average for women in psychology are very similar.

For sociology,

$$\bar{X} = \frac{\sum_{i=1}^{N} X_i}{N}$$

$$= \frac{8 + 18 + 14 + 14 + 8 + 15 + 12 + 17 + 12 + 19}{10}$$

$$= \frac{137}{10}$$

$$= 13.7\%$$

[2] Sylvia Fleis Fava, "The Status of Women in Professional Sociology," *American Sociological Review*, **25** (April, 1960), 271–276.

For psychology,

$$\bar{X} = \frac{\sum_{i=1}^{N} X_i}{N}$$

$$= \frac{17 + 15 + 13 + 14 + 14 + 11 + 12 + 14 + 16 + 15}{10}$$

$$= \frac{141}{10}$$

$$= 14.1\%$$

It would seem that these fields differ very little with respect to the proportion of women they attract and admit to Ph.D. level degrees. But what happens when we take variability into account? Perhaps they are not as similar as a comparison of their means would lead us to believe.

For sociology (Table 6.6),

Table 6.6

Year	X_i	x_i	x_i^2
1949	8	−5.7	32.49
1950	18	4.3	18.49
1951	14	.3	.09
1952	14	.3	.09
1953	8	−5.7	32.49
1954	15	1.3	1.69
1955	12	−1.7	2.89
1956	17	3.3	10.89
1957	12	−1.7	2.89
1958	19	5.3	28.09
Total	137	0	130.10

$$s = \sqrt{\frac{\sum_{i=1}^{N} (X_i - \bar{X})^2}{N}}$$

$$= \sqrt{\frac{130.10}{10}}$$

$$= \sqrt{13.01}$$

$$= 3.6\%$$

For psychology (Table 6.7),

Table 6.7

Year	X_i	x_i	x_i^2
1949	17	2.9	8.41
1950	15	.9	.81
1951	13	−1.1	1.21
1952	14	− .1	.01
1953	14	− .1	.01
1954	11	−3.1	9.61
1955	12	−2.1	4.41
1956	14	− .1	.01
1957	16	1.9	3.61
1958	15	.9	.81
Total	141	0	28.90

$$\begin{aligned} s &= \sqrt{\frac{\sum_{i=1}^{N}(X_i - \bar{X})^2}{N}} \\ &= \sqrt{\frac{28.90}{10}} \\ &= \sqrt{2.89} \\ &= 1.7\% \end{aligned}$$

Here we see a marked difference. Although their averages are nearly alike, sociology shows much more variability than psychology when it comes to recruiting women at the Ph.D. level. The proportion of women in sociology differs more from year to year. This may suggest a number of interpretations. Perhaps it is true that psychologists have worked out a policy with respect to women in the profession, whereas sociologists are still experimenting. At any rate, these results do indicate that the mean is a better over-all summary of the percentage of women in psychology from year to year than it is for sociology.

Summary of Procedure. Whenever data are distributed in an interval scale, Formula 6.2 may be used to calculate s.

Other Statistics. Both v, the variation ratio, and d, the decile range, may be used for summarizing variation in interval scales. Since neither of these statistics makes use of the equal interval character of the data, however, their utility is limited.

The square of the standard deviation (s^2) is called the *variance*. It results as an intermediate step in the calculation of the standard deviation before the square root is extracted. The variance is sometimes used directly as an index of variation. It cannot be interpreted in terms of areas of the curve as can the standard deviation, but it has great utility in more advanced statistical work. We shall therefore have occasion to examine the variance in later chapters.

The only other statistic you are likely to encounter as an index of variation for interval-scale data is the *mean deviation* or *average deviation.* Some of the older literature made use of this statistic. The mean deviation is calculated by taking the deviation of each of the scores from the mean without reference to its sign. The symbol for this is

$$|X_i - \bar{X}|$$

where the vertical lines designate absolute values—they tell you to drop the negative signs. Then, taking these values, you calculate an ordinary mean

$$\text{mean deviation} = \frac{\sum_{i=1}^{N} |X_i - \bar{X}|}{N}$$

The mean deviation is easy to interpret, but it cannot be used as a building block for more advanced statistical procedures.

Section C

Describing Association between Two Variables

As we saw in Chapter 2, one of the main tasks of statistics is to help us to describe the relatedness or association between variables. This relatedness goes by many names. To the statistician it is association or correlation. To the practical scientist it is often contingency or dependence or agreement, but the basic idea is the same: two characteristics are associated or correlated to the degree that one may be guessed accurately from the other.

Suppose you are told that an American's name has been dropped into a hat and that you are to guess that person's sex. If you know that there are slightly more women than men in America, you will probably guess that the person is female. But your chances of making an error are very great; you have a slightly better than fifty-fifty chance of being right. Now let us suppose you are told that the person in question is a coal miner. Since you know that there are very few women who are miners, you change your guess to male. In this case your chances of being correct are much, much higher. They are higher because, to some extent at least, sex and occupation are associated.

Whenever knowledge of the values taken by one variable helps us to guess the values taken by another, they are associated. If such knowledge is of no help in making guesses, the variables are not associated. But the fact of observable association does not imply a causal relationship. When we know that two variables are associated, we cannot tell which is the producer and which the product or even that both are not the products of some third variable. It is possible, for example, to demonstrate association between the salaries of Presbyterian ministers in Massachusetts and the price of rum in Havana. Few of us, however, would be prepared to argue that a change in either of these variables caused the change in the other. The fact is that they are probably both the results of a third variable: shifts in the basic economy of the Western World.

We must be careful, then, when we interpret association between variables. Association means only that variables vary together in a patterned way.

To be practically useful, observed patterns of association need not necessarily be based on theory. Often associations that do not "make sense" may be used to solve practical problems. We know, for example, that responses to certain questions by prison inmates are related to their parole success. The reasons for these relationships are often not clear, but nonetheless the responses to the questions may be used for parole prediction. In such instances understanding is not necessary; the face of association may be used in the solution of practical problems.

We can always observe and describe association in the rather loose way we have just stated, or we can adopt a statistical language in order to make our description more precise. Using statistical procedures we can obtain a single number which serves as an accurate description of the degree of association between two variables. Such a number is usually called a *coefficient* of association or correlation. Most such coefficients vary between 0 and 1. A value of 0 indicates that the variables are independent—that there is no association. And increasing values from 0 to 1 indicate increasing association between the variables.

There is a wide range of statistical techniques for describing the degree of association between two variables. Although several of these techniques are similar in their basic approach, they differ with respect to the type of data for which they are appropriate and in terms of computational detail. Computed coefficients cannot be compared therefore unless they are produced by the same coefficient.

Various associational techniques are appropriate for one or another type of data. But they all require that the data be provided in the form of a *joint bivariate distribution*. That is, a series of individual cases must be observed and the values of two variable characteristics must be recorded

Individual	Variable X Value	Variable Y Value
A	1	4
B	10	2
C	5	3
D	7	1
E	9	3
etc.	etc.	etc.

for each case. The data must be recorded so that we can tell the value of each variable for each case. One way of recording such data is by tabulating the joint distribution.

Another procedure accomplishes the same purpose through tabulating the frequencies in a contingency table (Table C.1).

Table C.1. *Contingency Table*

Variable Y Values	Variable X Values 5	4	3	2	1	Total
5	6	0	0	0	0	6
4	2	2	3	1	0	8
3	0	2	7	2	1	12
2	0	2	4	3	1	10
1	2	0	1	1	9	13
Total	10	6	15	7	11	49

The numbers listed within such a table are frequencies of joint occurrence of an X score and a Y score. The upper left entry, for example, indicates that 6 individuals scored 5 on variable X and 5 on variable Y. One or another of these procedures for recording data is appropriate for determining any coefficient of association.

The chapters in Section C will be concerned with problems of describing the degree of association between two variables under various circumstances.

7 Describing Association between Nominal Scales

A great number of techniques for describing the degree of association between two nominal scales have been proposed. One of these, Guttman's coefficient of predictability, is more generally useful than most of the others. It imposes no restrictions on the number of classes in the scales, it requires no unrealistic assumptions about the distributions of the variables, and it is directly interpretable. Furthermore, this coefficient has great intuitive appeal—it makes better sense than most of the others. This chapter therefore will be concerned primarily with Guttman's coefficient of predictability.

Guttman's coefficient has no standard symbol. Sometimes it is called G, and sometimes g. Increasingly, it is assigned the Greek letter lambda (λ).

Guttman's Coefficient of Predictability

Function. As we have seen, association may be viewed as a problem in guessing. Two variables are said to be associated if knowledge of values of one of them helps us to guess values of the other. A coefficient of association should be a single number which summarizes the degree to which such knowledge of one variable helps in guessing the other. If this knowledge makes our guesses perfect, the coefficient conventionally registers 1.00. If, on the other hand, the knowledge provides no help at all, the coefficient usually takes a value of 0. Increasing ability to make accurate guesses of one variable on the basis of knowledge of the other, then, is reflected by increasing values of the coefficient from 0 to 1.00.

Guttman's coefficient, λ, meets these requirements. It is an index of the degree of association between two nominal scales.

Rationale. If we present a problem in logic to 50 college students and rate their performance, we may obtain the following results.

Passed	30
Failed	20
Total	50

Suppose, then, we are asked to make one guess, either passed or failed, which best represents the performance of the whole group. Think back to Chapter 5 and remember that the mode is the best guess under these circumstances. This can be seen if we evaluate each of our two possible guesses here. If you guess that every individual in the group passed (the modal category), 20 out of your 50 guesses will be incorrect. If, on the other hand, you choose to guess that they all failed (the nonmodal category), 30 out of your 50 guesses will be wrong. It is clear therefore that guessing the modal category yields fewer errors in the long run. In this example we guess "passed," and our error is 20 in 50. We shall call this the "dependent" variable.

Now suppose we are given some information for each student on another variable. This new variable we shall call "independent" since we shall use it to help us try to guess values of the dependent variable. Let us say we know something about the previous course work of each of these students. Twenty-five have taken courses in mathematics, and 25 have not. If we know which students have taken mathematics and which have not, we can set up the contingency table in Table 7.1.

Table 7.1. *Contingency Table*

	Response to Logic Problem		Total
	Passed	Failed	
Previous work in mathematics	22	3	25
No previous work in mathematics	8	17	25
Total	30	20	50

With this information we can make new guesses about the students' performance in logic, this time taking experience in mathematics into account. Students who are trained in mathematics can be separated from those without previous training, and we can guess performance in logic for each category separately. If training in mathematics is associated with performance in logic, this operation will reduce our error in guessing.

First, we take only those students who have had previous work in mathematics. Twenty-two of these 25 students passed the logic problem, so our guess is that the group as a whole passed and our error is 3 in 25. For students without previous work in mathematics the modal performance is failure, so "failed" would be our guess. Our error here is 8 out of these 25 students.

Without considering previous mathematics background our minimum error in guessing performance in logic for 50 students was 20. However, when we took mathematical background into account, we made only 3 errors for mathematics students and 8 for those who had no mathematics—11 in all. Predicting performance in logic on the basis of experience in mathematics has allowed us to reduce our error from 20 to 11. We can summarize this reduction by computing its ratio to the amount of original error.

$$\frac{\text{Amount of reduction in error}}{\text{Amount of original error}}$$

In this case,

$$\frac{20 - 11}{20} = \frac{9}{20} = .45$$

To put this into words: 45% of our errors in guessing the performance of these students on a problem in logic can be eliminated if we take previous background in mathematics into account.

So far we have examined only the problem of guessing performance in logic on the basis of mathematical background. We may, however, be concerned with the opposite problem: guessing background in mathematics (the new dependent variable) on the basis of performance in logic (the new independent variable). In order to accomplish this we must compute the amount of error we would make in guessing mathematical background without considering logic at all, and the amount of reduction in error in such guessing when we take performance in logic into account.

If we refer to Table 7.1, we can see that 25 of the 50 students have had work in mathematics. Thus, when we are asked to guess whether or not these students have had mathematical training, we may guess either way. In any case our error is 25 out of the 50. Perhaps, however, when we take performance in logic into account this error can be reduced. First, for those who passed the logic problem, we must guess that they all have had training in mathematics, and our error is 8 in 30. And for those who failed, we must guess that they lack mathematical training, and we make 3 errors in 20 guesses. Taking performance in logic into account, then, reduces our frequency of error in guessing mathematical training from 25 to 11.

The ratio here is equal to

$$\frac{\text{Amount of reduction in error}}{\text{Amount of original error}}$$

$$\frac{25 - 11}{25} = \frac{14}{25} = .56$$

This, then, is our first measure of association. It summarizes the degree to which knowledge of the values taken by one variable helps in guessing the values taken by another. It is called λ_a. The subscript *a* indicates that it is asymmetrical—that guessing is only one-way.

Sometimes we want a coefficient that is symmetrical—one that allows us to summarize the mutual predictability between two variables. In computing the coefficient of predictability this is accomplished by combining the two asymmetrical coefficients

$$\frac{\text{Amount of reduction in error in both variables}}{\text{Amount of original error in both variables}}$$

$$\frac{(20 - 11) + (25 - 11)}{20 + 25} = \frac{9 + 14}{45} = \frac{23}{45} = .51$$

The coefficient of predictability in this case is .51. We have eliminated 51% of our errors through guessing each of our variables on the basis of the other.

Had we been able to eliminate all the errors, our computation would have run

$$\frac{(20 - 0) + (25 - 0)}{20 + 25} = \frac{45}{45} = 1.00$$

a perfect association. And if we had eliminated no errors at all we should have obtained

$$\frac{(20 - 20) + (25 - 25)}{20 + 25} = \frac{0}{45} = 0.00$$

or no association at all. As it is we achieved a moderate association—we were able to eliminate a sizable proportion of error.

Procedure. What has just been described is not one but two related coefficients. In the first case the values taken by one variable were guessed on the basis of knowledge of the other. In the second case guesses were made both ways. The first is called λ_a; it is used whenever we want to evaluate one-way guesses. The second is simply λ; it refers to symmetrical two-way guessing.

Either λ_a or λ may be computed by means of the processes described. However, somewhat less cumbersome general formulas may be used. For λ_a,

$$\lambda_a = \frac{\sum f_i - F_d}{N - F_d} \tag{7.1}$$

where f_i = the maximum frequency found within each subclass of the independent variable,

F_d = the maximum frequency found among the totals of the dependent variable,

N = the number of cases.

If we go back to the data on logic and mathematics we can apply this formula. Suppose we wish to guess performance in logic with and without consideration of mathematical background.

To find $\sum f_i$ we add the largest frequency for those students with previous work in mathematics (22) to the largest for those without mathematics (17). F_d is the maximum frequency in response to the logic problem (30) and N, of course, is 50. Substituting in the formula,

$$\lambda_a = \frac{\sum f_i - F_d}{N - F_d} = \frac{(22 + 17) - 30}{50 - 30} = \frac{39 - 30}{20} = \frac{9}{20} = .45$$

We can, of course, also guess whether students have had previous mathematics on the basis of their performance in logic. In this case, $\sum f_i$ is the sum of the maximum frequency for those passing the logic problem (22) and the maximum for those failing (17). F_d is the largest frequency in the totals for experience with mathematics (25). Therefore

$$\lambda_a = \frac{\sum f_i - F_d}{N - F_d} = \frac{(22 + 17) - 25}{50 - 25} = \frac{39 - 25}{25} = \frac{14}{25} = .56$$

A somewhat different expression is more convenient for computing λ. It is expressed symbolically as follows:

$$\lambda = \frac{\sum f_r + \sum f_c - (F_r + F_c)}{2N - (F_r + F_c)} \tag{7.2}$$

where f_r = the maximum frequency occurring within a row,
f_c = the maximum frequency occurring within a column,
F_r = the maximum frequency occurring in a row total,
F_c = the maximum frequency occurring in a column total,
N = the number of cases.

For our earlier data $\sum f_r$ is the sum of the largest frequency in the top row (22) and the largest in the bottom (17). Then $\sum f_c$ is the sum of the largest frequency in the first column (22) and the largest in the second (17). F_r is the largest of the row totals (25) and F_c is the largest of the column totals (30). N is 50. Substituting in the formula for our data,

$$\begin{aligned}\lambda &= \frac{\sum f_r + \sum f_c - (F_r + F_c)}{2N - (F_r + F_c)} \\ &= \frac{39 + 39 - (25 + 30)}{2(50) - (25 + 30)} \\ &= \frac{78 - 55}{100 - 55} \\ &= \frac{23}{45} \\ &= .511\end{aligned}$$

This procedure may be used for computing λ in all cases.

Example

Lystad has reported a study of the relationship between achievement of status and the occurrence of schizophrenia in certain subgroups of the population of New Orleans.[1] In this study she contrasted the kind of mobility exhibited by a sample of hospitalized schizophrenic patients with that shown by an equivalent sample of normal individuals. Mobility was classified in terms of occupational change; individuals were rated as having moved up or down or as having remained at the same level in occupational prestige during their work careers. Here results are summarized in Table 7.1. Lystad's question is not entirely clear. From the context, however, she seems to be interested in the degree to which schizophrenia can be guessed from a knowledge of mobility. λ_a may be used to answer this question.

[1] Mary H. Lystad, "Social Mobility among Selected Groups of Schizophrenic Patients," *American Sociological Review*, **22** (June, 1957), 288–292.

Table 7.2. Status Mobility of Schizophrenic Patients and Controls

Group	Mobility			Total
	Upward	Downward	None	
Schizophrenics	12	43	39	94
Controls	19	22	53	94
Total	31	65	92	188

$$\begin{aligned}\lambda_a &= \frac{f_i - F_d}{N - F_d}\\ &= \frac{(19 + 43 + 53) - 94}{188 - 94}\\ &= \frac{115 - 94}{94}\\ &= \frac{21}{94}\\ &= .22\end{aligned}$$

Thus a knowledge of history of mobility will eliminate 22% of the errors we make in guessing schizophrenia. This is some improvement; it suggests that there is a relationship between schizophrenia and social mobility for the sample in question.

For illustration, if we assume that Lystad was interested in the mutual predictability between her two variables, we have

$$\begin{aligned}\lambda &= \frac{\sum f_r + \sum f_c - (F_r + F_c)}{2N - (F_r + F_c)}\\ &= \frac{(43 + 53) - (19 + 43 + 53) - (94 + 92)}{2(188) - (94 + 92)}\\ &= \frac{25}{190}\\ &= .13\end{aligned}$$

Thus a knowledge of each of these variables eliminates only 13% of the errors we make in guessing each from the other. History of mobility is more useful for guessing schizophrenia than schizophrenia is for guessing mobility.

Summary of Procedure. The following steps must be taken in the computation of λ or λ_a:

1. Arrange the frequencies observed in the two nominal scales in a contingency table.

2. If the problem requires guessing values of only one variable on the basis of the other, determine $\sum f_i$, F_d, and N, and calculate λ_a from formula 7.1.

3. If an index of mutual predictability is required, determine $\sum f_r$, $\sum f_c$, F_r, F_c, and N and calculate λ from Formula 7.2.

Other Statistics. At the beginning of this chapter it was mentioned that a great many statistics are used to measure the degree of association between nominal scales. The reader will continually run across one or another of these in the literature of social science. Most of these statistics vary between 0 and 1, but they are distributed differently. That is, although they all increase as association increases, they do so at different rates. An index of association obtained by means of one of these procedures cannot be compared with one resulting from a different procedure. Only when both are calculated by a single technique can two associations be compared, and not always even then.

The more common techniques used for computing the degree of association between nominal scales are the following.

YULE'S *Q*. *Q* is called the coefficient of association. It is easy to compute and its interpretation is relatively direct. *Q*, however, is limited in that it can be applied only when both variables are two-valued or dichotomous. See Moroney (1953) for a discussion of *Q*.

YULE'S *Y*. *Y*, the coefficient of colligation, is an alternative to *Q*, but it is rarely used. Like *Q*, it can be used only when both variables are expressed as dichotomies. See Yule and Kendall (1950) for a discussion of *Y*.

PEARSON'S *C*. *C* is called Pearson's coefficient of mean square contingency or merely the coefficient of contingency. Although it may be applied to nominal scales possessing any number of categories, *C* cannot achieve a value of 1, even for perfect association. *C* is described in Peatman (1947), McNemar (1955), and Siegel (1956).

TSCHUPROW'S *T*. *T* is a variant of *C* which was designed to achieve a value of one for perfect association. However, *T* cannot take a value of one unless the number of columns is equal to the number of rows. See Hagood and Price (1952) for a discussion of *T*.

PHI. Phi (ϕ) or point correlation (sometimes designated r_4) is like *Q* and *Y* in that it can be used only when both variables are expressed as dichotomies. And, like *C* and *T*, phi does not always vary between 0 and 1. Phi is discussed in Peatman (1947).

TETRACHORIC CORRELATION. r_t may also be applied only when both variables are dichotomies. Furthermore, it requires the assumption that both dichotomies represent divisions in variables that are normally distributed. It is discussed in McNemar (1955).

8 Describing Association between Ordinal Scales

Perhaps the most generally useful ordinal measure of association is one developed by Goodman and Kruskal. They call their coefficient *gamma* (γ) or G, and at least one other writer has symbolized it as o. Here, in order to be consistent with the form used by its authors, it will be called G.

Goodman and Kruskal's Coefficient of Ordinal Association

Rationale. In Chapter 7 we examined the problem of association between nominal scales. Association was understood as a matter of guessing values of one variable on the basis of values of another. For nominal scales this involved guessing a person's class on one scale from his class on another. And since nominal scales are unordered sets of classes, this procedure made sense.

For ordinal scales association may still be viewed as a matter of guessing. However, since ordinal scales are made up of ordered classes, the nature of our guesses must change. We are no longer interested in guessing class membership; instead we are concerned with guessing order. The problem here is the degree to which an individual's relative position or rank in one ordinal scale is predictable from his rank in another.

There are two conditions under which rankings are completely predictable from each other. If all the individuals are ranked in exactly the same order on two ordinal scales, the scales are in perfect *agreement*. If all the individuals are ranked in exactly the opposite order on two ordinal scales—if the highest individual on one scale is lowest on the other and so on—the scales are in perfect *inversion*. In either of these cases, perfect agreement or perfect inversion, we can guess a person's rank on one of the scales from his rank on the other scale without making any errors at all.

In general, the degree to which we can guess an individual's rank on one ordinal scale from his rank on another is determined by the degree to which the two ranking systems tend toward either agreement or inversion. The degree of association, or the degree of predictability, between two ordinal scales is dependent on the amount of agreement or inversion in the order of the scales. To determine the degree of association between such scales, then, we must examine the degree to which they exhibit agreements or inversions in order.

Both perfect agreement and perfect inversion are complete association; both produce a coefficient of ordinal association of 1.00. If our coefficient is to be useful, however, it is necessary that we distinguish between a value of 1.00 based on perfect agreement and one based on perfect inversion. This is accomplished by using a plus or a minus sign. The sign shows whether the association is based on agreements or inversions in the order of the ranks. If two sets of ranks are in perfect agreement, G is $+1$. (In practice, we do not record the plus sign; if there is no sign we assume that the intention is plus.) When two sets of ranks are in perfect inversion, G is -1. Remember that both are cases of perfect association; the only difference lies in the direction of that association. All other arrangements produce absolute values less than 1, and as these values increase from 0 to $+1$ *or* -1 they express increasing association between the two rankings.

As an example let us suppose that we ask two judges to rank five students in terms of their relative sociability. We may designate the five students as *A*, *B*, *C*, *D*, and *E*, and let us say, our judges provide the following rankings.

Student	Judge *X*	Judge *Y*
A	4	5
B	1	2
C	3	3
D	2	1
E	5	4

The order of the students is rearranged so that the ranks of Judge *X* are in their natural order: no smaller number lies above a larger number; we obtain the arrangement in Table 8.1.

Table 8.1

Student	Judge *X*	Judge *Y*	Inversions	Agreements
E	5	4	0	0
A	4	5	1	0
C	3	3	0	2
D	2	1	0	3
B	1	2	1	3
Totals			2	8

When we look at the rankings of Judge Y, we see that there is a tendency toward agreement—a progression from higher to lower numbers—but that this agreement is not perfect. If there were perfect agreement, no smaller number would be above a larger one. If we begin at the bottom of the rankings of Judge Y, we see that the first number is 2. Rank 1 lies above it; so we have a case of a departure from perfect agreement, an inversion, which is tabulated in the column marked "Inversions." There are no inversions for ranks 1 or 3, but rank 4 lies above rank 5, so this generates another inversion; there are two inversions in all.

We can tabulate agreements in a similar fashion. Whenever a larger number lies above a smaller one in the rankings of Judge Y, his rankings are in the same order as those of Judge X. To apply this criterion to the rankings of Judge Y, we begin with the first of his ranks, 2, at the bottom of the table. There are three larger numbers above this number (3, 4, 5), three above 1, and two above 3. The total number of agreements is therefore 8.

In effect, counting inversions and agreements is a process of comparing each number in the Y series with each of those above it. If the rankings in the Y series are identical with those in X, each one of these comparisons generates one agreement, and there are no inversions at all (Table 8.2).

Table 8.2

Student	Judge X	Judge Y	Inversions	Agreements
A	5	5	0	0
B	4	4	0	1
C	3	3	0	2
D	2	2	0	3
E	1	1	0	4
Totals			0	10

If the Y series is the exact reverse of X, each comparison generates an inversion and there are no agreements at all (Table 8.3).

Table 8.3

Student	Judge X	Judge Y	Inversions	Agreements
A	5	1	0	0
B	4	2	1	0
C	3	3	2	0
D	2	4	3	0
E	1	5	4	0
Totals			10	0

Thus each comparison in the Y series is capable of generating either an agreement or an inversion, never both. The maximum possible number of either agreements or inversions is equal to the total number of observed agreements plus the total number of observed inversions. In the original example, there are 2 inversions and 8 agreements, and the maximum is 2 + 8, which equals 10.

If we subtract the number of inversions from the number of agreements, we have an index of the relative dominance of either one. If agreements predominate, the sign of the difference is plus, and if inversions predominate, its sign is negative. The size of this difference, regardless of its sign, indicates the *net* predominance of *either* agreements or inversions. Then if we compute the ratio of this difference to its maximum possible value, we have a coefficient of association which will always vary between -1 and $+1$. For our example,

$$\frac{\text{Number of agreements} - \text{number of inversions}}{\text{Number of agreements} + \text{number of inversions}} = \frac{8 - 2}{8 + 2} = .60 = G$$

This is Kruskal and Goodman's coefficient of ordinal association. It is a ratio of the amount of predominance of agreement or inversion between two sets of rankings to the maximum possible agreement or inversion. We can interpret this ratio to mean that there is 60% greater agreement or concordance than disagreement or discordance between our judges in ranking these five students in sociability.

If our two rankings were in exactly the same order, they would generate 10 agreements and 0 inversions and G would be

$$\frac{10 - 0}{10 + 0} = 1.0$$

or if the rankings of Judge Y were exactly opposite to those of Judge X, G would be

$$\frac{0 - 10}{0 + 10} = -1.0$$

Or if the rankings generate equal numbers of agreements and inversions, as in Table 8.4, G will be

$$\frac{5 - 5}{5 + 5} = 0.0$$

Thus, G is a coefficient of association between two sets of ordered observations based on their mutual predictability in terms of the relative number of agreements and inversions in the order of the rankings.

Table 8.4

Student	Judge X	Judge Y	Inversions	Agreements
A	5	4	0	3
B	4	3	0	2
C	3	1	0	0
D	2	2	1	0
E	1	5	4	0
Totals			5	5

Procedure. In Chapter 6 we say that ordinal scales may occur in either of two forms: (1) a series of individuals or objects may be arranged such that each ranks either higher or lower than each of the others or (2) there may be ties wherein several individuals will occupy the same rank. This distinction is important in computing G. Hence we shall discuss separately techniques for computing G without ties and with ties.

COMPUTING G WITHOUT TIES. The general formula presented earlier can be used for computing G when ties are absent. This computing formula is expressed symbolically as follows:

$$G = \frac{f_a - f_i}{f_a + f_i} \tag{8.1}$$

where f_a = the frequency of agreements,
f_i = the frequency of inversions.

This computational procedure may be applied to all sets of tieless ranks.

Example

Frumkin has reported a study in which he compares two sets of rankings of ten items referring to family interest.[1] Sixty family interest items were rated in terms of their assumed significance for family adjustment by fifty-two graduate students, teachers, and others in sociology and psychology at Ohio State University. The ten items exhibiting the highest mean ratings were expressed as an ordinal scale, ranked in assumed importance for family adjustment. Then 107 married couples were studied, and the relative importance of the ten family interest items in contributing to their actual marriage adjustment (according to the Burgess scale) was

[1] Robert M. Frumkin, "Family Interests Crucial to Marital Adjustment," *Alpha Kappa Deltan*, **24** (Autumn, 1953), 23–27.

established. This provided a second independent ranking of the ten family interest items, this time based on empirical criteria. The question, then, is to determine the extent of agreement between expert judgments of the relative importance of these family interests and their actual importance for a sample of married couples. If we wish to determine the degree to which these two ranking methods agree in ranking these interests, we may employ G.

Table 8.5. *Judges' and Empirical Rankings of the Contribution to Marital Adjustment of Ten Family Interest Items*

Family Interest	Judges Ranks, X	Empirical Ranks, Y	f_i	f_a
Demonstrating affection	10	9	0	0
Planning for the future	9	6	0	1
Planning saving or investment	8	10	2	0
Training children	7	1	0	3
Planning family budget	6	8	2	2
Making plans for children	5	7	2	3
Planning home decorations	4	4	1	5
Arranging and preparing meals	3	5	2	5
Going shopping	2	3	1	7
Housecleaning	1	2	1	8
Totals			11	34

$$
\begin{aligned}
G &= \frac{f_a - f_i}{f_a + f_i} \\
&= \frac{34 - 11}{34 + 11} \\
&= \frac{23}{45} = .51
\end{aligned}
$$

Thus the rank association between the judges' ranks and the empirical ranks is .51. There is a 51% greater agreement than disagreement between these two sets of rankings.

COMPUTING G WITH TIED RANKS. There is no variation in the formula we use for computing G when ties are present. The only difference is that in the presence of ties it is simpler to employ another method for determining f_a and f_i.

Suppose we are able to rank 50 people very crudely in, say, attitude toward spending money and in social class background. We can summarize their rankings in an ordered contingency table (Table 8.6).

Table 8.6

Social Class Background Rank	Rank in Attitude Toward Spending Money: More Spendthrift, 2	Rank in Attitude Toward Spending Money: Less Spendthrift, 1	Total
Upper, 3	2	3	5
Middle, 2	15	20	35
Lower, 1	8	2	10
Total	25	25	50

Clearly, these are both ordinal variables, although crude ones. Their crudity is indicated by the number of ties in each rank. Nevertheless we can calculate a coefficient of rank association between these variables and attempt to determine the degree to which class level and attitude about money are related for our 50 people.

To compute f_a we multiply the frequency in each cell by the sum of the frequencies in all the cells that lie *both below and to the right of it.* By adding these products together, we obtain f_a.

$$f_a = 2(20 + 2) + (15)(2) = 74$$

To compute f_i we multiply the frequency in each cell by the sum of the frequencies in the cells which lie *both below and to the left of it* and add these products, thus

$$f_i = 3(15 + 8) + (20)(8) = 229$$

Now we may compute G in the usual way.

$$G = \frac{f_a - f_i}{f_a + f_i}$$
$$= \frac{74 - 229}{74 + 229} = \frac{-155}{303} = -.51$$

The coefficient of rank association is $-.51$. The negative sign indicates that this association is based on the predominance of inversions: that high ranks on one variable tend to coincide with low ranks on the other. To put this into words, there is 51% more inversion than agreement in the rankings of these characteristics. In general, the higher the class, the less spendthrift tendency, or conversely, the greater the spendthrift tendency, the lower the class.

This computational procedure may be applied to all cases involving tied ranks.

Example

In a study of mobility in Rome, Lehner questioned 1692 men.[2] Each of these men was ranked according to his occupation and according to the occupation of his father. Occupations were divided into six prestige ranks.

6 Government officials; executives of large industries.
5 Large farm owners; executives of middle-sized industrial, commercial, or financial enterprises; professionals.
4 Government employees; employees of large industries; landlords.
3 White collar workers; artisans with employees; small merchants.
2 Agricultural foremen; artisans without employees; service personnel; skilled workers.
1 Salaried agricultural workers; unskilled workers.

The question is to determine the degree to which the occupations of sons are ranked in the same order as those of their fathers—the degree to which occupational rank is passed on from father to son. Lehner's data are reported in Table 8.7.

Table 8.7. *Rankings of Roman Men according to Occupation and Father's Occupation*

Occupational Ranks of Sons	Occupational Ranks of Fathers						Total
	6	5	4	3	2	1	
6	7	9	13	4	1	0	34
5	1	27	10	22	7	5	72
4	8	19	22	36	8	0	93
3	5	30	37	227	152	31	482
2	0	5	12	96	453	194	760
1	0	2	1	13	45	190	251
Total	21	92	95	398	666	420	1692

For this table,

$$f_a = (7)(27 + 10 + 22 + 7 + 5 + 19 + 22 + 36 + 8 + 0 + 30 + 37 + 227 + 152 + 31 + 5 + 12 + 96 + 453 + 194 + 2 + 1 + 13 + 45 + 190) + (9)(10 + 22 + 7 + 5 \cdots + (453)(190) = 671{,}672$$

$$f_i = (9)(1 + 8 + 5 + 0 + 0) + (13)(1 + 27 + 8 + 19 + 5 + 30 + 0 + 5 + 0 + 2) + (4)(1 + 27 + 10 + 8 + 19 + \cdots + (194)(45) = 86{,}833$$

[2] Alessandro Lehner, "Sur la Mesure de la Mobilité Sociale," *Transactions of the Second World Congress of Sociology*, Vol. II, London: International Sociological Association, 1954, pp. 119–127.

Then

$$G = \frac{f_a - f_i}{f_a + f_i}$$
$$= \frac{671{,}672 - 86{,}833}{671{,}672 + 86{,}833}$$
$$= \frac{584{,}834}{758{,}505} = .77$$

We must conclude for this sample that there is a rather large positive association between fathers' occupational level and the occupational level of sons. There is 77% more agreement than inversion in ranking.

Summary of Procedure. The steps of procedure in the use of Goodman and Kruskal's coefficient of ordinal association are the following.

1. Order the observations on the X variable from 1 to the highest rank. Order the observations on the Y variable in the same manner.
2. Determine whether two or more cases are tied for a single rank either in X or Y.
3. If no ties occur, carry through the following steps.
   (*a*) Arrange the list of N subjects so that their ranks on the X variable are in their natural order (from highest to lowest).
   (*b*) Determine the value of f_a to f_i from the order of the Y ranks.
   (*c*) Determine the value of G by applying Formula 8.1.
4. If ties do occur, carry through the following steps.
   (*a*) Arrange the two rankings in an ordered contingency table.
   (*b*) Tabulate the frequency of occurrence for each cell in the table.
   (*c*) Determine the values of f_a and f_i from these frequencies.
   (*d*) Determine the value of G by applying Formula 8.1.

Other Statistics. KENDALL'S TAU. Kendall's coefficient is frequently used in problems similar to those for which we have employed G. If there are no ties in either set of ranks, *tau* equals G exactly. Tau, differs however, when it comes to tied ranks. See Siegel (1956) for a discussion of this statistic.

SPEARMAN'S RHO. Spearman's coefficient, *rho*, is also often used to determine the degree of association between two ordinal scales. For discussion of rho see Siegel (1956).

Both tau and rho are difficult to calculate when ties are present.

FLANAGAN'S COEFFICIENT OF CORRELATION. Flanagan has proposed a method of computing a coefficient of correlation when the problem is one of determining the relationship between a test score and the distribution of responses on an item contained in the test. Actually, however, his statistic is appropriate as a coefficient of rank correlation whenever one of the variables is expressed in only two ranks and the other has a relatively large number of ranks. This statistic is discussed in Walker and Lev (1953).

9 Describing Association between Interval Scales

There is only one statistic that is commonly employed to describe the degree of association between two interval scales: Pearson's coefficient of correlation. This statistic is sometimes known as Pearson's correlation, or zero-order correlation, or linear correlation, or often simply as *the* coefficient of correlation. It is almost universally symbolized by a lower case r. This chapter will be concerned with applications of Pearson's r.

Pearson's Coefficient of Correlation

Function. Pearson's r describes the degree and direction of linear association between two variables, each of which is expressed in an interval scale. An explanation of the idea underlying linear association follows.

Rationale. We have already had a great deal of experience in viewing association in terms of guessing. Pearson's r may be viewed from this same perspective. Although it is possible to understand r from any of several different points of view, perhaps it makes most sense when it is described in terms of guessing. Like other measures of association, Pearson's r increases as our guesses become more accurate. However, as we have seen, there are different procedures to evaluate the accuracy of guessing. λ is an index of improvement in guessing; it is a ratio of reduction in error to original error in guessing. G, however, is an index of over-all accuracy; it is a ratio of the dominance of correct guesses to the total number of guesses made. The general model of r is identical with that of λ; it is a ratio of reduction in error to original error.

$$\frac{\text{Amount of reduction in error}}{\text{Amount of original error}}$$

Pearson's r is distinct, however, in terms of how guesses are made and how errors are tabulated. Association in nominal scales involved the notion of guessing class membership; in ordinal scales the problem was one of guessing order; and when it comes to interval scales, association is a question of guessing scores or values on measures.

Let us take an example to see how guesses are made and errors are determined. Suppose we have a distribution of scores on an interval scale. We have, let us say, a group of nine students. Each is scored in terms of the number of A's he received in a given school term. We shall call this variable, number of A's, Y.

Y: 5 4 4 3 1 1 0 0 0

What we are looking for is the one value of Y that best represents the entire distribution. We must determine the score that produces the smallest total amount of error when it is used as a guess of each and every score in the entire distribution. In order to specify such a value we must determine what is meant by the "smallest total amount of error."

In Chapter 6 the variance was defined as the square of the standard deviation. The variance is the mean of the squared differences of the scores in a distribution from the mean of that distribution.

$$s^2 = \frac{\sum_{i=1}^{N}(X_i - \bar{X})^2}{N}$$

This idea may be generalized. We may conceive of the variance of a set of scores around any guessed value. Then

$$\frac{\sum_{i=1}^{N}(X_i - g)^2}{N}$$

where g is any guessed value.

If we take this definition of the variance as our index of error in guessing the scores in a distribution, the mean is the best guess for any interval scale. Since it is the "point of balance," the mean of the squared differences of all the observations from the mean is less than the mean of the squared differences of all the observations from any other point. Symbolically,

$$\frac{\sum_{i=1}^{N}(X_i - \bar{X})^2}{N} < \frac{\sum_{i=1}^{N}(X_i - g)^2}{N}$$

where g is any point other than the mean.

We can try this for the distribution of A's for our nine students. First we calculate the mean.

$$\bar{Y} = \frac{\sum_{i=1}^{N} Y_i}{N}$$

$$= \frac{18}{9}$$

$$= 2$$

Then the variance around the mean is as shown in Table 9.1.

Table 9.1

Y	$Y - \bar{Y}$	$(Y - \bar{Y})^2$
5	3	9
4	2	4
4	2	4
3	1	1
1	−1	1
1	−1	1
0	−2	4
0	−2	4
0	−2	4
		32

$$s^2 = \frac{\sum_{i=1}^{N}(Y_i - \bar{Y})^2}{N} = \frac{32}{9} = 3.55$$

We can try guessing other values and compute the variance around them. If we guess $g = 1$ (Table 9.2),

Table 9.2

Y	$Y - 1$	$(Y - 1)^2$
5	4	16
4	3	9
4	3	9
3	2	4
1	0	0
1	0	0
0	−1	1
0	−1	1
0	−1	1
		41

$$s^2_{(1)} = \frac{\sum_{i=1}^{N}(Y_i - 1)^2}{N} = \frac{41}{9} = 4.33$$

If we guess $g = 3$ (Table 9.3),

Table 9.3

Y	$Y - 3$	$(Y - 3)^2$
5	2	4
4	1	1
4	1	1
3	0	0
1	−2	4
1	−2	4
0	−3	9
0	−3	9
0	−3	9
		41

$$s^2_{(3)} = \frac{\sum_{i=1}^{N} (Y_i - 3)^2}{N} = \frac{41}{9} = 4.33$$

Of all possible guessed values for a distribution, the mean will produce the smallest average squared deviation from all the scores in the distribution. Because of this property, the mean is called a *least-squares* guess for the values in a distribution. In this sense it is a "best" guess. The error resulting from guessing the mean may be determined by calculating the variance.

Table 9.4

X Number of Hours Studied per Day	Y Number of A's
8	5
6	4
4	4
4	3
4	1
3	1
3	0
2	0
2	0

The mean number of A's for our nine students, then, is 2. And the variance is 3.55. The question in correlation is the degree to which we can reduce this error through guessing the number of A's on the basis of some other variable instead of guessing the mean. Suppose we collect information from each of our students on the number of hours he studies per day, rounded to the nearest whole hour. With this information we can investigate the degree to which time spent in study may help us to guess the number of A's. Our investigation may give us the combined distribution on the two variables shown in Table 9.4.

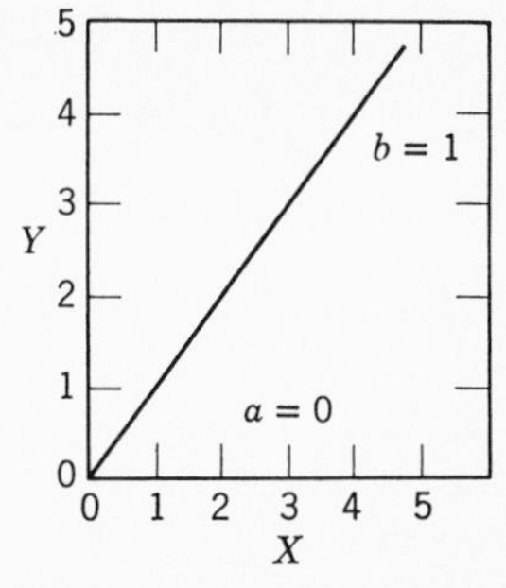

Fig. 9.1. This illustration shows a situation in which Y increases 1 unit for every unit increase in X.

$X = 0\ 1\ 2\ 3\ 4\ 5$
$Y = 0\ 1\ 2\ 3\ 4\ 5$

If the variables are associated, our new guesses should be more accurate than our first guess of the mean, and our error reduced. What we need, then, is a way of guessing scores on one variable on the basis of scores on another. When interval measures are involved, the use of the linear equation provides such a way.

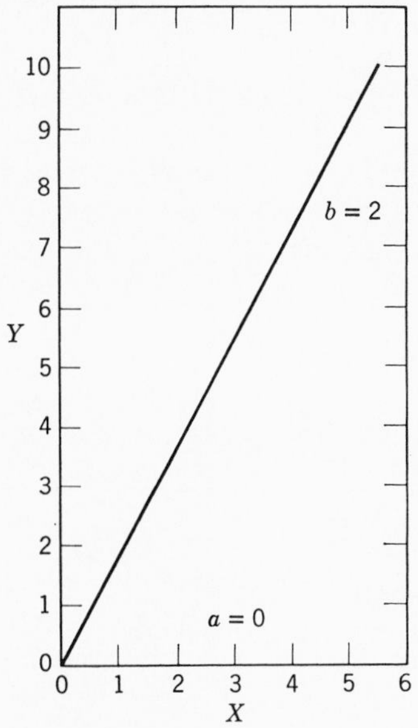

The reasoning underlying the use of linear equations runs as follows. When we are dealing with interval scales we are interested in guessing scores of one variable from our knowledge of scores on the other. In order to guess scores of one variable unambiguously from scores of another, it is necessary that there be some systematic or functional relationship between the values of one and the values of the other. The simplest relationship we might observe—the one with which we shall be concerned—is one in which a given amount of change in the value of one variable (Y) always accompanies a given amount of change in the value of the other (X). An example of this could be a situation in which every increase

Fig. 9.2. Y increases 2 units per unit increase in X.

$X = 0\ 1\ 2\ 3\ 4\ 5 \quad Y = 0\ 2\ 4\ 6\ 8\ 10$

of 1 unit in variable X is accompanied by an increase of 1 unit in Y, or every increase of 1 unit in X might be accompanied by a decrease of 3 units in Y.

Pictorially, this situation may always be represented by a straight line. Figures 9.1, 9.2, and 9.3 will make this clear.

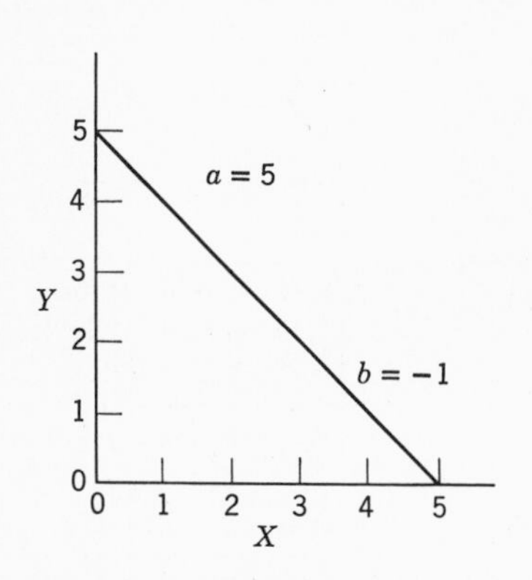

Fig. 9.3. Y decreases 1 unit for every unit increase in X.

$X = 0\ 1\ 2\ 3\ 4\ 5$
$Y = 5\ 4\ 3\ 2\ 1\ 0$

From the diagrams it will be seen that whenever the rate of increase or decrease is constant, the relationship between two variables can be represented by a straight line.

If all scores fall on a straight line, any particular value of Y is determined by a value of X. All we need to know in order to make such a determination is (1) the rate of change in Y as X changes and (2) a Y value for some particular value of X. Clearly, if we know the value of Y for some value of X and the rate of change in Y as X changes, we can determine a Y value for any value of X.

In the general case, if all the scores fall on a straight line,

$$Y_i = a + bX_i$$

That is, any particular value of Y is equal to a plus b times some X value. This expression describes a linear or straight-line relation.

b is called the slope of the line. It is the rate of change in Y per unit increase in X.

$$b = \frac{\Delta Y}{\Delta X}$$

where ΔY is the number of units change in Y when two Y values are compared, and ΔX is the number of units change in the corresponding X

Table 9.5. *Data of Fig.* 9.1

X	Y	ΔX	ΔY
0	0	1	1
1	1	1	1
2	2	1	1
3	3	1	1
4	4	1	1
5	5		

values. As an example, let us look at the data of Fig. 9.1 in Table 9.5. As X increases from 0 to 1, an increase of 1 unit, Y also increases from 0 to 1, and so on. Thus

$$b = \frac{\Delta Y}{\Delta X} = \frac{1}{1} = 1$$

throughout Table 9.5.

Table 9.6 shows the data of Fig. 9.2.

Table 9.6. *Data of Fig.* 9.2

X	Y	ΔX	ΔY
0	0	1	2
1	2	1	2
2	4	1	2
3	6	1	2
4	8	1	2
5	10		

And

$$b = \frac{\Delta Y}{\Delta X} = \frac{2}{1} = 2$$

The data for Fig. 9.3 are tabulated in Table 9.7.

Table 9.7. *Data of Fig.* 9.3

X	Y	ΔX	ΔY
0	5	1	−1
1	4	1	−1
2	3	1	−1
3	2	1	−1
4	1	1	−1
5	0		

$$b = \frac{\Delta Y}{\Delta X} = \frac{-1}{1} = -1$$

Note that in each case, and in *every* linear equation, the ratio of $\Delta Y/\Delta X$ is constant throughout the table.

a is simply the value of Y when $X = 0$. In the preceding illustrations a can be read from the tables. In other cases it may be determined by extending the tables until $X = 0$. Suppose we have data as in Table 9.8.

Table 9.8

X	Y	ΔX	ΔY
10	20	−1	3
9	23	−1	3
8	26	−1	3
7	29	−1	3
6	32	−1	3
5	35		

We can determine a by extending Table 9.8 according to ΔX and ΔY until $X = 0$ (Table 9.9).

Table 9.9

X	Y	ΔX	ΔY
10	20	−1	3
9	23	−1	3
8	26	−1	3
7	29	−1	3
6	32	−1	3
5	35	−1	3
4	38	−1	3
3	41	−1	3
2	44	−1	3
1	47	−1	3
0	50		

Thus $a = 50$.

This, then, is the reasoning underlying the linear equation. This equation, $Y = a + bX$, describes how changes in one variable accompany changes in another. We can now determine the ways such equations are used in Pearson's coefficient of correlation.

Let us begin by examining Fig. 9.4. This is a graph that represents our nine hypothetical observations on class grades and hours of study. This graph shows a general tendency for Y to increase as X increases, but this tendency is by no means completely regular. There is no straight line that would pass through each of these observations. The fact is that very few sets of actual observations ever fall exactly on a straight line.

What is needed, then, is a method for "fitting" a line to the observations so that the approximation is as close as possible. This line may then be used to guess values of Y on the basis of values of X.

$$Y'_i = a + bX_i$$

where Y'_i is a guessed value of Y.

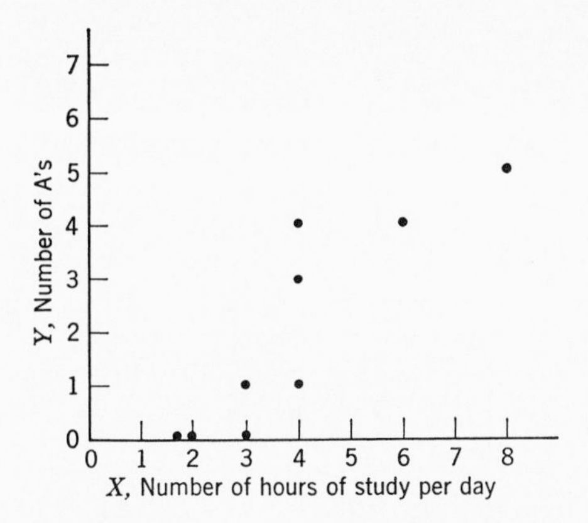

Fig. 9.4. Distribution of hypothetical data on number of A's and number of hours of study per day.

This set of guessed values of Y is called the *line of regression.* In any particular case, it is the one straight line that provides the "best" guesses of Y values on the basis of values of X. Thus the regression line has the same least-squares property as the mean. The variance around the guessed values of Y provided by the line of regression is less than the variance around any other line.

Obviously, a great many straight lines may come fairly close to the observations in Fig. 9.5. However, if our regression line is to minimize the variance around the guessed values of Y, its origin and slope must be determined with care.

The slope of the line is b. For any set of observations,

$$b = \frac{\sum_{i=1}^{N} x_i y_i}{\sum_{i=1}^{N} x_i^2}$$

In general, b describes the over-all amount of change in Y for every unit of change in X; it is positive if Y increases as X increases, and negative if Y decreases as X increases; its magnitude indicates the number of units of change in Y for every unit of increase in X. For example, if X and Y change at the same rate and in the same direction—if every unit of increase in X is accompanied by an equal unit of increase in y—$\sum xy = \sum x^2$ and $b = 1$.

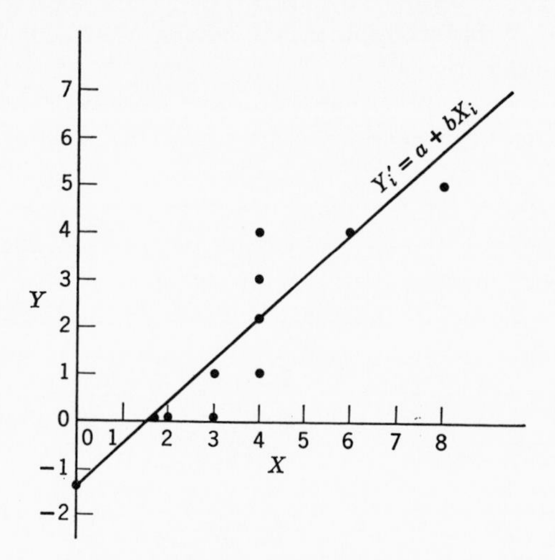

Fig. 9.5. Regression line fit to hypothetical data on number of A's and number of hours of study per day.

For our illustrative problem on study and grades see Table 9.10.

Table 9.10

	X	x	x^2	Y	y	xy
	8	4	16	5	3	12
	6	2	4	4	2	4
	4	0	0	4	2	0
	4	0	0	3	1	0
	4	0	0	1	−1	0
	3	−1	1	1	−1	1
	3	−1	1	0	−2	2
	2	−2	4	0	−2	4
	2	−2	4	0	−2	4
Σ	36	0	30	18	0	27

$$b = \frac{\sum_{i=1}^{N} x_i y_i}{\sum_{i=1}^{N} x_i^2}$$

$$= \frac{27}{30}$$

$$= .9$$

For the persons in this group, then, the number of A's tends to increase by .9 for every hour studied.

Now we can turn to the problem of a, the value of Y when X is zero. Common sense tells us that if we wish to guess the Y score equivalent to the mean of X in a distribution, we should guess the mean of Y. Furthermore, if we look at Table 9.10, we can see that b is reckoned in terms of deviation scores from the two means; it assumes that the straight line must pass through the intersection of the means. This suggests that if we know the two means and b in a particular case we can calculate a. Since

$$Y'_i = a + bX_i$$

and

$$\overline{Y} = a + b\overline{X}$$

then

$$a = \overline{Y} - b\overline{X}$$

In effect, all this computation does is begin with the known value of $Y(\overline{Y})$ when X is set at $\overline{X}$, and using b, it follows the changing values of Y down until $X = 0$; at this point $Y' = a$.

For our data,

$$\overline{X} = \frac{36}{9} = 4$$

$$\overline{Y} = \frac{18}{9} = 2$$

and

$$b = .9$$

so

$$\begin{aligned} a &= \overline{Y} - b\overline{X} \\ &= 2 - (.9)(4) \\ &= 2 - 3.6 \\ &= -1.6 \end{aligned}$$

This suggests that with no study ($X = 0$), we would guess that a person should receive -1.6 A's. This is, of course, ridiculous, given the problem at hand. It indicates one of the difficulties of extrapolating our generalizations beyond our observations. The line of regression is designed to summarize a relationship within the range of the observations. It is not safe to assume simply that it can be extended out of that range and retain any meaning.

In this case, however, this problem is not critical. The regression line has been extended to $X = 0$ only to determine its starting point. Now, with this information on a and b, we can determine the guessed values of Y for each value of X.

$$
\begin{aligned}
& Y' = a + bX \\
X = 8;\quad & Y' = -1.6 + (.9)(8) = 5.6 \\
X = 6;\quad & Y' = -1.6 + (.9)(6) = 3.8 \\
X = 4;\quad & Y' = -1.6 + (.9)(4) = 2.0 \\
X = 3;\quad & Y' = -1.6 + (.9)(3) = 1.1 \\
X = 2;\quad & Y' = -1.6 + (.9)(2) = .2
\end{aligned}
$$

This regression line, along with the observations, is shown in Fig. 9.5. This figure shows that in each case the guessed value of Y is somewhat less than perfect. We can compare these guessed values with our actual Y scores and determine how much error we have made (Table 9.11).

Table 9.11

	X	Y	Y'	$y' = Y - Y'$	$y'^2 = (Y - Y')^2$
	8	5	5.6	−.6	.36
	6	4	3.8	.2	.04
	4	4	2.0	2.0	4.00
	4	3	2.0	1.0	1.00
	4	1	2.0	−1.0	1.00
	3	1	1.1	−.1	.01
	3	0	1.1	−1.1	1.21
	2	0	.2	−.2	.04
	2	0	.2	−.2	.04
Σ	36	18	18.0	0	7.70

Then, by analogy to the variance around the mean,

$$
\begin{aligned}
s_{y'}^2 &= \frac{\sum_{i=1}^{N} (Y - Y')^2}{N} \\
&= \frac{7.70}{9} \\
&= .855
\end{aligned}
$$

This, then, is our summary of the error resulting from guessing values of Y on the basis of values of X. It is a mean squared deviation or variance and as such it may be compared directly with the variance around the mean of Y. In this case, the variance around the mean of Y is 3.55. This results from guessing $\bar{Y}$ for each observation without taking values of X into account. It is clear that when we take the amount of study into account, we can go a long way toward eliminating our error in guessing

Y values. Pearson's r provides a standard index of the degree of reduction of error in such cases.

$$r^2 = \frac{\text{amount of reduction in error}}{\text{amount of original error}}$$

$$= \frac{s_y{}^2 - s_{y'}^2}{s_y{}^2}$$

where $s_y{}^2$ = the variance of Y scores around $\bar{Y}$, the original error,
$s_{y'}^2$ = the variance of Y scores around Y'_i, the error in Y scores guessed on the basis of X scores.

In this problem,

$$r^2 = \frac{s_y{}^2 - s_{y'}^2}{s_y{}^2}$$

$$= \frac{3.55 - .855}{3.55}$$

$$= .76$$

Note that we have not computed r, but rather r^2. This was done because r^2 is easier to interpret directly. r^2 may be interpreted as the proportion of variance in Y which is associated with variation in X under the assumption of a linear relationship. In this example 76% of the variance in Y is associated with variation in X.

It is important to remember that r^2 cannot be directly interpreted in terms of reduction of number of errors in guessing. The reason for this restriction will be clear if we recall that our index of error was not based on deviations but rather on *squared* deviations. Our index of error, then, was just that, an *index* of error—not a *measure* of number of errors. So if we want to interpret r^2 in terms of proportional reduction in error in guessing, we must speak in terms of reduction of variance.

For most purposes it should be satisfactory to interpret r^2 in terms of associated variance. r^2 is equal to the proportion of variance in Y which can be predicted from X, and $1 - r^2$ is equal to the proportion which is unpredictable on the basis of X. These are generally called *explained variance* and *unexplained variance* respectively. It is clear that the greater the association between X and Y, the larger the explained variance, and the smaller the proportion of error in guessing Y scores on the basis of X scores.[1]

[1] The statistic r is remarkable for the number of different forms in which it can be expressed. r can be expressed and interpreted as a kind of mean, as a rate of change, and as a probability. For most purposes, however, the interpretation of r^2 given here is satisfactory. The student who is interested in other interpretations should see McNemar (1955).

So far we seem to have been concerned only with predicting Y scores on the basis of X values. However, we have already determined that many coefficients of correlation are symmetrical—they refer to guesses in both directions. Since the line of regression was fixed in terms of observed values of both X and Y

$$r_{xy} = r_{yx} = r$$

Had we reversed our variables, the answer would still remain the same. So r^2 is symmetrical. We can interpret it as the proportion of the variance in Y which is associated with variation in X, or as the proportion of variance in X which is associated with variation in Y, or as the proportion of variance shared by our two variables.

There is one deficiency in the procedure we have discussed so far, however. It always produces a positive value of r. It is understood that

$$r = \sqrt{r^2}$$

which is true. But if we compute r by using the procedure just described, r is always taken to be positive. Since r should be positive if Y increases, and negative if Y decreases, as X increases we need some method for calculation which can produce either a positive or a negative value. Actually, we could use this method and affix the sign of b (plus or minus) to our final r. Since the sign of b describes whether the variables are related directly or inversely, it would work. However, the computational procedure described in the next section provides the proper sign. Furthermore, it is a great deal easier to employ than the method discussed. This method is useful for understanding r, the following procedure for calculating it.

Procedure. A simple formula for calculating r is the following:

$$r = \frac{\sum_{i=1}^{N} X_i Y_i - \dfrac{\left(\sum_{i=1}^{N} X_i\right)\left(\sum_{i=1}^{N} Y_i\right)}{N}}{\sqrt{\sum_{i=1}^{N} X_i^2 - \dfrac{\left(\sum_{i=1}^{N} X_i\right)^2}{N} \quad \sum_{i=1}^{N} Y_i^2 - \dfrac{\left(\sum_{i=1}^{N} Y_i\right)^2}{N}}}$$

Or, since we always sum over the entire array from $i = 1$ to N, the formula may be put more simply,

$$r = \frac{\sum XY - \dfrac{(\sum X)(\sum Y)}{N}}{\sqrt{\left[\sum X^2 - \dfrac{(\sum X)^2}{N}\right]\left[\sum Y^2 - \dfrac{(\sum Y)^2}{N}\right]}} \tag{9.1}$$

If we apply this formula to the data of our earlier example, we obtain Table 9.12.

Table 9.12

	X	X^2	Y	Y^2	XY
	8	64	5	25	40
	6	36	4	16	24
	4	16	4	16	16
	4	16	3	9	12
	4	16	1	1	4
	3	9	1	1	3
	3	9	0	0	0
	2	4	0	0	0
	2	4	0	0	0
Σ	36	174	18	68	99

$$N = 9$$

$$r = \frac{\sum XY - \frac{(\sum X)(\sum Y)}{N}}{\sqrt{\left[\sum X^2 - \frac{(\sum X)^2}{N}\right]\left[\sum Y^2 - \frac{(\sum Y)^2}{N}\right]}}$$

$$= \frac{99 - \frac{(36)(18)}{9}}{\sqrt{\left[174 - \frac{(36)^2}{9}\right]\left[68 - \frac{(18)^2}{9}\right]}}$$

$$= \frac{99 - 72}{\sqrt{(174 - 44)(68 - 36)}}$$

$$= \frac{27}{\sqrt{(30)(32)}}$$

$$= \frac{27}{\sqrt{960}}$$

$$= \frac{27}{30.98}$$

$$= .87$$

and

$$r^2 = .76$$

This is the same result we obtained earlier. This procedure may be used to compute r in all cases.

Example

In an attempt to devise an index of social development, Naroll has collected data on craft specialization and organizational ramification for a sample of 30 societies.[2] Craft specialization was measured in terms of the number of craft specialties found among the members of a society, and organizational ramification was defined in terms of the number of

Table 9.13. *Scores on Number of Team Types and Number of Craft Specialties for Thirty Societies*

X Team Types	*Y* Craft Specialties
3	2
3	2
3	4
6	2
3	4
5	4
4	5
4	5
4	6
5	5
7	3
6	4
6	5
8	3
6	4
7	5
6	5
8	4
8	5
7	6
7	8
8	10
10	11
9	9
14	9
14	10
21	10
14	16
22	17
17	35

[2] Raoul Naroll, "A Preliminary Index of Social Development," *American Anthropologist*, **58** (August, 1956), 687–715.

groups of three or more people organized together in a clearly recognized superordinate-subordinate relationship; these were called teams. Naroll has proposed that both these variables are indicators of social evolution. According to his hypothesis both will increase as a society becomes more complex; if this is the case, they should be positively correlated. It is reasonable, therefore, to determine the degree of relationship between number of team types and number of craft specialties for this sample of societies. Pearson's r is appropriate for this purpose. Naroll's data are presented in Table 9.13.

From these data we can compute r (Table 9.14).

Table 9.14

X	X^2	Y	Y^2	XY
3	9	2	4	6
3	9	2	4	6
3	9	4	16	12
6	36	2	4	12
3	9	4	16	12
5	25	4	16	20
4	16	5	25	20
4	16	5	25	20
4	16	6	36	24
5	25	5	25	25
7	49	3	9	21
6	36	4	16	24
6	36	5	25	30
8	64	3	9	24
6	36	4	16	24
7	49	5	25	35
6	36	5	25	30
8	64	4	16	32
8	64	5	25	40
7	49	6	36	42
7	49	8	64	56
8	64	10	100	80
10	100	11	121	110
9	81	9	81	81
14	196	9	81	126
14	196	10	100	140
21	441	10	100	210
14	196	16	256	224
22	484	17	289	374
17	289	35	1225	595
$\sum$ 245	2749	218	2790	2455

$$r = \frac{\sum XY - \frac{(\sum X)(\sum Y)}{N}}{\sqrt{\left(\sum X^2 - \frac{(\sum X)^2}{N}\right)\left(\sum Y^2 - \frac{(\sum Y)^2}{N}\right)}}$$

$$= \frac{2455 - \frac{(245)(218)}{30}}{\sqrt{\left(2749 - \frac{(245)^2}{30}\right)\left(2790 - \frac{(218)^2}{30}\right)}}$$

$$= \frac{2455.000 - 1780.333}{\sqrt{(2749.000 - 2000.833)(2790.000 - 1584.133)}}$$

$$= \frac{674.667}{\sqrt{(748.167)(1205.867)}}$$

$$= \frac{674.667}{\sqrt{902{,}189.896}}$$

$$= \frac{674.667}{949.837}$$

$$= .71$$

and

$$r^2 = .50$$

Thus, for this sample, 50% of the variance in craft specialization is associated with organizational ramification.

Summary of Procedure. Pearson's r may be computed from data expressed in two interval scales. It is necessary to assume a linear relationship between the variables; then r may be calculated by applying Formula 9.1.

Other Statistics. One circumstance may arise when r is an inappropriate measure of association for interval data: when the assumption of linear relationship was untenable. In this case either the correlation ratio or a coefficient of curvilinear correlation is usually used. A discussion of these follows.

CORRELATION RATIO. The correlation ratio, eta, is sometimes employed as an alternative to Pearson's r when the assumption of linearity cannot be met. Since eta is not even sensitive to relationships in order, it is usually inappropriate to this problem. Application of eta will be discussed in Chapter 11.

COEFFICIENT OF CURVILINEAR CORRELATION. There are situations in which an assumption of linear relationship between two variables cannot be made. The relationship between time and the growth of an organism, for example, is typically not linear. Instead, the rate of growth tends to diminish as time goes on. In such cases there is no constant unit of change in Y for every unit of increase in X. The rate of change (b) is itself variable and this must be taken into account in developing a regression equation. Such equations will produce curved rather than straight lines; and correlation coefficients based on them are called curvilinear coefficients. Several are discussed in Ezekiel and Fox (1959).

10 Describing Association between One Nominal and One Ordinal Scale

Thus far we have discussed statistics that are useful for determining the degree of association between two variables when our data are expressed in nominal, ordinal, or interval scales. We have no assurance, however, that in any particular problem both variables will be recorded at the same level of measurement. Sometimes we will find that we wish to determine the degree of association between two variables, one of which is recorded as a nominal scale and one as an ordinal scale. This chapter will describe a technique for dealing with such problems. This technique was developed by the author as an extension of Wilcoxon's signed-ranks test. It is called the coefficient of differentiation; its symbol is θ (theta).

The Wilcoxon Model for Nominal-Ordinal Association

Function. The usual procedure for dealing with the problem of describing association between one nominal and one ordinal scale involves the use of a nominal scale statistic. Typically, when faced with this problem, the investigator ignores the order in the ordinal scale and computes λ or some other coefficient of nominal association. Attempts to justify this approach are usually based on the argument that one cannot talk about an ordered relationship between two variables when one of

Table 10.1

Nominal Scale, X Classes	Ordered Variable, Y Ranks					Totals
	5	4	3	2	1	
A	10	0	10	0	10	30
B	0	10	0	10	0	20
Totals	10	10	10	10	10	50

them possesses no order. Such an argument, however, does not stand up well under critical examination. Consider the following contingency table (Table 10.1).

If we ignore the order in Y and compute λ for this table, we obtain

$$\begin{aligned}\lambda &= \frac{\sum f_r + \sum f_c - (F_r + F_c)}{2N - (F_r + F_c)} \\ &= \frac{20 + 50 - (30 + 10)}{100 - (30 + 10)} \\ &= \frac{30}{60} = .50\end{aligned}$$

Now let us consider Table 10.2.

Table 10.2

Nominal Scale, X Classes	Ordered Variable, Y Ranks					Totals
	5	4	3	2	1	
A	10	10	10	0	0	30
B	0	0	0	10	10	20
Totals	10	10	10	10	10	50

If we again ignore the order in Y, λ for Table 10.2 is

$$\begin{aligned}\lambda &= \frac{\sum f_r + \sum f_c - (F_r + F_c)}{2N - (F_r + F_c)} \\ &= \frac{20 + 50 - (30 + 10)}{100 - (30 + 10)} \\ &= \frac{30}{60} \\ &= .50\end{aligned}$$

In each of these cases, then, we are able to reduce our error in guessing each variable from the other by 50%. However, if we compare Tables 10.1 and 10.2 we can see that they express very different types of relatedness. In both cases it is possible to guess a person's class membership in the nominal scale from his rank on the ordinal scale without error. And in both cases you will make errors in guessing exact ranks from class memberships. But if we guess *relative* ranking—higher or lower—instead of exact ranks, we can see the difference between the two tables. In

Table 10.2 members of class A all rank higher than those of class B, whereas in Table 10.1 there is no such ordered relationship. The presence of an ordered relationship of this sort suggests that there is a greater degree of association shown in Table 10.2.

The basic notion here is that a nominal scale and an ordinal scale are related to the degree that individuals in each one of the classes on the nominal scale tend to be ranked consistently higher or lower than persons in the other classes. This is Wilcoxon's model; it may be used in description of the degree of association between a nominal and an ordinal scale.

Rationale. As in other coefficients of association, the basic procedure in θ involves guessing or predicting. And since one of the variables is ordinal in the present case, θ is like G in that it requires that we guess the rank order of the individuals we examine. But here, unlike G, we cannot guess order on one variable from order on the other; instead we must guess order on one variable from classification on the other.

An example will show how this works. Suppose we are able to rank ten men and women in terms of their relative aggressiveness in a series of social situations. Our results may resemble Table 10.3.

Table 10.3

	Rank in Aggressiveness									
Sex	10	9	8	7	6	5	4	3	2	1
Male	1	1	1	1	0	1	0	1	0	0
Female	0	0	0	0	1	0	1	0	1	1

Now the question here is the degree to which we can predict the relative aggressiveness ranks of each of the sexes—the association between sex and rank in aggressiveness. This is accomplished by comparing the ranks of each individual in each nominal class with the ranks of all of the individuals in each of the other classes. When, as in this instance, only two classes are in the nominal scale (male and female), only one set of comparisons need be made. We must compare the rank of each male with the ranks of all the females. If we begin with the first male, whose rank is 10, we discover that 4 females rank below him (ranks 6, 4, 2, and 1), and no females rank higher. His scores, then, are 4 below and 0 above. We repeat this procedure for each of the males. For the male ranking 9, 4 are below; 0 are above. For the male ranking 8, 4 are below; 0 are above. Also for the one ranking 7, 4 are below; 0 are above. But for the one ranking 5, 3 are below; 1 is above. And for the one ranking 3, 2 are below; 2 are above. If we total these frequencies and compute the difference between their values, we have an index of the relative ranking of the sexes. Thus

$$\text{Total below} = 4 + 4 + 4 + 4 + 3 + 2 = 21$$
$$\text{Total above} = 1 + 2 = 3$$
$$\text{Total below} - \text{Total above} = 21 - 3 = 18$$

If we divide this difference by the total number of comparisons made, we have a coefficient of association.

$$\frac{\text{Total below} - \text{Total above}}{\text{Total number of comparisons}}$$
$$\frac{21 - 3}{21 + 3} = \frac{18}{24} = .75$$

If we begin with the ranks of women, our result will be identical except for sign. The highest rank obtained by a woman is 6. We find 4 men above this rank and 2 below it. For rank 4, 5 are above; 1 is below. For rank 2, 6 are above; 0 are below. And for rank 1, 6 are above; 0 are below. For women then,

$$\frac{\text{Total below} - \text{Total above}}{\text{Total number of comparisons}}$$
$$\frac{3 - 21}{3 + 21} = -.75$$

Thus, in comparing the rankings of men and women, men rank higher in aggressiveness in 75% more cases than they rank lower. The magnitude of association is, of course, the same whichever way we compute it. The only difference is its sign. But since only one of our variables is ordered, the sign is meaningless—it reflects only which class in the nominal scale we count from. If we drop the sign, the procedure just described becomes a general formula for θ. Thus,

$$\theta = \frac{|\text{Total below} - \text{Total above}|}{\text{Total number of comparisons}}$$

where the vertical lines, $|\quad|$, indicate that the difference is to be recorded without reference to its sign.

If all the men ranked higher than any of the women as in Table 10.4,

Table 10.4

	Rank in Aggressiveness									
Sex	10	9	8	7	6	5	4	3	2	1
Male	1	1	1	1	1	1	0	0	0	0
Female	0	0	0	0	0	0	1	1	1	1

our scores for men will be

$$\text{below} = 24$$
$$\text{above} = 0$$

and θ

$$\theta = \frac{|24 - 0|}{0 + 24} = \frac{24}{24} = 1.0$$

indicating perfect association. If the men and women were equally distributed according to aggressiveness, our scores for men will be as shown in Table 10.5.

Table 10.5

	Rank in Aggressiveness									
Sex	10	9	8	7	6	5	4	3	2	1
Male	1	0	1	0	1	1	0	1	0	1
Female	0	1	0	1	0	0	1	0	1	0

$$\text{below} = 12$$
$$\text{above} = 12$$

and θ

$$\theta = \frac{|12 - 12|}{12 + 12} = \frac{0}{24} = 0.0$$

or no association at all.

θ is a measure of association between a nominal scale and an ordinal scale. It may vary between 0 and 1 and its magnitude may be interpreted in terms of comparisons of the rankings of individuals in different nominal-scale classes. θ is the difference between the proportion of comparisons in which members of one class predominate and the proportion in which members of another class predominate.

Procedure. For computing θ a slight modification of the procedure described provides a more generally useful statistic. This modification will allow us to compute θ when we have ties in rankings as well as in the no-tie case described earlier. The computing formula for θ, then, is

$$\theta = \frac{\sum D_i}{T_2} \tag{10.1}$$

where $D_i = |f_b - f_a|$ or the frequency below minus the frequency above for each pair of classes in the nominal scale, and T_2 is computed by multiplying the total frequency for each nominal class by the totals for each of the other classes two at a time and summing the products. This value is equal to the total number of comparisons made which we computed earlier.

This formula requires that we assume that the ordered variable is continuous and that ties in ranking result simply from crude classification on that variable. Thus ties arise through our inability to determine which observation ranks higher and which ranks lower. Half of the ties, therefore, are assigned to one order and half to the other. But since we are dealing with differences, $|(f_b - \frac{1}{2}f_{\text{ties}}) - (f_a - \frac{1}{2}f_{\text{ties}})|$, the frequency of ties has no effect on the result and can be dropped from the computation.

Let us go back to the data of Table 10.3 and compute θ using Formula 10.1. We can compute f_b by multiplying each frequency in Table 10.3 (in this case they are all ones) by the sum of the frequencies which are both below and to the right of it and adding them together, and we obtain:

$$\begin{aligned}
\text{For } 10:&\quad (1)(4) = 4\\
9:&\quad (1)(4) = 4\\
8:&\quad (1)(4) = 4\\
7:&\quad (1)(4) = 4\\
5:&\quad (1)(3) = 3\\
3:&\quad (1)(2) = \underline{2}\\
&\qquad\qquad\quad 21
\end{aligned}$$

And f_a may be calculated by multiplying each frequency in Table 10.3 by the sum of the frequencies which are both below and to the left of it and adding these together.

$$\begin{aligned}
\text{For } 10:&\quad (1)(0) = 0\\
9:&\quad (1)(0) = 0\\
8:&\quad (1)(0) = 0\\
7:&\quad (1)(0) = 0\\
5:&\quad (1)(1) = 1\\
3:&\quad (1)(2) = \underline{2}\\
&\qquad\qquad\quad 3
\end{aligned}$$

Then $D_i = f_b - f_a = 21 - 3 = 18$, and since we have only two classes in the nominal scale, there are no other comparisons to be made. Therefore there is only one D_i, and $\sum D_i = D_i$.

$$T_2 = (6)(4) = 24$$

We are now prepared to calculate θ.

$$\theta = \frac{\sum D_i}{T_2} = \frac{18}{24} = .75$$

Using Formula 10.1 we obtain the same value we just computed.

When the nominal scale has more than two classes, computing θ is a little more involved. Let us take another example. Suppose we have a group of people classified in terms of their marital status and we are able to rank them in social adjustment. Our results may be arranged as in Table 10.6.

Table 10.6

Marital Status	Rank in Social Adjustment 5	4	3	2	1	Total Frequency
Single	1	2	5	2	0	10
Married	10	5	5	0	0	20
Widowed	0	0	2	2	1	5
Divorced	0	0	0	2	3	5

If we want to determine the degree of association between marital status and social adjustment for our sample, we can compute θ.

First, we calculate f_b for the comparison between the single and the married persons.

$$\begin{aligned}
\text{For rank } 5&: \ (1)(5+5) = 10\\
4&: \ (2)(5) = 10\\
3&: \ (5)(0) = 0\\
2&: \ (2)(0) = 0\\
1&: \ (0)(0) = 0\\
& \quad\quad \overline{20}
\end{aligned}$$

f_a for this same comparison is

$$\begin{aligned}
\text{For rank } 5&: \ (1)(0) = 0\\
4&: \ (2)(10) = 20\\
3&: \ (5)(10+5) = 75\\
2&: \ (2)(10+5+5) = 40\\
1&: \ (0)(10+4+4) = 0\\
& \quad\quad \overline{135}
\end{aligned}$$

D_i for this comparison, then, is

$$\begin{aligned} D_i &= |f_b - f_a| \\ &= |20 - 135| \\ &= 115 \end{aligned}$$

Now we can compare single persons with those who are widowed. f_b is

$$\begin{aligned} \text{For rank } 5\text{:} &\quad (1)(2 + 2 + 1) = 5 \\ 4\text{:} &\quad (2)(2 + 2 + 1) = 10 \\ 3\text{:} &\quad (5)(2 + 1) = 15 \\ 2\text{:} &\quad (2)(1) = 2 \\ 1\text{:} &\quad (0)(0) = \underline{0} \\ & \qquad\qquad\qquad 32 \end{aligned}$$

And f_a is

$$\begin{aligned} \text{For rank } 5\text{:} &\quad (1)(0) = 0 \\ 4\text{:} &\quad (2)(0) = 0 \\ 3\text{:} &\quad (5)(0) = 0 \\ 2\text{:} &\quad (2)(2) = 4 \\ 1\text{:} &\quad (0)(2 + 2) = \underline{0} \\ & \qquad\qquad\quad 4 \end{aligned}$$

D_i for this comparison is

$$\begin{aligned} D_i &= |f_b - f_a| \\ &= |32 - 41| \\ &= 28 \end{aligned}$$

We may now compare single with divorced persons and compute f_b.

$$\begin{aligned} \text{For rank } 5\text{:} &\quad (1)(2 + 3) = 5 \\ 4\text{:} &\quad (2)(2 + 3) = 10 \\ 3\text{:} &\quad (5)(2 + 3) = 25 \\ 2\text{:} &\quad (2)(3) = 6 \\ 1\text{:} &\quad (0)(0) = \underline{0} \\ & \qquad\qquad\quad 46 \end{aligned}$$

And f_a

$$\begin{aligned} \text{For rank } 5\text{:} &\quad (1)(0) = 0 \\ 4\text{:} &\quad (2)(0) = 0 \\ 3\text{:} &\quad (5)(0) = 0 \\ 2\text{:} &\quad (2)(0) = 0 \\ 1\text{:} &\quad (0)(2) = \underline{0} \\ & \qquad\qquad 0 \end{aligned}$$

Then

$$\begin{aligned} D_i &= |f_b - f_a| \\ &= |46 - 0| \\ &= 46 \end{aligned}$$

Now we must compare the married with the widowed. By the same procedure,

$$\begin{aligned} f_b &= 90 \\ f_a &= 0 \\ D_i &= 90 \end{aligned}$$

Comparing married persons with those divorced,

$$\begin{aligned} f_b &= 100 \\ f_a &= 0 \\ D_i &= 100 \end{aligned}$$

Comparing widowed with divorced persons—our last comparison,

$$\begin{aligned} f_b &= 16 \\ f_a &= 2 \\ D_i &= 14 \end{aligned}$$

To find the total number of comparisons we multiply each of our total frequencies by each of the others and add them together.

$$T_2 = (10)(20) + (10)(5) + (10)(5) + (20)(5) + (20)(5) + (5)(5) = 525$$

We are now ready to compute θ.

$$\begin{aligned} \theta &= \frac{\sum D_i}{T_2} \\ &= \frac{115 + 28 + 46 + 90 + 100 + 14}{525} \\ &= \frac{393}{525} \\ &= .75 \end{aligned}$$

Thus for these 40 individuals we can predict social adjustment on the basis of marital status rather well. θ shows that in 75% of the comparisons made persons in the various marital status classes show systematic differences in social adjustment.

This statistic θ may be applied whenever we wish to know the degree of association between an ordinal and a nominal scale.

Example

Smith and Monane studied courtship values among students at the University of Colorado.[1] Each student was given a questionnaire on which he was asked to specify the trait he most desired in a date. Responses were collected and classified into five categories: Companionability, desirable physical appearance, social graces, intelligence and education, and miscellaneous responses. Background data on the students were collected, and the investigators attempted to discover the relationship between preferred trait and several of these background characteristics.

One of the background characteristics with which Smith and Monane were concerned was family income rank. They hypothesized that students who desired different traits in a date might come from families with differing income ranks. θ is appropriate to explore that possibility.

Table 10.7 presents the data collected by Smith and Monane. The category of miscellaneous responses has been eliminated in order to simplify our analysis.

Table 10.7. *Preferred Traits in a Date according to Family Income*

Preferred Trait	Family Income Rank				Total Frequencies
	4	3	2	1	
A. Companionability	52	28	40	34	154
B. Desirable physical appearance	7	9	16	10	42
C. Social graces	8	4	10	9	31
D. Intelligence and education	12	6	7	5	30

Comparison $A:B$

$$\begin{aligned} f_b &= (52)(9 + 16 + 10) = 1820 \\ & (28)(16 + 10) = 728 \\ & (40)(10) = 400 \\ & \overline{2948} \end{aligned}$$

$$\begin{aligned} f_a &= (28)(7) = 196 \\ & (40)(9 + 7) = 640 \\ & (34)(16 + 9 + 7) = 1088 \\ & \overline{1924} \end{aligned}$$

$$D_i = |f_b - f_a| = |2948 - 1924| = 1024$$

[1] Elinor Smith and H. H. Greenberg Monane, "Courtship Values in a Youth Sample," *American Sociological Review*, **18** (December, 1953), 635–640.

Comparison $A:C$

$$\begin{aligned} f_b = {} & (52)(4 + 10 + 9) = 1196 \\ & (28)(10 + 9) = 532 \\ & (40)(9) = 360 \\ & \overline{2088} \end{aligned}$$

$$\begin{aligned} f_a = {} & (28)(8) = 224 \\ & (40)(8 + 4) = 480 \\ & (34)(8 + 4 + 10) = 748 \\ & \overline{1452} \end{aligned}$$

$$D_i = |f_b - f_a| = |2088 - 1452| = 636$$

Comparison $A:D$

$$D_i = |f_b - f_a| = |1472 - 1906| = 434$$

Comparison $B:C$

$$D_i = |f_b - f_a| = |476 - 484| = 8$$

Comparison $B:D$

$$D_i = |f_b - f_a| = |314 - 646| = 322$$

Comparison $C:D$

$$D_i = |f_b - f_a| = |242 - 453| = 211$$

Then

$$\sum D_i = 1024 + 636 + 434 + 8 + 322 + 211 = 2635$$

And

$$T_2 = (154)(42) + (154)(31) + (154)(30) + (42)(31) + (42)(30) + (31)(30) = 19{,}354$$

Then

$$\theta = \frac{\sum D_i}{T_2} = \frac{2635}{19{,}354} = .14$$

For these data only 14% of the comparisons among individuals expressing different courtship values show consistent differences in family income levels; in such a case any attempt to predict family income level on the basis of desired trait would be relatively unproductive.

Summary of Procedure. In order to compute θ the following steps must be taken.

1. Arrange the frequencies in a contingency table.
2. Compare each class in the nominal scale with each other class and record the number of observations in the latter which are below (f_b) and the number above (f_a) the former.
3. Compute the difference between f_b and f_a (without regard to its sign) for every pair of classes and add these differences together.
4. Calculate the total number of possible comparisons T_2.
5. Compute θ according to Formula 10.1.

Other Statistics. No other statistics are available for computing the degree of association between one nominal and one ordinal scale. It is always possible to reduce the ordinal scale to a nominal level and compute λ, but such procedure will result in a less sensitive measure of association.

11 Describing Association between One Nominal and One Interval Scale

Only one statistic is appropriate for describing the degree of association between one nominal and one interval scale: the correlation ratio. It is always possible to simplify the interval scale to an ordinal level and compute G or to reduce it to a nominal scale and employ λ. Using either of these approaches, however, would involve throwing information away; the correlation ratio provides the most sensitive index of association in this case. This chapter therefore will be concerned with the correlation ratio. The correlation ratio is usually symbolized as η (eta).

Function. η may be used to describe the degree of association between two variables when one of them is expressed in a nominal scale and one in an interval scale.

Rationale. We have been viewing association as a problem in guessing. Various kinds of guesses have been used, but, in general, the more accurate the guesses of values of one variable on the basis of values of the other, the greater the association. For λ and Pearson's r, this accuracy was evaluated in terms of the degree to which we could guess values of one variable correctly *without* knowledge of the other. In these instances the final coefficient of association was an index of improvement in accuracy of guessing—the greater the improvement, the higher the coefficient.

This is true also of η; the correlation ratio is an index of improvement in guessing. As in λ and r, we first guess a typical score in a distribution; then we guess again—this time on the basis of the distribution of another variable—and compute a ratio expressing the proportion of reduction of error or degree of improvement in guessing.

Let us take an example. Suppose we are given information on the number of packs of cigarettes purchased per week by each person in a group of 40. We can record these data in a frequency table like Table 11.1.

Now if we are asked to guess the typical number of packs purchased by any member of this group, we should guess the mean. The mean, as we

Table 11.1

Number of Packs of Cigarettes Purchased per Week, Y	Frequency, f
0	3
1	1
2	2
3	3
4	4
5	4
6	4
7	4
8	4
9	6
10	3
11	2
Total	40

have seen, is the best guess of a typical score in the distribution of an interval scale. In this case we designate the number of packs purchased as Y.

We can use a simplified method to calculate the mean for a frequency distribution of this sort. The general definition of the mean is

$$\bar{Y} = \frac{\sum_{i=1}^{N} Y_i}{N}$$

But several of the values of Y repeat—they have frequencies greater than 1. Here each Y value is simply multiplied by its associated frequency before summing.

$$\bar{Y} = \frac{\sum_{i=1}^{N} fY_i}{N}$$

This results in the same value of the mean as that calculated by our earlier formula (see Table 11.2). Then

$$\begin{aligned} \bar{Y} &= \frac{\sum_{i=1}^{N} fY_i}{N} \\ &= \frac{240}{40} \\ &= 6 \end{aligned}$$

Table 11.2

Y	f	fY
0	3	0
1	1	1
2	2	4
3	3	9
4	4	16
5	4	20
6	4	24
7	4	28
8	4	32
9	6	54
10	3	30
11	2	22
Σ	40	240

The best guess, then, is that a member of this group buys 6 packs of cigarettes a week.

In order to evaluate the efficiency of this guess we must obtain an index of the variation around the mean—the variance as shown in Table 11.3 (again, frequencies are used in the same manner).

Table 11.3

Y	$y = Y - \bar{Y}$	y^2	f	fy^2
0	−6	36	3	108
1	−5	25	1	25
2	−4	16	2	32
3	−3	9	3	27
4	−2	4	4	16
5	−1	1	4	4
6	0	0	4	0
7	1	1	4	4
8	2	4	4	16
9	3	9	6	54
10	4	16	3	48
11	5	25	2	50
Σ			40	384

$$s_y^2 = \frac{\sum_{i=1}^{N} fy_i^2}{N} = \frac{384}{40} = 9.6$$

Thus the variance in this distribution is 9.6. This is an index of error in guessing the mean of cigarette purchase for each member of this group.

Let us suppose now, reasonably enough, that we hypothesize that cigarette buying may be related to sex. (Men, we may guess, smoke more, and furthermore they probably purchase cigarettes which they give, one at a time, to women.) The problem therefore is to determine the degree of relatedness between sex and cigarette purchase for this group. In our terms, we wish to determine the degree to which knowledge of sex can help us to reduce our error in guessing cigarette buying. So we shall divide the frequency distribution by sex (Table 11.4).

Table 11.4

Number of Packs of Cigarettes Purchased per Week, Y	Sex, X		
	Males	Females	Total
0	0	3	3
1	0	1	1
2	0	2	2
3	0	3	3
4	0	4	4
5	0	4	4
6	0	4	4
7	1	3	4
8	2	2	4
9	4	2	6
10	2	1	3
11	1	1	2
Σ	10	30	40

We can now guess purchase and summarize the error for each sex separately. The error for males is shown in Table 11.5.

$$\bar{Y} = \frac{\sum_{i=1}^{N} fY_i}{N} = \frac{90}{10} = 9$$

$$s_y^2 = \frac{\sum_{i=1}^{N} fy_i^2}{N} = \frac{12}{10} = 1.2$$

Table 11.5

Y	f	fY	$y = Y - \bar{Y}$	y^2	fy^2
7	1	7	−2	4	4
8	2	16	−1	1	2
9	4	36	0	0	0
10	2	20	1	1	2
11	1	11	2	4	4
Σ	10	90			12

Table 11.6 shows a summary of errors for females.

Table 11.6

Y	f	fY	$y = Y - \bar{Y}$	y^2	fy^2
0	3	0	−5	25	75
1	1	1	−4	16	16
2	2	4	−3	99	18
3	3	9	−2	4	12
4	4	16	−1	1	4
5	4	20	0	0	0
6	4	24	1	1	4
7	3	21	2	4	12
8	2	16	3	9	18
9	2	18	4	16	32
10	1	10	5	25	25
11	1	11	6	36	36
	30	150			252

$$\bar{Y} = \frac{\sum_{i=1}^{N} fY_i}{N} = \frac{150}{30} = 5$$

$$s_y^2 = \frac{\sum_{i=1}^{N} fy_i^2}{N} = \frac{252}{30} = 8.4$$

The variance for males is 1.2, and that for females is 8.4. This means that if we guess the mean of males (9) for each male, our index of error is 1.2. And if we guess the mean of females (5) for each female, the index is 8.4. These values represent the error in guessing cigarette purchase for each sex separately; combined they produce an index of error in guessing cigarette purchase *when sex is taken into account.*

The index we want is simply a weighted average.

$$s_w^2 = \frac{\sum_{i=1}^{k} n_j s_j^2}{N}$$

where n_j = the number of observations in a nominal scale subgroup,
s_j^2 = the variance of Y-scores in that subgroup,
k = the number of subgroups,
N = the total number of observations,
s_w^2 = the average variance within subgroups.

In this case we have two subgroups

$$k = 2$$
$$n_1 = 10 \qquad n_2 = 30$$
$$s_1^2 = 1.2 \qquad s_2^2 = 8.4$$

And

$$\begin{aligned} s_w^2 &= \frac{(10)(1.2) + (30)(8.4)}{40} \\ &= \frac{12 + 252}{40} \\ &= \frac{264}{40} \\ &= 6.6 \end{aligned}$$

The average variance within the sex subgroups is 6.6. This is the index of error we obtain when we guess the mean number of packs purchased for each sex separately, compute the variance around each mean, and combine these into a single index. It is an index of error in guessing cigarette purchase when we take sex into account.

Now we can compute η using the same general model we used for λ and Pearson's r.

$$\frac{\text{Reduction in error}}{\text{Original error}}$$

In this case, like Pearson's r, the variance is our summary of error, thus

$$\begin{aligned}\eta^2 &= \frac{s_y^2 - s_w^2}{s_y^2}\\ &= \frac{9.6 - 6.6}{9.6}\\ &= \frac{3}{9.6}\\ &= .31\end{aligned}$$

And

$$\begin{aligned}\eta &= \sqrt{\eta^2}\\ &= \sqrt{.31}\\ &= .56\end{aligned}$$

η is equal to .56. Here, however, like Pearson's r, we are not simply counting errors; instead we are using the variance as our summary of error. Since it refers directly to variance, η^2 is easier to interpret; it is equal to the proportion of variance in Y (the measured variable) which is associated with subclasses in X (the nominal scale). Or, to put it another way, η^2 is the proportion of variance in Y which is eliminated by taking X into account. In this instance 31% of the variance in cigarette purchase is associated with sex, and $(1 - \eta^2)$ 69% of the variance is left over—it is not associated with sex.

The correlation ratio varies between 0 and 1. Since it involves the use of an unordered nominal scale, we cannot talk of an ordered relationship, and η therefore never takes a minus sign. The magnitude of η^2 expresses the proportion of shared variance between X and Y. η^2 (and hence η) is zero whenever guessing Y values cannot be enhanced by taking X values into account. In such a case $\bar{Y}$ for each X subgroup is equal to the grand mean for all Y scores, and the variance for the subgroups equals the variance for the whole distribution (Table 11.7).

Table 11.7

Y scores	f	fX_a	fX_b	fX_c
1	3	1	1	1
2	6	2	2	2
3	12	4	4	4
4	6	2	2	2
5	3	1	1	1
Total	30	10	10	10

Here we have 3 classes in our nominal (X) scale: a, b, and c. The mean of the whole Y distribution is 3 and the variance is also 3. For each of the X subgroups, $\bar{Y}$ equals 3 and s_w^2 equals 3 for all of them. Then

$$\eta^2 = \frac{3 - 3}{3} = \frac{0}{3} = 0$$

Hence taking X into account in no way reduces our error in guessing Y. There is no association between X and Y.

But if we take a case where each score in Y is confined to a particular X class, we obtain a different picture (Table 11.8).

Table 11.8

		X Subgroups				
Y scores	f	fX_a	fX_b	fX_c	fX_d	fX_e
1	3	3	0	0	0	0
2	6	0	0	0	6	0
3	12	0	12	0	0	0
4	6	0	0	6	0	0
5	3	0	0	0	0	3
Total	30	3	12	6	6	3

Here we have 5 classes in X (a through e), and each X class contains only one Y score. Again the mean of the whole Y distribution is 3 and the variance is 3. However, the means of the various X classes differ, and $s_w^2 = 0$. Then

$$\eta^2 = \frac{3 - 0}{3} = \frac{3}{3} = 1.0$$

All the variance in Y is associated with variation in X. Given knowledge of X, it is possible to predict Y perfectly.

In general, then, η is an index of the degree to which scores on an interval scale can be predicted from classes in a nominal scale. It may be used to measure association whenever we are dealing with the relationship between one nominal and one ordinal scale.

Procedure. The correlation ratio may be computed by the procedure described earlier. However, that procedure involves a series of extra steps; it may be simplified to the following general computational formula:

$$\eta^2 = \frac{\sum_{j=1}^{k} n_j(\bar{Y}_j - \bar{Y})^2}{\sum_{i=1}^{N} (Y_i - \bar{Y})^2} \qquad (11.1)$$

where n_j = the number of observations in an X subgroup,
$\overline{Y}_j$ = the mean of a subgroup,
$\overline{Y}$ = the grand mean,
k = the number of subgroups,
Y_i = a score on the interval scale,
N = the total number of observations.

Let us apply this formula to the data of our earlier illustrations (Table 11.9).

Table 11.9

Total Group						Male Subgroup		Female Subgroup	
Y	f	fY	$Y - \overline{Y}$	y^2	fy^2	f	fY	f	fY
0	3	0	−6	36	108	0	0	3	0
1	1	1	−5	25	25	0	0	1	1
2	2	4	−4	16	32	0	0	2	4
3	3	9	−3	9	27	0	0	3	9
4	4	16	−2	4	16	0	0	4	16
5	4	20	−1	1	4	0	0	4	20
6	4	24	0	0	0	0	0	4	24
7	4	28	1	1	4	1	7	3	21
8	4	32	2	4	16	2	16	2	16
9	6	54	3	9	54	4	36	2	18
10	3	30	4	16	48	2	20	1	10
11	2	22	5	25	50	1	11	1	11
	40	240			384	10	90	30	150

$$\overline{Y} = \frac{240}{40} = 6$$

$$\overline{Y}_{\text{males}} = \frac{90}{10} = 9$$

$$\overline{Y}_{\text{females}} = \frac{150}{30} = 5$$

Then

$$(\overline{Y}_{\text{males}} - \overline{Y})^2 = (9 - 6)^2 = 3^2 = 9$$
$$n_{\text{males}} = 10$$

and

$$(\overline{Y}_{\text{females}} - \overline{Y})^2 = (5 - 6)^2 = -1^2 = 1$$
$$n_{\text{females}} = 30$$

We can now compute η^2.

$$\eta^2 = \frac{\sum_{j=1}^{k} n_j(\bar{Y}_j - \bar{Y})^2}{\sum_{i=1}^{N} (Y_i - \bar{Y})^2}$$

$$= \frac{(10)(9) + (30)(1)}{384}$$

$$= \frac{120}{384}$$

$$= .31$$

This is a general formula which may be used to compute η in all cases.

Example

Chapman and Volkmann examined the effect of reference group on the level of aspiration of 86 psychology students.[1] Each student was told he was to be given a 50-item test in literature. Before the test the students were required to guess the number of items they would answer correctly. Twenty-two students (Group A) were given no further instructions. Another 22 (Group B) were told that a group of authors and literary critics had made an average score of 37.2 correct answers. Twenty-two more (Group C) were informed that a group of psychology students had made that average. The remaining 20 (Group D) were told that an average of 37.2 had been achieved by a group of unselected W. P. A. workers.

One variable in this study was the four class nominal scale—reference group. Group A had no reference group, Group B had a group of experts, Group C had a group of psychology students like themselves, and Group D had a group whom they might be expected to view as their inferiors. The other variable was the level of aspiration; each student's anticipated score on the literary test was recorded. The purpose of the study was to determine the degree of association between reference group and level of aspiration. The correlation ratio is appropriate for this problem.

The results of Chapman and Volkmann's study are shown in Table 11.10. Note that this table shows only the summary data for these 86 students. For our purposes we need not refer to the actual scores of individuals.

[1] Dwight W. Chapman and John Volkmann, "A Social Determinant of the Level of Aspiration," *Journal of Abnormal and Social Psychology*, **34** (1939), 225–238.

Table 11.10. *Aspiration Levels of Students Classified according to Reference Group*

	Reference Group				
	A None	*B* Experts	*C* Own	*D* Inferiors	Total Group
$\bar{Y}_j$	26.95	23.09	31.09	33.05	28.44
$\bar{Y}_j - \bar{Y}$	−1.49	−5.35	2.65	4.61	
$(\bar{Y}_j - \bar{Y})^2$	2.22	28.622	7.022	21.252	
n_j	22	22	22	20	
$n_j(\bar{Y}_j - \bar{Y})^2$	48.840	629.684	154.684	425.040	
$(Y_i - \bar{Y})^2$					4375.88

$$\eta^2 = \frac{\sum_{j=1}^{k} n_j(\bar{Y}_j - \bar{Y})^2}{\sum_{i=1}^{N} (Y_i - \bar{Y})^2}$$

$$= \frac{48.840 + 629.684 + 154.484 + 425.040}{4375.88}$$

$$= \frac{1258.048}{4375.88}$$

$$= .29 \quad \text{and} \quad \eta = .54$$

Thus 29% of the variance in level of aspiration is associated with variation in reference group.

Summary of Procedure. The following steps may be taken to compute η.

1. Let Y be the measured variable; compute $\bar{Y}$ for the total group, and $\bar{Y}_j$ for each of the subgroups classified according to the nominal scale.
2. Compute the squared deviations of each of the subgroup means from the grand mean: $(\bar{Y}_j - \bar{Y})^2$.
3. Multiply each of these squared deviations by the number of cases in the subgroup $n_j(\bar{Y}_j - \bar{Y})^2$ and sum for all k subgroups.
4. Calculate the sum of squared deviations for the entire group $\sum_{i=1}^{N} (Y_i - \bar{Y})^2$.
5. Compute η according to Formula 11.1.

Other Statistics. There are no other statistics which are appropriate for describing the degree of association between a nominal scale and an interval scale.

12 Describing Association between One Ordinal and One Interval Scale

There is no single solution to the problem of describing the degree of association between one ordinal and one interval scale. There are the usual inefficient alternatives involving simplifying one or the other of the scales and computing a less sensitive measure of association. And there are two procedures which are designed specifically for problems involving one ordinal and one interval scale: multiserial correlation and point-multiserial correlation.

Both procedures require that some assumption be made about the relative size of the intervals in the ordinal scale. For multiserial correlation it is necessary to assume that the intervals between the ranks are spaced according to a standard distribution. This distribution is imposed on the data in order to convert the ranks into scores on an assumed interval scale. But for point-multiserial correlation it is assumed that the ranks themselves are equally spaced and may be treated as scores on an interval scale.

In most instances the assumption that the ranks in a set are equally spaced appears unlikely. The fact that we use ordinal scales at all is a consequence of the fact that we cannot work out a way to establish equal intervals. If, in order to compute a coefficient of association, we assume equal intervals instead of demonstrating them, the meaning of the statistic we compute is unclear. The multiserial coefficient, then, is probably the best alternative in most cases. It has several limitations, as we shall see, but these are probably less restrictive in general than are the limitations involved in the point-multiserial.

Since there is no standard symbol for the coefficient of multiserial correlation, we shall use M.

Jaspen's Coefficient of Multiserial Correlation

Function. M may be used to measure the degree of association between an ordinal and an interval scale whenever the investigator is willing to assume (1) that there is a linear relationship between the variables and (2) that a normal distribution constitutes a reasonable image of what the ordinal variable might look like if we were able to measure it with greater precision.

Rationale. When we are able to measure a variable on an interval scale, we frequently find that a large sample of observations on that scale will be normally distributed. This is certainly not always true; income, for example, measured in dollars, is an extremely skewed distribution, and certain conforming behaviors seem to produce a distribution shaped something like the letter J. But many of the things we have measured carefully have turned out to be normally distributed.

What if we are unable to measure some variable in which we are interested; what if we can only rank our observations? The idea here is that ranking is a relatively inefficient method of scaling observations; but if we are willing to *assume* that the variable in question would be normally distributed if we could measure it on an interval scale, then it is possible to make some adjustments which will enhance the efficiency of our scaling. We can, in fact, transform our ordinal scale into an interval scale if we are ready to make this assumption. Suppose we administer an attitude scale to ten students and we are able to rank them into four classes in terms of their attitude toward spending money. Our results might resemble Table 12.1.

Table 12.1

Rank	Attitude	f
4	Very favorable	1
3	Mildly favorable	5
2	Mildly unfavorable	3
1	Very unfavorable	1
		10

In this table we have been unable to establish equal intervals. We know the people ranking *very favorable* are bigger spenders (at least verbally) than those classified as *mildly favorable*, but we do not know how much bigger. However, in this situation it would not seem unreasonable to assume that if we were able to measure attitude toward spending money in an interval scale it would be normally distributed. We should expect most people to be relatively moderate and few to be either extreme spendthrifts or extreme skinflints. Let us therefore make the assumption of normality and see where it leads us.

When we assume a normal distribution, the idea is that our ranking system is composed of crude, uneven categories. Each individual has a value on the assumed interval scale, but all we know from our ranking system is that he falls into one or another of the broad categories. We can express, however, our distribution in terms of the proportion of persons falling into each rank (Table 12.2).

Table 12.2

Rank	Attitude	f	Proportion
4	Very favorable	1	.10
3	Mildly favorable	5	.50
2	Mildly unfavorable	3	.30
1	Very unfavorable	1	.10
		10	1.00

If we take a standard normal curve, we can divide it into the corresponding proportions (Fig. 12.1). From these proportions of the normal curve we can assign each individual a score on the assumed underlying interval scale.

A normal curve is constructed so that if we know how far a score departs from the mean we can tell the proportions of scores above and below it. By knowing the proportions of scores above and below a particular score we can, of course, determine how far it departs from the mean. In Fig. 12.1 we have divided the curve into four segments; we can look at the table of the normal curve (Table C in the Appendix) and determine the deviation scores which are equivalent to each of the points of division. According to the table the deviation score (z) below which .10 of the cases fall is -1.2816. This then is the z score which divides those persons in rank 1 from those in rank 2. Everyone in rank 1 scores below -1.2816; everyone in ranks 2, 3, and 4 scores above this score. We can repeat this process for the other two dividing points; the new information about the distribution appears in Fig. 12.2. We can see that when we apply the normal curve to our data, we can determine critical

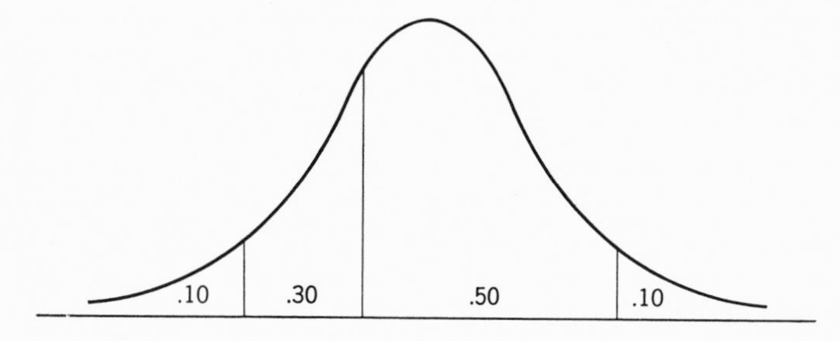

Fig. 12.1.

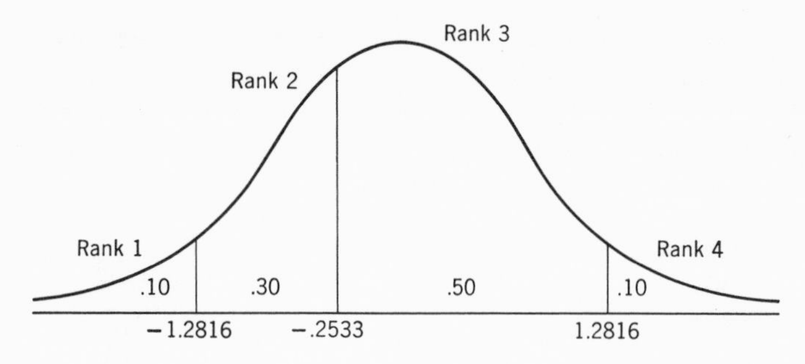

Fig. 12.2.

deviation scores above which and below which each of our ranks can be found. We know, for example, that everyone in rank 4 must score above 1.2816. Because of the crudity of our rankings, however, we cannot tell how far above that score any individual falls. The best we can do is assign each individual in this rank the average deviation score in this segment of the normal curve.

Here another attribute of the normal curve comes into play. The height of the curve or ordinate and the deviation scores are related in such a way that the mean deviation score of any segment of the curve may be determined from a knowledge of the ordinates which bound that segment. The general formula for determining this mean is

$$\bar{z} = \frac{o_b - o_a}{p}$$

where o_b = the height of the ordinate (read from Table C) below the segment in question,

o_a = the height of the ordinate above the segment,

p = the proportion of cases within the segment.

In this case Table C reveals that the ordinate above which .10 of the cases fall is .1755, and the ordinate above which none of the cases fall is, of course, 0. These are the boundaries of the segment with which we are concerned. Now if we apply our formula,

$$\begin{aligned} \bar{z}_4 &= \frac{o_b - o_a}{p} \\ &= \frac{.1755 - 0}{.10} \\ &= \frac{.1755}{.10} \\ &= 1.755 \end{aligned}$$

The average deviation score for individuals ranking 4 is 1.755.

For the individuals ranking 3, we must use caution when we use Table C. We are interested in the ordinate above which .50 + .10 = .60 of the cases fall. But the table reads only to .50. We must look therefore for the ordinate *below* which .40 of the cases fall: .3863. This is o_b, and we have already determined o_a to be .1755. $\bar{z}_3$ may be computed as follows:

$$\bar{z}_3 = \frac{.3863 - .1755}{.50}$$
$$= \frac{.2108}{.50}$$
$$= .4216$$

For those who rank 2,

$$\bar{z}_2 = \frac{.1755 - .3863}{.30}$$
$$= \frac{-.2108}{.30}$$
$$= -.7020$$

And for those who rank 1,

$$\bar{z}_1 = \frac{0 - .1755}{.10}$$
$$= \frac{-.1755}{10}$$
$$= -1.755$$

We have normalized our ranks. Each individual has been assigned a deviation score equivalent to his position in the rankings. These are an approximation of the deviation scores we should expect to have obtained

Table 12.3

Rank of Attitude toward Spending Money	$\bar{z}$ Score of Attitude toward Spending Money	*Y* Number of Dates per Week
4	1.755	4
3	.4216	5
3	.4216	4
3	.4216	3
3	.4216	3
3	.4216	3
2	−.7027	2
2	−.7027	3
2	−.7027	2
1	−1.755	1

had we been able to measure attitude toward saving money in an interval scale. Admittedly, these are only crude approximations, and they are based on the assumptions of normality, but they do form a workable set of equal-interval scores.

If our problem were one of association—if we wanted to correlate attitude toward spending money among our students with, say, number of dates per week—we could now compute Pearson's r. The attitude ranks have been transformed into equal-interval deviation scores, so r is the appropriate statistic.

Let us suppose we collected data on number of dates per week for the ten students. We might have the joint bivariate distribution shown in Table 12.3.

Using our $\bar{z}$ scores, then, we can compute r. Let us designate number of dates per week as Y (Table 12.4).

Table 12.4

	Y	Y^2	$\bar{z}$	$\bar{z}^2$	$Y\bar{z}$
	4	16	1.7550	3.080	7.020
	5	25	.4216	.178	2.108
	4	16	.4216	.178	1.686
	3	9	.4216	.178	1.265
	3	9	.4216	.178	1.265
	3	9	.4216	.178	1.265
	2	4	−.7027	.494	−1.405
	3	9	−.7027	.494	−2.108
	2	4	−.7027	.494	−1.405
	1	1	−1.7550	3.080	−1.755
Σ	30	102	0	8.532	7.936

$$r = \frac{\sum Y\bar{z} - \dfrac{(\sum Y)(\sum \bar{z})}{N}}{\sqrt{\sum Y^2 - \dfrac{(\sum Y)^2}{N}\,\sum \bar{z}^2 - \dfrac{(\sum \bar{z})^2}{N}}}$$

$$= \frac{7.936 - \dfrac{(30)(0)}{10}}{\sqrt{102 - \dfrac{(30)^2}{10}\,8.532 - \dfrac{(0)^2}{10}}}$$

$$= \frac{7.936}{\sqrt{(12)(8.532)}}$$

$$= \frac{7.936}{10.130}$$

$$= .783$$

The obtained r, then, is .78. This r, however, is in need of correction. A correction factor is necessitated by the fact that our normalized scores are expressed in several relatively broad categories instead of as individual scores. Classing a variable in broad categories tends to lower the variance of its distribution. If we divide our obtained r by the standard deviation of the broadly classed variable, the coefficient of correlation is raised in order to compensate for the broad categories. In this case,

$$\begin{aligned} r_{\text{corrected}} &= \frac{r}{s_z} = M \\ &= \frac{.783}{.924} \\ &= .85 \end{aligned}$$

The transformation of ranks changes the interpretation of r. Our obtained r would involve not only the usual assumption of linearity but also the assumption that the ranked variable would be normally distributed if we were able to measure it in an interval scale. Such an r can be interpreted not in terms of a proportion of shared variance, but rather in terms of the proportion of variance we should expect to be shared if we were actually able to measure our ranked variable.

In this case $r = .85$ and $r^2 = .72$. Therefore we might expect that 72% of the variance in number of dates per week for our sample would have been explained by attitude toward spending money had we been able to measure the attitude in an interval scale.

Procedure. Multiserial correlation combines the operations of normalizing ranks and determining the coefficient of correlation in a single procedure. It is simply an adaptation of Pearson's r which includes the steps necessary to determine mean deviation scores on the ranked variable, as well as the correction factor which compensates for the bias when the number of ranks is small.

Symbolically expressed, the general formula for M is

$$M = \frac{\sum \bar{Y}_{\text{sub}}(o_b - o_a)}{s_y \sum \frac{(o_b - o_a)^2}{p}} \tag{12.1}$$

where $\bar{Y}_{\text{sub}}$ = the mean Y score for a subgroup on the ranked variable,
$o_b - o_a$ = the normal curve ordinate below the subgroup in question minus the ordinate above that subgroup,
p = the proportion of cases in a subgroup,
s_y = the standard deviation of all the Y scores.

Let us apply this formula to the data of our earlier example (Table 12.5).

Table 12.5

Ranks	Y Scores	$\bar{Y}_{\text{sub}}$	p	o_b	o_a	$o_b - o_a$	$(o_b - o_a)^2$	$\frac{(o_b - o_a)^2}{p}$	$\bar{Y}_{\text{sub}}(o_b - o_a)$
4	4	4	.10	.1755	0	.1755	.0308	.3080	.7020
3	5, 4, 3, 3, 3,	3.6	.50	.3863	.1755	.2108	.0444	.0888	.7589
2	3, 2, 2,	2.333	.30	.1755	.3863	−.2108	.0444	.1480	−.4918
1	1	1	.10	0	.1755	−.1755	.0308	.3080	−.1755
Totals			1.00			0		.8528	.7936

$$s_y = \sqrt{\frac{\sum y^2}{N}} = \sqrt{\frac{12}{10}} = \sqrt{1.2} = 1.095$$

$$M = \frac{\sum \bar{Y}_{\text{sub}}(o_b - o_a)}{s_y \sum \frac{(o_b - o_a)^2}{p}}$$

$$= \frac{.7936}{(1.095)(.8528)}$$

$$= \frac{.7936}{.9338}$$

$$= .85$$

Thus Formula 12.1 yields the same result as our earlier, more involved computations. Formula 12.1 may be used to compute M in all cases.

Example

Curtis has reported a study of the relationship between intelligence and susceptibility to hypnosis.[1] He selected 32 subjects, ranging from 16 to 32 years of age and representing a wide variety of regional and social class backgrounds. Each subject was given a Stanford-Binet Intelligence Test, and each was subjected to an hypnotic session. In these sessions the subjects were exposed to a standardized set of hypnotic stimuli; suggestions ranged from eye closure, through an hallucination of a fly, to post-hypnotic amnesia. Responses to these suggestions were recorded, and each subject was assigned a score on a hypnotic suggestibility scale. These scores, however, were somewhat arbitrary, and although Curtis treated them as scores on an interval scale, they might be more realistically viewed as a set of crude ranks. For the present reanalysis, therefore, hypnotic susceptibility has been collapsed into an ordinal scale consisting of four ranks.

[1] James W. Curtis, "A Study of the Relationship Between Hypnotic Susceptibility and Intelligence," *Journal of Experimental Psychology*, **33** (October, 1943), 337–339.

Table 12.6 shows the intelligence test scores and the hypnotic susceptibility ranks of these 32 individuals. M is appropriate to describe the relationship between these two variables.

Table 12.6. *Intelligence Test Scores for Various Ranks in Hypnotic Susceptibility*

Rank in Susceptibility to Hypnosis			
4	3	2	1
136	144	139	128
131	137	134	111
126	134	133	104
116	131	132	103
	129	130	103
	126	129	101
	122	123	101
	117	117	
	111	116	
	109	112	
		106	

If we adopt the procedure described earlier, we obtain Table 12.7.

Table 12.7

X Ranks	$\bar{Y}_{sub}$	p	o_b	o_a	$o_b - o_a$	$(o_b - o_a)^2$	$\frac{(o_b - o_a)^2}{p}$	$\bar{Y}_{sub}(o_b - o_a)$
4	127.25	.13	.2115	0	.2115	.0448	.3446	26.9388
3	126.00	.31	.3978	.2155	.1863	.0347	.1020	23.4738
2	124.64	.34	.2961	.3978	−.1017	.0103	.0332	−12.6759
1	107.28	.22	0	.2961	−.2961	.0877	.3986	−31.7656
Totals		1.00			0		.8784	5.9711

$$s_y = \sqrt{\frac{\sum y^2}{N}} = \sqrt{153.37} = 12.38$$

$$M = \frac{\sum \bar{Y}_{sub}(o_b - o_a)}{s_y \sum \frac{(o_b - o_a)^2}{p}}$$

$$= \frac{5.9711}{(12.38)(.8784)}$$

$$= \frac{5.9711}{10.8746}$$

$$= .55$$

Thus the multiserial correlation between intelligence and susceptibility to hypnosis for these 32 subjects is .55* and $M^2 = .30$. This suggests that if we were able to measure susceptibility to hypnosis in an interval scale and if it were normally distributed, we should expect it to correlate with intelligence about .55. Under this assumption, then, and with this qualification, intelligence and susceptibility to hypnosis share about 30% of their variance for these subjects.

Summary of Procedure. To compute M it is necessary to assume a linear relationship between the two variables. Furthermore, we must assume that the values of the ordinal scale would be normally distributed if they had been measured in an interval scale. If these assumptions are made, M may be computed by performing the following operations:

1. Determine $\bar{Y}_{\text{sub}}$—the mean Y score for each subgroup on the ranked variable.
2. From a table of the normal curve determine the ordinates which bound each ranked subgroup.
3. Subtract the ordinate above from the ordinate below each subgroup.
4. Compute the proportion of cases in each subgroup.
5. Calculate the standard deviation of the measured variable.
6. Compute M according to Formula 12.1.

Other Statistics. Any of the following several procedures is often applied to problems of association between an ordinal and an interval scale.

BISERIAL CORRELATION. Biserial r is nothing but the special case of M applied when the ordinal scale has only two ranks. It differs from M only in that there is a special computing formula for r_{biserial} which is convenient for a two-rank ordinal scale. This computing formula can be found in McNemar (1955), Walker and Lev (1953), and in most other introductory texts.

POINT-MULTISERIAL CORRELATION. Point-multiserial r was discussed at the beginning of this chapter. It requires the assumption that the intervals in the ordinal scale are equal. Such an assumption would probably rule out its use in all except very special circumstances. Point-multiserial correlation is discussed in Peters and Van Voorhis (1940) under the general discussion of Pearson's r.

* It may be noted that the Pearson's r between intelligence and Curtis' arbitrary scores in susceptibility to hypnosis was .50.

POINT-BISERIAL CORRELATION. Point-biserial correlation is the special case of point-multiserial correlation where the ordinal scale is limited to two ranks. All the limitations of point-multiserial apply also to point-biserial *r*.

Section D

Statistical Inference

In science, and in any day-to-day experience, we collect information in terms of a necessarily limited field of experience. Each of us looks around, but we do not merely observe, we look for recurrent or regular patterns in our experience. And then we tend to think and talk in terms of generalizations of these apparent regularities. Thus we may see a few crows and decide that "crows are black." Or, after some jarring experiences with young ladies, a young man might be prone to report that "women have a logic all their own." In this fashion we can learn that "football players are stupid," "members of Eta Eta Kappa Fraternity are drunks," or that "we tend to think and talk in terms of generalizations of apparent regularities." In each of these examples a person has more or less limited experience with a few cases of a general class of subject matter, but in each he *generalizes* that experience to the whole class. The need for such generalization is apparent. If we had to deal with each situation we met as an entirely new event—if we could discover no consistencies in our observations—it would be next to impossible to cope with even the simplest of problems. So we seek consistencies, we make generalizations, and we use our generalizations to guide our behavior.

It should be clear, however, that not all generalizations built on partial observation are equally valid. Some seem to stand up in the light of further experience; others do not. Here again is a place where statistical tools can be helpful. The tools of statistics can be used to differentiate between "good" and "bad" generalizations—those which are likely to stand up under further observation and those which are not.

Populations and Samples

In the language of statistics, the name of the class of cases to which we wish to generalize is the *population* or *universe*. Thus we may wish to make statements about the population of crows, or women, or football players, or fraternity members, or even about such a complex class as middle-class American males of Irish descent between the ages of 17 and 24 who are attending engineering school.

In the usual situation we use a word or phrase to delineate a class of objects that have at least one characteristic in common, and about which we wish to talk. But almost always it is impossible to examine each and every member of the class in question. Realistically, we must settle for a look at a part or *sample* of that class. We can look at a few crows, some women, or samples of football players, fraternity men, or young Irish-American engineering students. But we must be careful that they are *probability samples* of the population in question.

When an investigator has a probability sample, he may use the rules of probability theory to evaluate any generalizations he wishes to make about the population from which the sample was drawn. A nonprobability sample, on the other hand, cannot provide the same type of evaluations of generalizations.

Various procedures have been devised for probability sampling. However, regardless of the particular design, all probability sampling ultimately depends on the principle of *randomness.* This is the basic technique of control which underlies all probability sampling.

We might choose a sample of N observations from a population. This set would be a simple random sample from the population if it were selected in such a way that every possible set of that same size had an equal probability of being chosen. This usually boils down to a procedure which provides that every *observation* in the population has an equal chance of appearing in the sample. If, for example, an investigator is interested in studying the political opinions of the student body of some specific university, he can obtain a list of the students, write each of their names on a separate slip of paper, put the slips into a bowl, shuffle them, and blindfolded, select a sample of any desired size. This lottery procedure would not guarantee that the sample was representative of the population in every respect. But it would avoid systematic bias and it would enable us to use the laws of probability to evaluate its representativeness. Only when our samples are based on random procedures can we determine how representative they are. A nonrandom sample *might* be quite adequate, but we could never be sure.

In practice, simple random sampling from specified populations is not always possible or desirable. A list of all the individuals in a given universe is usually unobtainable, and the cooperation of every individual who is selected cannot be guaranteed. Furthermore, other information about the population is sometimes available that can be used to increase the sampling efficiency.

Stratified random sampling is often extremely useful, especially in public opinion polling. When certain relevant characteristics of the universe are known, it may be divided according to these known characteristics, and each subgroup sampled individually. Thus, if an investigator is studying the opinions of daytime radio listeners, and he suspects that sex might be an important factor in these opinions, he can sample randomly within each sex group. Such a procedure would guarantee sufficient numbers of each sex to permit comparisons.

An important point to remember in using samples of this sort is that they are stratified *random* samples. Dividing a universe according to its relevant characteristics merely provides a series of subuniverses; it does not free the investigator from his responsibility to sample randomly. Random procedures must be employed to select individuals within each subsample —those possessing the appropriate characteristics of the subgroup. Without such controls, systematic bias of one sort or another is not controlled.

Some investigators have used a modified form of stratified sampling called the *quota sample*. Quotas are determined according to the relative proportion of each subgroup in the universe and interviewers are assigned to fill these quotas. An interviewer may be instructed to select five males under 25 years of age, all in the highest socioeconomic class, ten females over 60 years, in the lowest class, and so on, depending on the relevant proportions in the universe. Thus the interviewer controls the actual sampling. This is usually an economical technique, and sometimes a successful one, but there is a chance of bias. Too much is left to the interviewers. In such a situation interviewers often tend to avoid rundown neighborhoods and interview only the most willing subjects. Such seemingly trivial actions may seriously bias the results of a survey. Quota sampling, then, may be an effective low-budget method, but great care must be taken in its use. The universe must be properly stratified, and the selection and training of interviewers must be very carefully performed.

Some investigators seem to confuse randomness with accident; they use a class in a university or people on a street corner and have no systematic sampling plan. These are *accidental samples*; they cannot be evaluated. One has no idea of what, if any, population they represent. A school class which happens to be convenient is not necessarily representative of students in a school, and a group passing a street corner may or may not represent a neighborhood. A good example of misleading results of poor sampling is the report in many newspapers from their "Inquiring Reporter." Effective probability sampling always requires an explicit program designed to provide a random selection of observations. Only when the sample is random is it safe to generalize research findings to the population from which the sample was drawn. The ways in which data are employed in making generalizations must depend partly on the sampling technique which was used in their collection. The remainder of this book will consider only the most general case, that in which data were collected according to a simple random sampling plan. Kish has provided an excellent review of the modifications in procedure which should be used when various stratified sampling designs are selected.[1]

Even when we have a random sample of some specified population, the tools of statistics cannot guarantee a correct inference from our observation to the state of affairs in the population from which the sample was drawn. Whenever we generalize from observed cases to those we have not seen, we are, at best, guessing. Statistical procedures direct us to the inferences that have the highest *probability* of being true. In order to see how this happens, we must sidetrack briefly and discuss a little bit of probability theory.

Probability theory, like sampling, is a subject for study in its own right. We can, however, examine a few of its principles and provide some basis for understanding statistical inference.

Let us imagine a perfectly balanced coin. By perfectly balanced we mean that in the imaginary population of all possible tosses of this coin, the proportion of heads is *exactly* 50%. Granted that this is an extremely hypothetical state of affairs, we can at least conceive of such a coin. When we toss our coin, it will have to fall in one of two possible ways, heads or tails. With a perfectly balanced coin we know that these two outcomes are equally probable—we are just as likely to get a head as a tail. And since there are two possible outcomes, we can define the probability of obtaining either one (say heads) as one-in-two or $\frac{1}{2}$ or .50.

In general, whenever several events are equally probable we can define the probability of occurrence of any one of them as one in the total number of possibilities. Thus

$$\begin{array}{c}\text{Probability of any one of a}\\ \text{set of equally likely events}\end{array} = \frac{1}{\text{number of events}}$$

So the probability of tails is, of course, also one-in-two, or $\frac{1}{2}$ or .50. We can represent this situation pictorially by means of the tree diagram in Fig. D.1.

[1] "Confidence Intervals for Clustered Samples," *American Sociological Review*, **22** (1957), pp. 154–165; "Some Statistical Problems in Research Design," *American Sociological Review*, **24** (1959), pp. 328–338.

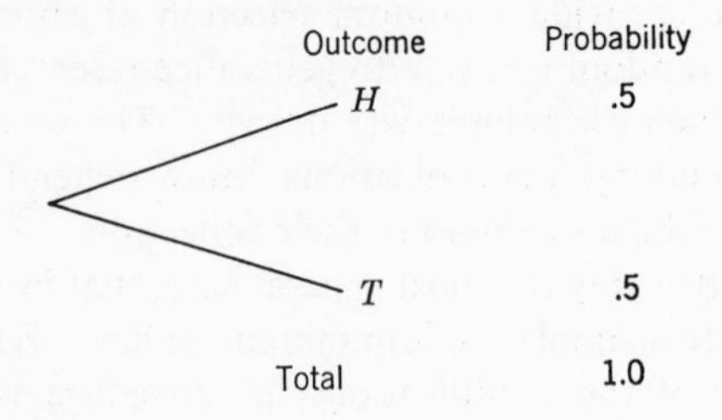

Fig. D.1.

Note that the probabilities of the separate outcomes total to 1.0. Whenever probabilities are assigned to each of the possible outcomes of an experiment, they must total to 1.0. This suggests simply that some one of the possible outcomes *must* occur. The coin must fall with either a head or a tail showing.

This operation also illustrates another property of probabilities called the *rule of addition.* This rule states that the *probability of alternatives is equal to the sum of their separate probabilities.* To illustrate this rule let us imagine a six-sided fair die. When we roll such a die, any of the six alternative outcomes can occur (Fig. D.2). If we ask the probability of obtaining a 1 *or* a 2 *or* a 3—any one of these alternatives—the answer will be

$$\tfrac{1}{6} + \tfrac{1}{6} + \tfrac{1}{6} = \tfrac{1}{2}$$

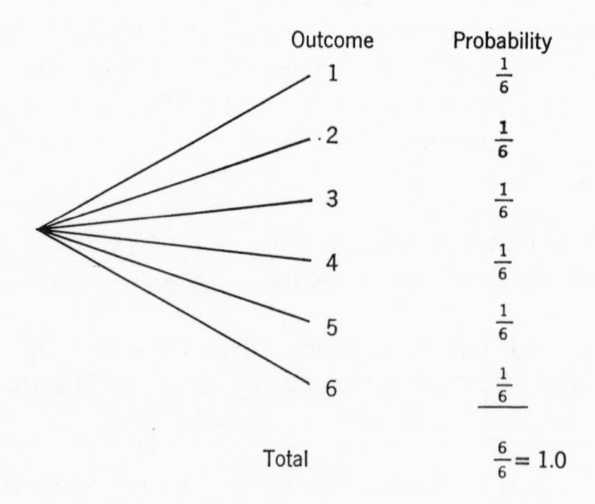

Fig. D.2.

Let us go back to our coin and suppose we toss it twice. What are the chances of obtaining heads twice in a row? Figure D.3 shows four possible outcomes. We assume that they are equally likely, so each is assigned a probability of $\frac{1}{4}$ or .25. The probability of two heads therefore is .25 as Fig. D.3 shows.

There is an important consequence of the assumption that these four outcomes are equally likely. It is the notion that successive outcomes of tossing our coin are *independent*. This means that the result of the first toss has no effect on the outcome of the second. Since the coin has no memory, this seems to be a reasonable assumption; but if it were not true we should have to calculate our probabilities in a different way.

With the assumption of independence, there is a way of getting the results of a tree diagram without actually listing and counting the possible outcomes. We can apply the *rule of multiplication.* It states that *the probability of the combination of independent events is equal to the product of their separate probabilities.*

We may use the rule of multiplication to calculate the probability of obtaining heads on each of two successive tosses of our coin. For the first toss the probability of heads is $\frac{1}{2}$. And for the second (independent) toss it is also $\frac{1}{2}$. Therefore the probability of obtaining heads on both tosses is

$$(\tfrac{1}{2})(\tfrac{1}{2}) = (\tfrac{1}{2})^2 = \tfrac{1}{4} = .25$$

So far we have been listing all the possible outcomes of our coin tossing. Often, however, we are interested in relative proportions of heads and tails rather than in specific sequences of outcomes. If a coin is tossed twice, and our interest is in proportion of heads, there are three, not four, possible outcomes: 100% heads, 50% heads, and 0% heads. But, viewed this way, these outcomes are not equally likely. There is only one way to get 100%

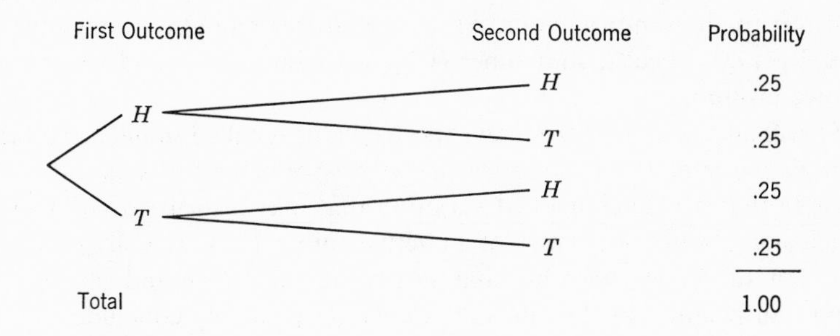

Fig. D.3.

heads and only one way to get 100% tails, but there are two ways to get 50% heads. This is shown in Table D.1.

Table D.1

Events			
First Toss	Second Toss	Percent of Heads	Probability
H	*H*	100	.25
H	*T*	50	.25
T	*H*	50	.25
T	*T*	0	.25

Therefore the probability of 50% heads is .25 (for head, then tail) plus .25 (for tail, then head), which equals .50.

This same reasoning can be extended to three, four, or an indefinite number of coin tosses. For ten tosses of a coin there are $2^{10} = 1024$ possible sequences of heads and tails. They are all equally likely. If we drew a tree diagram for ten tosses, we would discover that 252 of these 1024 outcomes involve 50% heads. The chances of getting exactly half heads are therefore about .25. On the other hand, there is only one way we could get 100% heads (10 in a row), so the probability of such an outcome is 1 in 1024 or about .001. It *could* happen, but, with a perfect coin, ten heads in a row is an extremely unlikely event.

Let us suppose we actually throw our perfect coin ten times. Although we can specify the likelihood of any particular proportion of heads or tails, we cannot anticipate the actual outcome. We expect the proportion of heads to be about .5, but it actually may depart from that expectation. But if we tossed our coin ten more times, and ten more, and ten more, and so on, over a very large number of sets of ten tosses, the average proportion of heads would approximate .5 quite closely. The important thing to note here is that over a large number of samples of ten tosses each, we should expect to get *exactly* 50% heads only about one-quarter of the time. The rest of the samples would vary around this amount—sometimes we would get 40% heads, sometimes 60%, sometimes 30%, and so on—in a chance fashion.

This chance variation from an expected value is called *sampling variation* or *sampling error*. It is not error in the sense of being a mistake; it is only error in that it is uncontrolled variation that may lead us to an incorrect conclusion about the balance of an actual coin. If we actually toss a fair coin ten times, we *may* hit that nearly one-in-a-thousand chance and obtain all heads. In this instance we would probably conclude that the balance of the coin was something less than perfect, but we would be mistaken; the result would be a chance outcome as a result of sampling error. (The chances of this happening, however, are less than one in one thousand.)

For this coin-tossing problem we can easily determine the likelihood of any particular outcome. On the basis of our assumption that the coin is perfectly balanced we can determine the probability of heads (or of tails) on any particular toss. Then we can list the possible outcomes with a tree diagram, and, by using the rules of addition and multiplication, assign a probability value to each. Such a list of all possible outcomes along with the probability value of each is called the *sampling distribution* of a statistic. Thus, when we observe some particular sample statistic, we need to look only at the sampling distribution of that statistic to determine the likelihood of such an outcome. It is important to note, however, that the sampling distribution is known only if we make an assumption about the nature of the population under study. In this case we assumed that the coin was unbiased, which led us to assign a probability of .5 to heads and one of .5 to tails. Without this or some other initial assumption we could never work out a sampling distribution. There are two ways of approaching this *problem of the initial assumptions* we make. We shall take them up under the topic of inference.

Inference

The two procedures for making statistical inferences to a population on the basis of a look at a sample are called *testing hypotheses* and *estimation*. We shall examine them in turn.

Testing Hypotheses

When a research worker does an experiment or a survey he has some hypotheses about the outcome of his investigation. The simple fact that he has chosen a problem for study suggests that some sort of hypothesis has led him to his choice. But hypotheses are typically stated in general terms—they refer to populations of observations. Research studies, however, are usually restricted to examinations of samples of observations, not entire populations. So the object of statistical tests of hypotheses is to guide us in making inferences from observed samples to hypothesized populations. Such tests tell whether our hypotheses are more or less believable in the light of our sample observations.

Any test of an hypothesis must begin with the hypothesis. We propose that the population is arranged in some specified fashion; for example, we might hypothesize that a given coin is perfectly balanced. On the basis of the hypothesis, we can determine the probability of each possible outcome as we have done earlier. Some would turn out to be rather probable, and some would be extremely unlikely. Then we may try our experiment—actually toss our coin and observe the result. And we are prepared to evaluate the outcome. If the observed result turns out to be reasonably probable, we can take it as evidence *for* our hypothesis. But if the result turns out to be extremely unlikely, we are obliged to question our original hypothesis and consider some alternative explanation.

We can use statistical tests whenever we can specify an hypothesis for which the sampling distribution of the statistic in question is known. Thus, for a coin-tossing experiment, a test is possible because we are able to list the probability of each possible outcome in the light of our hypothesis that the coin is perfectly balanced.

Research Hypothesis and Null Hypothesis. There are many hypotheses which can be tested, any for which the sampling distribution of the statistic in question is known. In practice, though, the hypothesis with which behavioral scientists are commonly concerned is the proposal that there is some association or relationship between two variables, X and Y, for some specified population. Sometimes this is extended further, and we propose a direction (plus or minus) for that hypothesized association as well, but this is not necessary to the hypothesis. The question of direction will be discussed later. The fact remains that the typical behavioral science hypothesis suggests the presence of association in a population. It is this hypothesis which will be examined for various types of data in the following chapters.

Let us look at this hypothesis of association. First, we can see that it seems rather vague. How can we possibly specify the sampling distribution of a statistic for a population described in such general terms as exhibiting association? It would be like trying to work out the probability of a particular set of coin tosses on the basis of a general hunch that the coin was biased. Biased in what way? How much? The ambiguity of the hypothesis prevents us from working out a sampling distribution. But if we state the negation of our hypothesis—if we propose a *null hypothesis*—the sampling distribution becomes apparent. For the coin we have described, our null hypothesis is that the coin is perfectly balanced; for the question of association, the null hypothesis states that, in the population, the association is zero. Then, for both these cases, we can conduct our study and either reject or fail to reject the null hypothesis. And, in either case, since the null is the rejection of our research hypothesis, we are led to reject or fail to reject our original alternative. The null hypothesis, then, is the standard—allowing us to assume a known sampling distribution—which is the common denominator of statistical tests.

Sampling Distributions. The fact that we need to know the sampling distribution of a statistic in order to test the null hypothesis has already been established. In the discussion of probability we saw some of the thinking that goes into working out such distributions. It was evident also that the job of listing all the possible outcomes and determining the probability of each would be quite a task. If we had to do this job every time we wanted a statistical test, we would accomplish very little research. But, fortunately, the sampling distributions of all the statistics we will be studying have already been worked out and listed in tables. The users of statistical tests need only learn to use the tables.

We can go back to the coin-tossing problem and see how this works. We have a coin, let us say, and we suspect it of bias. We are prepared to toss it twenty times and we want to infer from this sample to the population of all possible tosses of this particular coin.

Table D.2

Proportion of Heads	Probability
1.00	.000*
.95	.000*
.90	.000*
.85	.001
.80	.005
.75	.015
.70	.037
.65	.074
.60	.120
.55	.160
.50	.176
.45	.160
.40	.120
.35	.074
.30	.037
.25	.015
.20	.005
.15	.001
.10	.000*
.05	.000*
.00	.000*
	1.000

* These probabilities are so small they round off to zero in three places. The value for 100% heads, for example, is .0000019.

Here our null hypothesis is the negation of the notion of bias; it is that the coin is perfectly balanced. We already know that under these conditions the probability of a head is .5. By applying the rules of multiplication and addition, we can work out the whole sampling distribution of twenty tosses under these conditions. If we calculate these probabilities for all the possible proportions of heads, we obtain the distribution in Table D.2.

This, then, is a list of the probabilities that a perfectly balanced coin will fall with a given proportion of heads showing when it is tossed twenty times. Now we are left with the problem of drawing a clearcut line between results which support the null hypothesis and results which are so unlikely that they will lead us to reject the idea that this is a perfect coin. These unlikely results fall into a *region of rejection.*

Region of Rejection. The region of rejection is defined in such a way that any observed outcome which falls into its range requires that the null hypothesis be rejected. It includes a predetermined proportion of cases in the sampling distribution. This proportion is called *alpha* (α), and it is usually set at either .05 or .01. If $\alpha = .05$ this means that if an observed outcome is among the 95% more likely possibilities, the null hypothesis is *not* rejected. But if it falls into the least likely 5%, we reject the null hypothesis. If $\alpha = .01$, these values are 99% and 1% respectively.

Now let us look at our coin-tossing problem and see how this works. Under the null hypothesis, the expected outcome is 50% heads. This has a probability of .176. We should therefore expect to get exactly 50% heads in about 17.6% of our samples. The probability of 55% heads is .160, as is the probability of 45% heads. Then, by the law of addition, the probability that the outcome will fall in the range 45% to 55% heads is $.176 + .160 + .160 = .496$. By continuing to accumulate these probabilities, we obtain Table D.3.

Now if $\alpha = .05$, we want to find the range within which the 95% most likely results fall. For this problem, the nearest value is the range of .30 to .70, which contains 95.8% of the cases. This means that if we tossed our coin twenty times and we obtained anything from 30% to 70% heads, we would not reject the null hypothesis that the coin was unbiased. But if our result shows less than 30% or more than 70% heads, it would fall into the region of rejection; we would reject our null hypothesis and suspect the coin of bias.

For $\alpha = .01$ we want the most likely 99%. The nearest probability above .99 is .998 for the range of 20% to 80%. So, in this case an observed value would have to show less than 20% or more than 80% heads before we could reject the null hypothesis.

Table D.3

Range of Proportion of Heads	Probability of a Result Falling within That Range
.50	.176
.45– .55	.496
.40– .60	.736
.35– .65	.884
.30– .70	.958
.25– .75	.988
.20– .80	.998
.15– .85	.999+
.10– .90	.999+
.05– .95	.999+
.00–1.00	1.000

One- and Two-Tailed Tests. So far, we have been dealing with a problem for which our hypothesis was very general. We suspect our coin of bias—no more than that. But suppose that for some theoretical reasons we are able to specify this hypothesis further. We hypothesize, let us say, that the coin is biased toward showing heads. Now in this case our null hypothesis is the same: the coin is unbiased. But we need a new way to cumulate probabilities for this new research hypothesis. We are no longer interested in extreme departures from expectation in the direction of tails—we are interested only in heads. So when we start cumulating probabilities, we shall look only at the end with a high proportion of heads (Table D.4).

Table D.4

Range of Proportion of Heads	Probability of a Result Falling within That Range
.00– .50	.588
.00– .55	.748
.00– .60	.868
.00– .65	.942
.00– .70	.979
.00– .75	.994
.00– .80	.999
.00– .85	.999+
.00– .90	.999+
.00– .95	.999+
.00–1.00	1.000

Note that this time we are cumulating the range from 0 to each specified level. We are concerned with only the top half (one tail) of the original distribution—the part where heads predominate. This is done because an extremely low proportion of heads would be evidence *against* rather than *for* our research hypothesis. This is called a *one-tailed test* as compared with our earlier *two-tailed test* where we were looking for departures from expectation no matter which direction they went.

In this one-tailed case, if $\alpha = .01$, the most likely 99% of the cases fall at the bottom of the original distribution (where the proportion of heads is low or moderate). The nearest value to .99 is .994 for the range from 0 to 75% of the cases. So the one-tailed region of rejection includes any outcomes which show more than 75% heads.

Note that we need fewer heads to reject the null hypothesis with a one-tailed test. This is because our test is sensitive to departures from expectation in only one direction. For the one-tailed test which we have been considering, where the hypothesis suggests a bias toward heads, even a strong preponderance of tails would still lead us to accept the null hypothesis.

False Results. This whole process of testing hypotheses looks fairly neat until this point. We can plan a study, choose a statistic, determine its sampling distribution, specify a region of rejection, and conduct a test—either one- or two-tailed—whichever is appropriate. But even with all this elegant and precise procedure, two types of errors are still possible.

Errors of the first kind, or *Type I errors*, occur when we reject a null hypothesis which is true: they are determined by the level of α. It is customary, you will remember, to set $\alpha = .05$ or .01. Then, if a given result falls in the area (5% or 1%) specified by α, we reject the null hypothesis. If the null hypothesis is true, a result falling in the region of rejection is an extremely unlikely event; but it is not impossible! At $\alpha = .05$, 5% of the observed results will fall into the region of rejection just by chance. So if we consistently use $\alpha = .05$, we shall reject 5 out of every 100 true null hypotheses. At $\alpha = .01$ we shall commit this Type I error once in every 100 tests. In the general case, the probability of a Type I error is equal to α.

This seems to suggest that it would be wise to make α small. We could make α equal .001 or even .00000001 for that matter. Such a course of action would result in an infinitesimal probability of a Type I error. But, unfortunately, it is not this simple—there are also errors of the second kind or *Type II errors*.

A Type II error consists of failing to reject a false null hypothesis. It is very difficult to determine the probability of a Type II error, but we can get a general idea of how it is calculated if we return to our earlier example of coin tossing.

Let us assume that the coin is really biased. Seventy-five percent of the population of all possible tosses are, let us say, heads. We are to toss the coin twenty times with the research hypothesis that the coin is biased toward heads. Under these conditions probabilities of each outcome would be as shown in Table D.5.

Table D.5

Proportion of Heads	Probability	Probability of This Proportion or More Heads
1.00	.003	.003
.95	.021	.024
.90	.067	.091
.85	.134	.225
.80	.190	.415
.75	.202	.617
.70	.169	.786
.65	.112	.898
.60	.061	.959
.55	.027	.986
.50	.010	.996
.45	.003	.999
.40	.000*	.999
.35	.000*	.999
.30	.000*	.999
.25	.000*	.999
.20	.000*	.999
.15	.000*	.999
.10	.000*	.999
.05	.000*	.999
.00	.000*	1.000

* These entries are so small they round off to zero in three places. Together, however, the nine entries have a probability of about .001.

When we did a one-tailed test at $\alpha = .01$ earlier, we discovered that the region of rejection included all results with 75% or more heads. Now, for illustration, we are assuming that the null hypothesis is false—that 75% of the population of tosses are really heads. We shall reject the null hypothesis whenever a result exhibits 75% or more heads, and that will account for $.003 + .021 + .067 + .134 + .190 + .202 = .617$, or 61.7% of the cases. But we shall accept the null hypothesis for 100% − 61.7% = 38.3% of these cases. Since the null hypothesis is actually false (75%

are actually heads), we shall make a Type II error 38.3% of the time; the risk is .383.

If, however, we had set $\alpha = .05$, we would reject the null hypothesis whenever 70% or more heads showed up. This would happen for $.617 + .169 = .786$, or 78.6% of the time. So at $\alpha = .05$, our risk of a Type II error is only $1.00 - .786 = .214$.

The unhappy conclusion to which we are forced on the basis of all of this is that the probabilities Type I and Type II errors are inversely related. When we minimize the risk of making an error of the first kind, we increase the likelihood of one of the second kind.

There is no need to despair, however; we have an out: the probability of Type II errors is also inversely related to sample size. The larger the sample we take, the smaller the risk of a Type II error. Hence a good practical solution in actual research is to increase sample size whenever it is important to minimize the risk of Type II errors. If our sample must be small, the risk of a Type II error is very great if $\alpha = .01$. Therefore, when N is small, we should generally let $\alpha = .05$ or even .10.

Estimation

Estimation involves a somewhat different approach to statistical inference. To test an hypothesis we begin with the hypothesis and then compute a sample statistic. But in statistical estimation we turn this process around; we use sample observations in order to guess population values. Estimation is based on the fact that in the absence of other information the best guess of an unknown population value (a parameter) is usually the corresponding sample value (statistic). A sample mean, for example, is a statistic, but it may be used to estimate the unknown value of the mean in the population from which the sample was drawn. The same is true of most of the other statistics we have examined. We have therefore three possible forms for any value we may consider: (1) we have a statistic calculated from sample data, (2) we have a corresponding population parameter, and (3) we have a sample estimate of the population parameter which may or may not differ from the sample statistic. Different symbols will be used wherever necessary to refer to these different forms. Italic type (s and r, for example) has been used to designate statistics calculated from samples. Boldface type ($\mathbf{s}$, $\mathbf{r}$) will be employed to refer to the corresponding population parameters. When estimates are intended, these boldface parameter symbols will have a caret above them ($\hat{\mathbf{s}}$, $\hat{\mathbf{r}}$).

In general, the sample statistics we have discussed may be used to estimate the values of their corresponding population parameters. But some sample statistics provide better estimates than others. An ideal estimator should provide an *unbiased* estimate of the unknown population parameter.

A sample statistic is an unbiased estimate of a population parameter if the average of a large number of sample estimates corresponds closely to the population value being estimated. The mean, for example, is unbiased. Suppose the mean I.Q. of the students in a college is 120. We can take a sample of students from that college, measure their intelligence, and compute a mean I.Q. This sample mean is an estimate of the true population value of I.Q. for these students. It probably would not be *exactly* correct, but if we repeated that same process again and again until we had a large number of samples—each with an estimated mean—the average of all those estimates would agree quite closely with the true value of 120.

A good estimate should be relatively *efficient* in addition to being one that is unbiased. When there are two or more possible sample estimates for a population value, the one which yields estimates with the smallest sampling error is the most efficient. In a normally distributed population, for example, the mean and the median coincide. Both the sample mean and the sample median could be used to provide estimates of the population mean. Both are unbiased; if we take a long series of samples from such a normally distributed population, the average of the sample means and the average of the sample medians will both coincide with the population mean. But the range of variation from sample to sample will be much greater among the medians. The sample mean therefore provides a more efficient estimate of the population mean; it is more efficient than the sample median.

Actually, it is not necessary for a statistic to be an unbiased estimator if it is efficient. We occasionally run into a statistic which has a slight bias, but which has a smaller sampling error than another. In such a case the biased estimator may be preferable to the unbiased one, providing that the bias is known. In that event we can usually correct for bias.

The sample standard deviation is a biased estimator, but it is simple to correct. The standard deviation was defined in Chapter 6 as

$$s = \sqrt{\frac{\sum_{i=1}^{N} x_i^2}{N}}$$

This statistic, however, is not an unbiased estimate of the population standard deviation. It may be corrected, however, to provide an unbiased estimate. We can do this very simply if we refer to the *variance*, the square of the standard deviation

$$s^2 = \frac{\sum_{i=1}^{N} x_i^2}{N}$$

This formula provides an accurate description of the variance in a sample, but, like the standard deviation, it is not an unbiased estimate of its population counterpart. A small correction is necessary in order to estimate the variance in the population,

$$\hat{\mathbf{s}}^2 = s^2 \frac{N}{N-1}$$

where $\hat{\mathbf{s}}^2$ equals the estimated population variance. Or this estimate can be calculated directly from the sum of the squared deviations

$$\hat{\mathbf{s}}^2 = \frac{\sum_{i=1}^{N} x_i^2}{N-1}$$

Analogously, the estimated population standard deviation is

$$\hat{\mathbf{s}} = \sqrt{\frac{\sum_{i=1}^{N} x_i^2}{N-1}}$$

Most sample statistics provide estimates of population parameters, but from our earlier discussion of probability, we know that such estimates will not necessarily be correct. The average of the statistics yielded by a large number of samples will approximate the population value, but the estimate provided by any one particular sample will be something less than perfect—it will reflect sampling variation. So when we make an estimate of a population value, we may properly be questioned about the degree of confidence which should be placed in such a statement.

This problem may be handled by the use of a *confidence interval.* We decide in advance how confident we would like to be, say 95% or 99%. This allows us to determine a range of values in which the true value is estimated to fall, instead of making a single estimate of the parameter. Instead of saying that the estimated population mean is 120, we may say that we estimate the population mean to be somewhere between 100 and 140. These boundaries are called *confidence limits*—they refer to our expectation about the value of an unknown population parameter.

However, a statement about a confidence interval is always accompanied by another type of statement, a *confidence coefficient.* This refers to our original decision on how sure we wanted to be. A confidence coefficient is a statement about our whole procedure. We might say, for example, that the limits, 100 to 140, are set at the 95% level of confidence. This means that out of a large number of repetitions of this same estimation procedure, about 95 out of every 100 studies will set limits which do include the true population value. In this way we can make estimates with any given degree of confidence. In general, if we demand a very high degree of confidence, say 99.9%, our limits will be relatively broad. And if we will settle for less assurance, we can specify a narrower range. Of course, if we can afford very large samples, it is possible to get both narrow limits and relatively high confidence.

An example may help to clarify these concepts. Let us go back to our coin-tossing problem and see how we can use our knowledge of sampling distributions to determine confidence intervals.

We have, let us say, tossed our coin twenty times and obtained 50% heads. The best single estimate of the population parameter, then, is 50%. That is to say, we are guessing that if we toss this coin in an endless series of tosses, half will be heads.

If we wish to evaluate this estimate, we must look at the sampling distribution of the percentage of heads for 20 tosses of a coin when the population parameter is 50%. This is the same distribution we worked out in Table D.3. There the parameter of 50% was assumed; here it is estimated on the basis of a sample observation, but the distribution is the same.

If we set our confidence coefficient at .95 and look at Table D.3, we see that the range from 35 to 65% heads includes about .88 of the cases, and the range from 30 to 70% includes .96. We must use the wider range and report that at the 95% level of confidence the true percentage of heads falls between 30 and 70%. By similar reasoning at the 99% level of confidence the true value falls between 20 and 80% heads. This sort of procedure is used whenever we wish to make confidence statements about sample observations.

The use of procedures of estimation is usually based on the assumption of a rather mature state of science. In order to recognize the need for estimating population values we must have theories that attempt to account for actual averages or absolute amounts of correlation. In the behavioral sciences, however, we have few theories of that sort so far. Instead, our theories usually yield hypotheses that suggest that members of an experimental group should have higher average performance scores (of undetermined amount) than members of a control group. Or we propose that variables X and Y should be correlated; often we are not even prepared to specify even the direction of association. For the most part therefore we rely on tests of hypotheses in most behavioral science research.

Estimates are used in population studies and in public opinion pools and other sample surveys. Often these are simply one-number estimates of means or proportions based on sample values. In such cases confidence intervals are usually neglected. In view of these considerations, most of the rest of the discussion in this book will center on the subject of testing hypotheses. This emphasis is not intended to represent the relative importance of estimates and tests. It is only an attempt to be realistic about their respective roles in current behavioral science research. The reader who is interested in following up this discussion is encouraged to look into Walker and Lev (1953) or Wallis and Roberts (1956).

The remaining six chapters are concerned with problems of testing the null hypothesis of no association for various levels of scaling. They all share a common core—a seven-step plan which represents a sort of ideal model for testing the null hypothesis. It is important that all seven steps be performed for every test and that they be performed in order. They will be introduced and reviewed briefly. The chapters will show how they are used.

1. *State your research hypothesis* (H_1). For the test considered here the only research hypotheses will be those which propose that a pair of variables are related. The critical point is simply to make sure that your statement is as precise and complete as possible and specifies direction of association if appropriate. This is necessary in order to allow you to make a later decision between a one-tailed and a two-tailed test.

2. *State the null hypothesis* (H_0). This step is necessary to draw attention to the fact that it is precisely this null hypothesis that is being subjected to statistical test.

3. *Choose a statistical test.* Choice should be made on the basis of scaling considerations and the assumptions involved in the several tests. A good choice will be a test that is appropriate for the level of scaling you are using and one that does not require you to throw information away by simplifying the scaling of your observations. Neither should it require you to make assumptions about your data which are obviously inappropriate for the problem at hand.

4. *Specify sample size* (N) *and level of significance* (α). The size of your sample will often be determined by economic considerations. Once it has been established, set α. Remember that if N is small, α should usually be set at .05 or greater to lower the probability of a Type II error.

5. *Find the sampling distribution of the test statistic under* H_0. For most statistics this is a simple job. Just locate the appropriate table. For some statistics, however, it is necessary to create your own tables.

6. *Define the region of rejection.* First you look at your research

hypothesis and decide whether a one- or two-tailed test is appropriate. Then on the basis of this choice and α specify the outcomes that will lead you to reject the null hypothesis.

7. *Compute the statistic and make your decision.* Here you simply follow the steps of the computing model for the statistic in question. When you have your result, compare it with the values in the region of rejection. If it falls in the region, reject H_0; if it lies outside the region, do not reject the null hypothesis.

These are the steps that should be followed in conducting a statistical test. They are somewhat pedantically put, and you will find that many investigators combine several steps into one operation. However, at the beginning, it is a good idea to think about them one by one.

13 Testing Hypotheses about Two Ordinal Scales

The general plan of organization of this book suggests that this chapter should be concerned with two nominal scales. The procedures for testing hypotheses about nominal scales, however, contain some rather difficult and special problems. We shall therefore postpone their discussion until the end of the book, and start this section with the relatively straightforward topic of tests for ordinal scales.

The Significance of *G*

Function. We have seen that even a perfectly balanced coin will occasionally turn up ten heads in ten consecutive tosses. Similarly, we shall sometimes observe association between two variables in a sample when no association exists in the population from which the sample was drawn. Chance variation from sample to sample is bound to produce an apparent association in some samples. But if we have only one sample, and it shows association, what may we conclude? Should we conclude that this is evidence of association in the population or might this be one of those random fluctuations—an apparent association resulting from sampling variation? We need a procedure that will allow us to make a decision in this matter, and the test of significance of G provides such a procedure. Specifically, this test allows us to evaluate the hypothesis that any association we have observed is the result of sampling variation from a population in which association is absent.

Rationale. Let us define an extremely simple problem and follow it through in order to understand the test for G. We have the hypothesis, let us say, that the prestige of an American college is positively related to the size of its endowment. We obtain a list of American colleges and randomly select four colleges as our sample. Each is ranked in relative prestige (X) and each is ranked in terms of the size of its endowment (Y). Our results might resemble Table 13.1.

Table 13.1

College	Rank in Prestige X	Rank in Endowment Y	Inversions	Agreements
A	4	4	0	0
B	3	3	0	1
C	2	1	0	2
D	1	2	1	2
Sum			1	5

$$G = \frac{f_a - f_i}{f_a + f_i} = \frac{5 - 1}{5 + 1} = \frac{4}{6} = .67$$

For the four observed cases, then, prestige and endowment are indeed related. And higher prestige tends to go with higher endowment as our hypothesis suggested. In general, these observations seem to support our hypothesis.

There is, however, another (null) hypothesis which may possibly explain these observations. We know that even when we sample from a population where there is no association, we can expect to observe association in some samples. Perhaps this is such a case; maybe the association we have observed is peculiar to this sample; maybe it represents no more than a random result of sampling variation from a population in which $G = 0$.

It would be useful to know the probability of this alternative hypothesis. If it were rather probable, we should have to continue to view it as plausible. If, on the other hand, our result were extremely unlikely on the basis of sampling variation, we would be safe in discounting sampling variation as an explanation of our results.

Let us begin by assuming that there is no association between X and Y in the population from which our sample was taken. We can then determine the sampling distribution for such a population and evaluate our results. If our observed value of G is so unlikely that it would occur by chance, say 5 samples out of every 100 or less ($\alpha = .05$), we shall reject our assumption that there is no association in the population. If, on the other hand, such a G would result from sampling variation more than 5 in every 100 samples, we shall be unable to reject the hypothesis of no association. What we need to know, then, is the sampling distribution of G when $N = 4$ and the population has no association at all.

If we draw a random sample of four cases from a population with no association, and arrange them in their natural order according to X ranks, there will be 24 possible arrangements of the Y ranks (Table 13.2).

Table 13.2

Order of X	Possible Y Orders																							
4	4	4	4	3	4	4	3	3	2	4	3	3	2	2	1	3	2	2	1	1	2	1	1	1
3	3	3	2	4	2	1	4	2	4	1	2	1	4	3	4	1	3	1	4	3	1	3	2	2
2	2	1	3	2	1	3	1	4	3	2	1	4	1	4	3	2	1	4	2	4	3	2	4	3
1	1	2	1	1	3	2	2	1	1	3	4	2	3	1	2	4	4	3	3	2	4	4	3	4

Since X and Y are taken to be unrelated, each of these 24 possible orders of Y ranks is equally likely—any particular one is as apt to occur as any other. The probability of any particular order in the Y ranks is therefore 1 in 24.

For each of the possible Y rankings there is an associated value of G. For the 24 rankings in Y, the possibilities are given in Table 13.3. From this table we can determine the probability of any observed outcome of G when $N = 4$ given that there is no correlation in the population. This reasoning parallels exactly our earlier consideration of coin tossing. It provides us with a list of the sampling distribution of G when $N = 4$.

From Table 13.3 we can see that the probability of getting a G of 1.0 is .042 if there is no association in the population. And the probability of a G of .67 *or higher* is $.125 + .042 = .167$. Since we have set $\alpha = .05$, we need a G of 1.0 before we can reject the null hypothesis of no association in the population. Our observed G is .67. It would be obtained *more* than five times in every 100 samples from such a population. Therefore we cannot reject the null hypothesis; we have insufficient evidence to conclude that prestige and endowment are positively related among American colleges.

This type of reasoning is characteristic of all tests of hypotheses. We begin with a research hypothesis, state a null hypothesis, set a level of α, specify the sampling distribution, and make a decision.

Sometimes we run into difficulty in determining the needed sampling distribution. Tables like Table 13.3 for $N = 4$ can be calculated for any value of N. They are based on the assumption, however, that there are no ties in either set of rankings. When ties are present, the task of determining exact probabilities becomes extremely difficult. What is needed therefore is some simpler way of determining the probabilities of the various outcomes.

Our simpler method for determining the sampling distribution of G depends on an approximation. If we can specify some known distribution that approximates the sampling distribution of G quite closely, we could avoid the problem of calculating exact probabilities. And if our approximating distribution were easy to calculate or, better still, already tabulated, our problem would be solved. The fact is that there is such a distribution that approximates G. It is our old standby, the normal distribution.

Table 13.3

Order of Y	Value of G	Probability of Occurrence	
4, 3, 2, 1	1.0	$\frac{1}{24}$	.042
4, 3, 1, 2		$\frac{1}{24}$	
4, 2, 3, 1	.67	$\frac{1}{24}$	.125
3, 4, 2, 1		$\frac{1}{24}$	
4, 2, 1, 3		$\frac{1}{24}$	
4, 1, 3, 2		$\frac{1}{24}$	
3, 4, 1, 2	.33	$\frac{1}{24}$	.208
3, 2, 4, 1		$\frac{1}{24}$	
2, 4, 3, 1		$\frac{1}{24}$	
4, 1, 2, 3		$\frac{1}{24}$	
3, 2, 1, 4		$\frac{1}{24}$	
3, 1, 4, 2	0	$\frac{1}{24}$	.250
2, 4, 1, 3		$\frac{1}{24}$	
2, 3, 4, 1		$\frac{1}{24}$	
1, 4, 3, 2		$\frac{1}{24}$	
3, 1, 3, 4		$\frac{1}{24}$	
2, 3, 1, 4		$\frac{1}{24}$	
2, 1, 4, 3	−.33	$\frac{1}{24}$	.208
1, 4, 2, 3		$\frac{1}{24}$	
1, 3, 4, 2		$\frac{1}{24}$	
2, 1, 3, 4		$\frac{1}{24}$	
1, 3, 2, 4	−.67	$\frac{1}{24}$	.125
1, 2, 4, 3		$\frac{1}{24}$	
1, 2, 3, 4	−1.0	$\frac{1}{24}$	.042

To see how the normal approximation is used we shall go back to the exact distribution of G without ties. When $N = 4$, as in Table 13.3, the sampling distribution of G has the shape of Fig. 13.1. This distribution

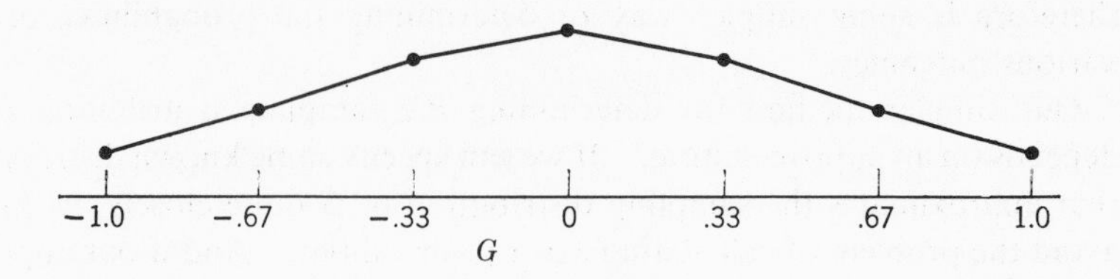

Fig. 13.1.

is symmetrical and unimodal: a G of zero has the greatest probability, and other values of G are relatively less probable as they depart from zero (either high or low).

When $N = 10$, G has the sampling distribution shape shown in Fig. 13.2. The striking thing about this diagram is its resemblance to the normal curve. It is a series of discrete steps, but its general shape is clearly normal. In fact, the normal curve is called the limiting distribution of G. With an infinite number of observations, the sampling distribution of G is exactly normal in form. And as a practical procedure, whenever we have ten or more observations, with or without ties, G is approximately normally distributed. This means that there is no need to calculate exact probabilities, providing that $N \geqslant 10$; we can get by with the approximation given by the normal curve tables. A portion of Table 13.3 of the sampling distribution of G when N equals 10 is given in Table 13.4. Both exact probabilities and their normal approximations are listed so that they may be compared. This table shows quite a close correspondence between

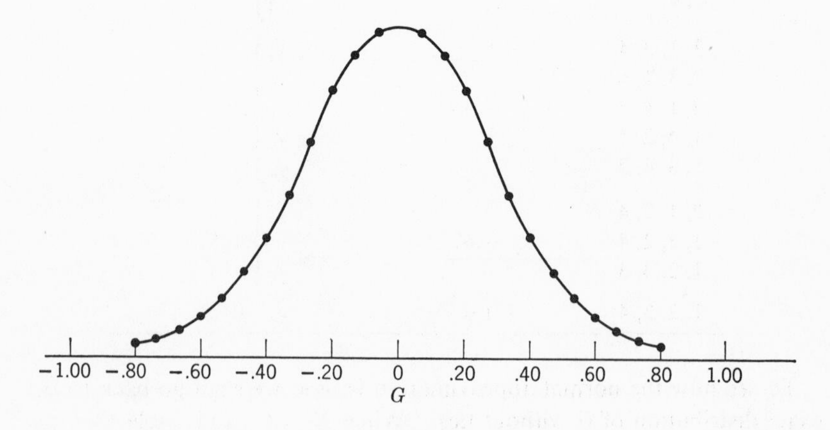

Fig. 13.2.

Table 13.4

	Cumulative Probability	
G	Exact	Normal Approximation
1.00	.000	.000
.95–1.00	.000	.000
.90–1.00	.000	.000
.86–1.00	.000	.000
.81–1.00	.000	.000
.77–1.00	.000	.001
.73–1.00	.001	.002
.68–1.00	.002	.003
.64–1.00	.005	.005
.59–1.00	.008	.008
.55–1.00	.014	.013
.51–1.00	.023	.020
.46–1.00	.036	.030
.42–1.00	.054	.046
.37–1.00	.078	.064
.33–1.00	.108	.090
.	.	.
.	.	.
.	.	.

the exact and approximate probabilities when N equals 10. And this correspondence will, of course, increase with larger sample sizes. The normal curve therefore provides a convenient shortcut for estimating the sampling distribution of G when N is 10 or more.

Procedure. We have seen that different distributions are used in testing the significance of G with and without ties in ranking. Therefore we shall discuss two different techniques for testing G: (1) when there are no ties and (2) when $N \geqslant 10$, and ties are present. These are both based on the reasoning described previously.

TESTING G WHEN THERE ARE NO TIES. Table E in the Appendix was constructed by the method of calculating exact probabilities described earlier. It lists the value of G that is needed to reject the null hypothesis for various levels of N and α, and for one- and two-tailed tests. Suppose, for example, we had a random sample of seven cases that produced a G of .71. We want, let us say, a one-tailed test at $\alpha = .05$. Table *E* has five columns, of which the first is headed N. We look down that column until we find 7, which is our sample size. Then we look across that row and find .62 in the column headed .05, and .81 in the column headed .01

under one-tailed tests. These are the critical values of G. With $N = 7$, sampling variation in G produces values as great as or greater than .62, 5 in every 100 samples, and values as great as or greater than .81, 1 in every 100 samples. This distribution might be illustrated as in Fig. 13.3. If we fit our computed value of $G = .71$ into this picture, we find that it falls above the 5% boundary. We may reject the null hypothesis at $\alpha = .05$; the idea of sampling variation from a population with no association does not stand up well as an explanation of our observations. We may therefore take our observations as evidence for association in the population from which we sampled.

Example

Ramsey and Smith have described a study in which seniors in Japanese and American high schools were asked to rate 23 occupations in terms of prestige.[1] Each student rated each occupation on a five-point scale from "very high" to "very low" prestige. Then the ratings were combined for the Japanese students and for the Americans and ranks were assigned. Table 13.5 shows these prestige ranks.

1. *Hypothesis.* H_1: Ramsey and Smith believe that there is general agreement in Japanese and American occupational prestige rankings.
2. *Null Hypothesis.* H_0: There is no positive association in order between Japanese and American occupational prestige rankings.
3. *Test.* Since this is a problem involving ordinal scales without ties, the exact test for G may be used.
4. *Significance Level.* Let $\alpha = .01$.
5. *Sampling Distribution.* The exact sampling distribution of G is listed in Table E in the Appendix.

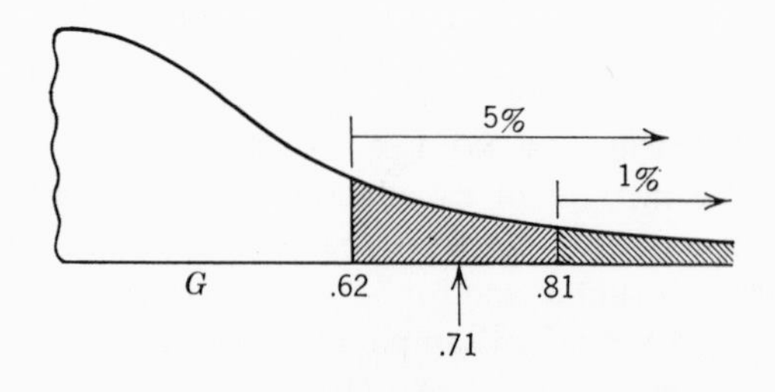

Fig. 13.3.

[1] Charles E. Ramsey and Robert J. Smith, "Japanese and American Perceptions of Occupations," *American Sociological Review*, **65** (March, 1960), 475–482.

Table 13.5. *Prestige Ranks of Twenty-Three Occupations by Japanese and American High School Seniors*

Occupation	Japanese Rank	American Rank
College professor	23	20
Doctor	22	23
Lawyer	21	22
Corporation executive	20	19
Author	19	18
Union Leader	18	16
Primary schoolteacher	17	14
Policeman	16	12
Small factory owner	15	9
Private secretary	14	13
Government clerk	13	10
Nurse	12	15
Priest (or minister)	11	21
Office worker	10	6
Beautician	9	5
Movie performer	8	17
Department-store clerk	7	3
Small shopkeeper	6	4
Soldier	5	11
Carpenter	4	7
Farm owner	3	8
Small shop salesclerk	2	2
Farm laborer	1	1

6. *Rejection Region.* The rejection region consists of all values of G which are so large that the probability associated with their occurrence under the null hypothesis is equal to or less than 1 in 100. Since H_1 predicts the direction of association, we may use a one-tailed test. Table E shows that for a one-tailed test at .01 when $N = 23$, a G of .35 or larger is necessary to reject H_0. If the results are in the hypothesized direction and if $G \geqslant .35$, we shall reject H_0.

7. *Decision.*

$$\begin{aligned} G &= \frac{f_a - f_i}{f_a + f_i} \\ &= \frac{208 - 45}{208 + 45} \\ &= \frac{163}{253} \\ &= .64 \end{aligned}$$

Table 13.6

X	Y	f_a	f_i
23	20	0	0
22	23	0	1
21	22	1	1
20	19	3	0
19	18	4	0
18	16	5	0
17	14	6	0
16	12	7	0
15	9	8	0
14	13	7	2
13	10	9	1
12	15	6	5
11	21	2	10
10	6	13	0
9	5	14	0
8	17	6	9
7	3	16	0
6	4	16	1
5	11	12	6
4	7	15	4
3	8	15	5
2	2	21	0
1	1	22	0
Total		208	45

The computed value of G is in the predicted direction and it is larger than .35, so we may reject the null hypothesis. It is unlikely that these samples came from populations in which rankings of occupations are not in some agreement.

TESTING G WHEN $N \geqslant 10$, AND TIES ARE PRESENT. When there are ties in either set of rankings, the exact probabilities of Table E are inappropriate. Instead we use the normal distribution to approximate the distribution we need.

In the preceding case it was possible to determine the exact pattern of variation in G for any given number of cases. When we use a normal approximation, however, we do not determine this exact pattern. We do know that when the null hypothesis is true, there is no association in the population. Here the number of agreements equals the number of inversions and the population value of G equals zero. Sampling variation, however, will still lead G to vary from sample to sample; our job is to find the pattern of this variation. Since we know that under these conditions G is approximately normally distributed, we can determine the pattern of its variation by means of the normal curve. When the null hypothesis is true, the expected value of G is zero, and its range of variation will depend on the size of the sample and the number of ties.

To determine a probability of an observation from a normal curve table, all we need to know is its value expressed in standard deviation (z) units. In this instance therefore we must determine the standard deviation of G. (When we are dealing with the sampling variation or sampling error of a statistic, such a standard deviation is usually called the *standard error*. This is just a question of naming, however; the standard error of G is the same standard deviation introduced in Chapter 6.)

If we calculate the standard error of an observed value of G, we can measure its departure from zero in a standard unit, and, using the normal curve, the probability of a departure as great as or greater than the one we observe. In effect, we are expressing our observed value of G in standard deviation units and evaluating its deviation in terms of the known deviation characteristics of the normal curve.

Our use of the normal approximation is simplified somewhat if we do not use G directly for our test. We can define a new value S that is related to G. The standard error of S is easier to calculate and it involves no loss of efficiency since there is a unique S for every G and a unique G for every S.

$$S = f_a - f_i \tag{13.1}$$

where f_a = the frequency of agreements,
f_i = the frequency of inversions, both defined as they were in Chapter 8.

It can be seen that S is simply the numerator of the expression for G. Since G is approximately normally distributed when $\mathbf{G} = 0$, S must be distributed in the same fashion.

The null hypothesis defines a population where $\mathbf{G} = 0$. In such a population, $\mathbf{S}$, of course, is also equal to zero. The departure of S from the value expected under the null hypothesis is therefore $S - 0$, which equals S. This departure may be expressed in standard deviation units simply by dividing it by its standard error

$$z = \frac{S}{s_S}$$

z, then, is the number of standard deviations by which an observed value of S departs from its expected value of zero.

Actually, it is necessary to adjust the value of S in any particular case in order to improve its approximation to the normal curve. The normal curve is smooth, whereas the exact distribution of S (and of G) is a series of steps. However, a small correction in the calculated value of S eliminates this difficulty. The formula for $\hat{S}$, the corrected value of S, is

$$\hat{S} = |S| - \frac{N}{(2)(R-1)(C-1)} \tag{13.2}$$

where R = the number of rows in the contingency table,
C = the number of columns in the table,
N = the number of observations.

In order to calculate the standard error of $\hat{S}$, we can use the following formula:

$$s_{\hat{S}} = \sqrt{\frac{U_2V_2}{N-1} - \frac{U_2V_3 + V_2U_3}{N(N-1)} + \frac{U_3V_3}{N(N-1)(N-2)}} \tag{13.3}$$

where U_2 = the sum of the products of the row totals taken two at a time,
V_2 = the sum of the products of the column totals taken two at a time,
U_3 = the sum of the products of the row totals taken three at a time,
V_3 = the sum of the products of the column totals taken three at a time,
N = the number of observations.

And z is, of course, calculated on the basis of these adjusted values:

$$z = \frac{\hat{S}}{s_{\hat{S}}} \tag{13.4}$$

Let us take an example and see how this works. Suppose we have two sets of ranks arranged as in Table 13.7.

Table 13.7

Ranks in Y	Ranks in X: 4	3	2	1	Total
2	4	5	0	1	10
1	0	2	6	4	12
Total	4	7	6	5	22

For Table 13.7,

$$U_2 = (10)(12) = 120$$
$$V_2 = (4)(7) + (4)(6) + (4)(5) + (7)(6) + (7)(5) + (6)(5) = 179$$
$$U_3 = 0, \text{ since there are only two row totals}$$
$$V_3 = (4)(7)(6) + (4)(7)(5) + (4)(6)(5) + (7)(6)(5) = 638$$
$$N = 22$$

And

$$\begin{aligned} s_{\hat{S}} &= \sqrt{\frac{U_2V_2}{N-1} - \frac{U_2V_3 + V_2U_3}{N(N-1)} + \frac{U_3V_3}{N(N-1)(N-2)}} \\ &= \sqrt{\frac{(120)(179)}{21} - \frac{(120)(638) + (179)(0)}{(22)(21)} + \frac{(638)(0)}{(22)(21)(20)}} \\ &= \sqrt{\frac{21{,}480}{21} - \frac{76{,}560 + 0}{462} + \frac{0}{9240}} \\ &= \sqrt{1022.86 - 165.07 + 0} \\ &= \sqrt{857.79} \\ &= 29.29 \end{aligned}$$

Furthermore,

$$\begin{aligned} S &= f_a - f_i \\ &= 98 - 8 \\ &= 90 \end{aligned}$$

And

$$\begin{aligned} \hat{S} &= |S| - \frac{N}{(2)(R-1)(C-1)} \\ &= 90 - \frac{22}{(2)(1)(3)} \\ &= 90 - \frac{22}{6} \\ &= 90 - 3.67 \\ &= 86.33 \end{aligned}$$

$\hat{S}$, then, may be expressed as a standard score

$$\begin{aligned} z &= \frac{\hat{S}}{s_{\hat{S}}} \\ &= \frac{86.33}{29.29} \\ &= 2.95 \end{aligned}$$

Significant values of z are listed in the bottom row of Table E. These are the values necessary to reject the null hypothesis at a given level of significance.

If, for example, we wanted a two-tailed test with $\alpha = .01$, the table shows $z = 2.576$. Our observed $z = 2.95$; it is larger so we can reject the hypothesis of no association.

Example

Ugurel-Semin has studied the generosity of school children in Ankara, Turkey.[1] A part of her study involved the attempt to determine the relationship between generous behavior in a social situation and economic background. Her data are shown in Table 13.8.

Table 13.8. *Generosity of 167 Children according to Economic Status*

	Economic Status			
Generosity	Rich	Middle Class	Poor	Total
Generous	23	19	53	95
Equal	5	13	31	49
Selfish	9	11	3	23
Total	37	43	87	167

1. *Hypothesis.* H_1: A reasonable research hypothesis might be that children from more plentiful backgrounds would be more generous.

2. *Null Hypothesis.* H_0: There is either no association or a negative association between economic status and generosity.

3. *Test.* Since we have two ordered variables and $N > 10$, we can use the normal approximation to test the significance of G through z.

4. *Significance Level.* Let $\alpha = .01$ for a one-tailed test.

5. *Sampling Distribution.* $\hat{S}$ is distributed approximately normally with $s_{\hat{S}}$ given in Formula 13.3. Appropriate normal deviates are listed at the bottom of Table E.

6. *Rejection Region.* The region of rejection consists of all the values of z which are so large that under the null hypothesis they would occur 1% of the time or less. Since we have a directional hypothesis, a one-tailed test is appropriate. Table E shows that under these conditions $z = 2.326$. Therefore we need an S which is positive (because according to H_1 we are doing a one-tailed test) and a z equal to or greater than 2.326 before we can reject H_0.

[1] Refia Ugurel-Semin, "Moral Behavior and Moral Judgment of Children," *Journal of Abnormal and Social Psychology*, **47**, suppl. (April, 1952), 463–474.

7. *Decision.* Table 13.8 shows the results of Ugurel-Semin's research. We can use this table to compute S and $\hat{S}$.

$$S = f_a - f_i$$
$$f_a = 2089$$
$$f_i = 3017$$
$$S = -928$$

It is negative, which is contrary to the expectation expressed in H_1. Therefore we automatically fail to reject H_0. We have no evidence that this sample came from a population where a wealthy background is associated with greater generosity.

Summary of Procedure. The following steps must be performed in order to test the significance of G.

1. If no ties are present, determine the significance of G directly from Table E. If G is larger than the tabulated value, reject H_0.
2. If ties are present and $N \geqslant 10$, carry through the following steps:
   (*a*) Determine $\hat{S}$ according to Formula 13.2.
   (*b*) Calculate its standard error ($s_{\hat{S}}$) according to Formula 13.3.
   (*c*) Determine z according to Formula 13.4.
   (*d*) Evaluate the significance of z by comparing it with the value in Table E. If the calculated value is larger than the one in this table, reject H_0.

Other Statistics. Two other tests that may be used to evaluate the null hypothesis when we have two ordinal scales are the test for the significance of Spearman's rank correlation coefficient and the test for the significance of Kendall's tau. In function these tests are equivalent to the test just described.

14 Testing Hypotheses about Two Interval Scales

The null hypothesis may be tested quite simply when our data are recorded in interval scales, but such a test is subject to one important restriction. In this chapter we shall examine the test procedure and the restriction on its use.

Test of the Significance of r

Function. When we have a sample of observations distributed on two interval scales, we can use Pearson's r to describe the degree of association between those two variables. But when r has been calculated, we may wish to know whether it may be generalized to the population from which the sample was drawn, or conversely, whether our calculated r might represent a sampling variation from a population where there is no correlation. The test of significance of r enables us to test the null hypothesis. We can determine the probability that any amount of linear association we may have observed in our sample is a chance variation from a population in which $\mathbf{r}$ is truly zero.

Rationale. The test for the significance of G was discussed in Chapter 13. In that discussion no mention was made of the distributions of the variables X and Y on which G was calculated. No comment was necessary since the test for G is *nonparametric*. That is, the distribution of G does not depend on the shapes of the distributions of the variables used in its calculation. No matter how X and Y are distributed, G always has the same pattern of variation.

Pearson's r, however, is a *parametric* statistic. The distribution of r depends on the shapes of the population distributions of X and Y, the variables from which it was calculated. And since the distribution of r is known only when both X and Y are normally distributed, we must demonstrate or assume such a normal bivariate population to test the significance of r.

Consider a population in which two variables X and Y are normally distributed. The correlation in the population **r** is, let us say, exactly zero. The values of r in successive samples drawn from such a population will vary around the true correlation of zero. If we draw a great many samples and compute r in each case, the mean of all the sample r's will be about zero. If each sample is small (say $N = 10$ to 20), the observed values of r will vary widely; but if each sample is large (say from 500 to 1000 cases), the observed r's will all cluster quite closely around the population value.

In either case, the pattern of their variation is predictable. When the sample size is large (about 30 or more), r is distributed normally; for small samples r exhibits a modified normal form called "Students'" distribution. But when either X or Y is not normal, the distribution of observed values of r is unknown. The significance of an observed value of r can be therefore tested only when the population values of X and Y are both normally distributed.

Clearly, short of a total enumeration of the entire population on a variable, there is no way of *knowing* whether that variable is normally distributed. But some variables, like height and weight, have been sampled a great deal and the preponderance of evidence strongly supports the assumption that they are normal. Others, like income, seem on repeated sampling to be skewed, and in such circumstances the assumption of normalcy would be questionable. In general, if a sample is unimodal and nearly symmetrical, it is not unreasonable to assume that it has been drawn from a normally distributed population. The great frequency with which normal distributions turn up in samples suggests that unless there is evidence to the contrary it is usually safe to assume a normal parent population.

When we are willing to make the assumption that both variables are normally distributed, we can test the significance of an observed r. Then the standard error of r is dependent entirely on the size of the sample from which it was calculated. The standard error of r does not depend directly on N, however. It depends on the number of *degrees of freedom*.

The idea of degrees of freedom (df) is based on the following reasoning. Suppose we are told to pick two numbers; there are no restrictions on our choice. We may pick 1 and 100, or 13 and 597, or any pair of numbers at all. We have two free choices; there are two degrees of freedom. Suppose, on the other hand, that our numbers must total to 10. Then we have only one *free* choice, since if we pick 7 the other number must be 3, and if we pick 1, the other must be 9; if we pick any number at all, the other one is necessarily fixed. We have therefore only one degree of freedom.

Whenever we calculate r we use up two cases—two degrees of freedom—in locating the line of regression. When $N = 2$, for example, r must equal either 1.0 or -1.0. Two points fix the regression line, and the line must necessarily pass through those points. Hence there can be no deviation of observations from the predicted regression scores. A coefficient of correlation makes sense, then, only when N is at least 3. The number of remaining degrees of freedom is always $N - 2$.

Procedure. To test the significance of an observed coefficient of correlation, check the observed r against the value listed in Table F with $\text{df} = N - 2$. If the observed r is equal to or larger than the tabulated value for the appropriate test, one-tailed or two-tailed, at the chosen level of significance, .05 or .01, reject the null hypothesis. If r is smaller than the value in the table, H_0 cannot be rejected.

Example

In part of a larger study of leadership, Berkowitz examined the relationship between the degree of sharing of leadership and the productivity of small groups.[1] Productivity was determined by the proportion of items on the agenda which were completed out of those brought up for consideration. And the degree of sharing of leadership was measured by a whole set of variables, including the percentage of participation by members other than the leader. The assumption made was that as members increased their participation they were taking over leadership functions.

Berkowitz conducted his study on 72 small groups drawn from industrial and governmental organizations. He examined the hypothesis that as leadership sharing increases productivity diminishes. His calculated value of r between these two variables was $-.20$.

1. *Hypothesis.* H_1: Berkowitz provided the directional hypothesis that as leadership sharing increases, productivity diminishes; therefore we may expect a negative correlation.

2. *Null Hypothesis.* H_0: There is a positive correlation or no correlation between leadership sharing and group productivity.

3. *Test.* Berkowitz provided no information on the shape of his distribution. In the absence of contradictory evidence, let us go along with his assumption that it was normal. If we make this assumption, we can test the coefficient of correlation for significance.

4. *Significance Level.* Let $\alpha = .01$.

[1] Leonard Berkowitz, "Sharing Leadership in Small Decision-Making Groups," *Journal of Abnormal and Social Psychology*, **48** (April, 1953), 231–238.

5. *Sampling Distribution.* Pearson's r has the distribution shown in Table F in the Appendix with df $= N - 2 = 72 - 2 = 70$.

6. *Rejection Region.* Since H_1 is directional, we can do a one-tailed test. α was set at .01 and the region of rejection consists of all values of r as great as or greater than the tabulated value. Table F shows that for a one-tailed test when $\alpha = .01$ and df $= 70$, an r of .274 or larger in the hypothesized direction will occur by chance one time in 100 when the population correlation is zero. We shall reject H_0 therefore if r is equal to or greater than .274.

7. *Decision.* If we look back to the coefficient, $-.20$, we can make our decision. It is negative as predicted, but it is not equal to or greater than .274. Therefore we cannot reject the null hypothesis. We must conclude that this sample might have come from a population where productivity is independent of leadership sharing.

Summary of Procedure. The significance of an observed coefficient of correlation may be tested by reference to Table F; if r is equal to or greater than the tabled value for the appropriate df and α, reject H_0.

Other Procedures of Inference. We have examined how a sample value of r may be used to test the hypothesis that the population value $\mathbf{r}$ is zero. This is, however, only one of many kinds of statistical inferences that can be made using r. In this section we shall examine some of the other ways in which the principles of inference may be used to make generalizations from samples to populations.

Pearson's r will be used here simply to illustrate some of the range and flexibility of inference procedures. r is particularly useful for this purpose. Its sampling distribution has been studied widely, and it is complicated enough to involve some of the more general problems of inference. Thus r can provide a sound basis for understanding the applications of the procedures of statistical inference to various sorts of problems.

The Sampling Distribution of r

When two variables X and Y are randomly sampled from a normally distributed population, the sample statistic r may be used to estimate the population parameter $\mathbf{r}$. This sample value is the most efficient estimator of its population counterpart. It is somewhat biased if the sample is small, but whenever N is at least as great as twenty-five or thirty observations such bias is negligible.

With only one sample (and $N \geqslant 30$) drawn from a population, the sample value r is the best available estimate of $\mathbf{r}$. But we cannot expect such an estimate to be exactly correct. Successive samples from the same population will yield different values of r and will therefore provide different estimates of **r**.

If the pattern of sampling variation is such that the values of the correlation coefficients in these successive samples vary widely, any one of them would provide a relatively poor estimate of **r**. If, on the other hand, successive sample values of r vary only a little, any one of them would provide a relatively good estimate of **r**. In order to evaluate a sample estimate of **r**, therefore, we need to know the sampling distribution of r under various conditions.

In the preceding discussion, the sampling distribution of r was characterized as normal. This occurs only when $\mathbf{r} = 0$, and even then it is only approximately true. A normal distribution extends indefinitely on both sides of its mean. This is shown in Fig. 14.1, which pictures a part of one tail of a normal curve. The further we go from the mean the fewer the number of cases we find, but that frequency never quite reaches zero. Now contrast this with the distribution of r shown in Fig. 14.2. The range of r is limited; r may not be greater than $+1$ or less than -1. The distribution of r therefore is truncated or cut off—it does not extend indefinitely in both directions.

When $\mathbf{r} = 0$, this is a trivial problem. Even with truncation the sampling distribution of r is close enough to the normal form for all practical purposes. Suppose, however, **r** is large. Then the departure of the sampling distribution of r from the normal distribution form becomes critical. Figure 14.3 shows the sampling distribution of r when $\mathbf{r} = .85$. Here the distribution is markedly skewed; its departure from normalcy is severe.

From this discussion it is clear that r is not generally normal in distribution form. In fact, there is no single distribution form for r. Instead its

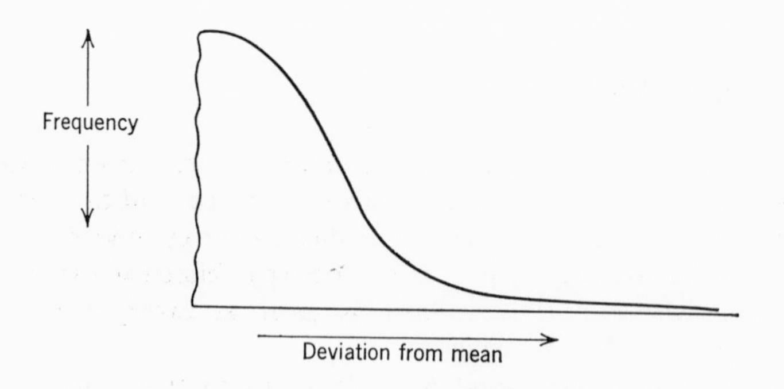

Fig. 14.1. Part of a tail of a normal distribution curve.

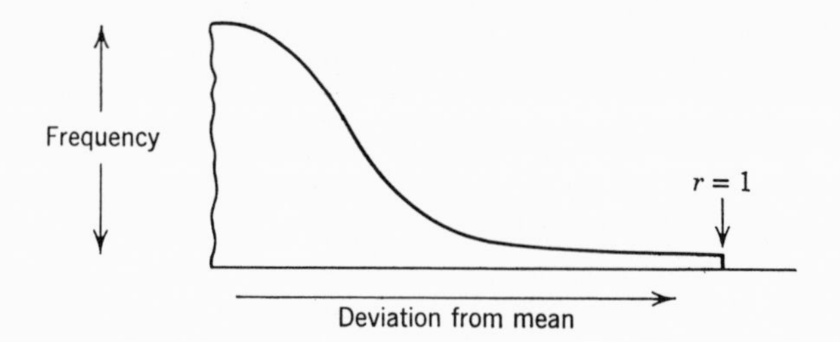

Fig. 14.2. Part of a tail of the sampling distribution of r when $\mathbf{r} = 0$.

pattern of sampling variation is expressed in a wide range of distribution forms depending on the magnitude of **r**. As **r** becomes larger, the distribution of sample r's is more and more skewed. The sampling variation of r, it seems, is quite complicated indeed.

Fortunately, there is a rather simple solution to all this complexity. Any value of r may be transformed into an equivalent value of a statistic called Z. And Z is always normally distributed. The rule for this transformation is

$$Z = 1.151293 \log \frac{1 + r}{1 - r}^{*}$$

Tables are available for converting r to Z or Z to r; a portion is shown in Table 14.1.

The sampling distribution of Z is normal. The mean of a large number of successive samples approaches **Z** (the value of Z associated with **r**)

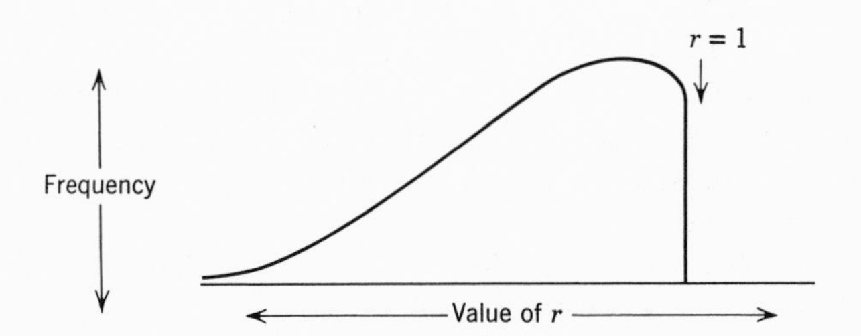

Fig. 14.3. The sampling distribution of r when $\mathbf{r} = .85$.

* If you are unfamiliar with logarithms, this statement will not convey much information. To follow the reasoning, however, it is sufficient simply to know that any value of r can be converted to a unique value of Z.

Table 14.1

r	Z
.00	.00
.10	.10
.20	.20
.30	.31
.40	.42
.50	.55
.60	.69
.70	.87
.80	1.10
.90	1.47
1.00	∞

quite closely. The standard deviation (properly standard error) is

$$s_z = \frac{1}{\sqrt{N - 3}}$$

Z therefore provides a neat solution to the problem of the general distribution of r. Although the distribution of r is quite complex, that for Z is quite simple. Any value of r may be transformed to an equivalent value of Z, and these Z values may be used to make estimates and test hypotheses.

Estimating r

Let us assume that we have a random sample of 100 students from a large college. Two variables are defined, high school standing and college grade point average. Pearson's r is calculated; it turns out to be .60 for these 100 students. What is wanted, however, is not merely a description of the correlation for this particular sample, but an index of correlation for the entire student body. If the population of college students is very large, it is not practical to consider studying all the students. We may therefore use our sample result in order to estimate the correlation for the entire student body.

For Pearson's r such estimation is quite direct. Since $N > 30$, $r = \hat{\mathbf{r}}$. Our best estimate of $\mathbf{r}$ therefore is .60.

So far, the job is only half done. We have estimated $\mathbf{r}$ for the population in question, but we have no idea whether we have provided a good or a poor estimate. With a sample of this size is our estimate likely to be close to or far from the true value?

In order to answer this question we shall use a confidence interval.

This provides a range of values which, over repeated trials, includes the actual parameter a given proportion of the time. Let us assume that we wish to establish a range with a confidence coefficient of .95. On repeated sampling such a procedure provides ranges that include the true population value in 95 out of every 100 trials.

Confidence intervals are determined by the sampling distribution of the statistic in question. We shall be concerned here with the distribution of Z since it is Z and not r that has the simple distribution form.

Our estimate of **r** is .60. The corresponding value of Z, .69, may be read from Table 14.1. What is needed is a range of values of Z around $\hat{\mathbf{z}} = .69$ that includes the middle 95% of a normal distribution.

We have already used the normal curve table to go from areas of the curve to standard scores. Table C shows that the area from the mean to 1.96 standard deviations ($z = 1.96$) includes 47.5% of the cases. The area from -1.96 standard deviations to $+1.96$ standard deviations includes therefore the middle 95% of the distribution in Fig. 14.4.

The standard error of Z is

$$\begin{aligned} s_z &= \frac{1}{\sqrt{N-3}} \\ &= \frac{1}{\sqrt{97}} \\ &= \frac{1}{9.85} \\ &= .10 \end{aligned}$$

This is our standard deviation. Now we want the range from $+1.96s_z$ to $-1.96s_z$. And since

$$\begin{aligned} 1.96s_z &= (1.96)(.10) \\ &= .196 \end{aligned}$$

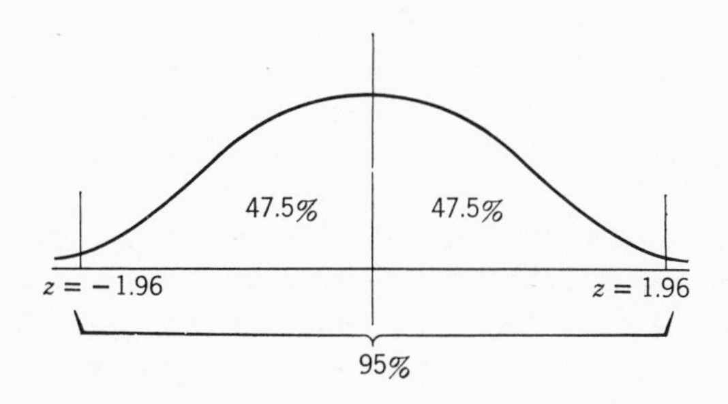

Fig. 14.4.

this means that the range we want is from

$$\hat{\mathbf{z}} + .196$$

to

$$\hat{\mathbf{z}} - .196$$

Therefore the upper limit of the range is

$$.69 + .196 = .886$$

and the lower limit is

$$.69 - .196 = .494$$

We can now convert these Z values back to values of r according to a complete table like Table 14.1. We get a range of r from .46 to .71. A confidence interval constructed in this manner is large enough to include the true population value in 95% of its applications. The statement that **r** may be found between .46 and .71 has a probability of .95 of being true.

Other Tests of Hypotheses

In considering the previous tests of hypotheses, we were concerned with only one test, $\mathbf{r} = 0$. But this discussion of confidence intervals suggests that other tests are possible. We may for example, wish to test the hypothesis that $\mathbf{r} = A$, where A is any arbitrary value. We are seldom able to develop hypotheses suggesting specific levels of correlation in behavioral science, but our knowledge of the sampling distribution of Z clearly permits tests of hypotheses of this sort.

Let us suppose that a great deal of theoretical or empirical work has been done in the prediction of college performance. That work, we shall assume, suggests that the actual correlation between high school standing and college performance is .80. This value might be taken as an hypothesis for research. Specifically, the hypothesis to be treated is $\mathbf{r} = 80$ or $\mathbf{r} - 80 = 0$. Thus, if we sampled from this population of college students, and calculated the correlation between performance and high school standing, we should expect our observed r to be close to .80. Because of sampling variation, we would not expect to get exactly .80 in any given sample.

Now suppose we did draw the sample of 100 college students described earlier. Pearson's r is calculated and it is .60. This result departs from the expected value of .80, but we do not know whether this is a large or a small departure. If **r** is really .80, what is the probability of getting an r of .60 in a sample of 100? To answer this question we must use the Z transformation.

In this case we are concerned with the departure of Z from its expected value. The actual hypothesis we will test therefore is

$$Z_{\mathbf{r}} = Z_A$$

or

$$Z_{\mathbf{r}} - Z_A = 0$$

Let $\alpha = .01$. Since Z is normally distributed, differences between Z's are also normal. The expected difference $Z_{\mathbf{r}} - Z_A$ is 0. We shall test whether the observed difference is relatively likely or relatively unlikely under the hypothesis of no difference.

The sampling distribution of $Z_{\mathbf{r}} - Z_A$ may be found in the table of the normal curve. Table C may be used. The region of rejection includes all values of $Z_{\mathbf{r}} - Z_A$ which are so large that they could be expected to occur once or fewer times in every 100 samples. Table C shows that an observation that departs from its expected value by 2.58 or more standard deviations ($z = 2.58$) will occur 1% of the time. This, then, is our region of rejection. If the observed difference between $Z_{\mathbf{r}}$ and Z_A is greater than 2.58 standard deviations, we may reject our hypothesis.

The standard error of Z is

$$\begin{aligned} s_z &= \frac{1}{\sqrt{N-3}} \\ &= \frac{1}{\sqrt{97}} \\ &= \frac{1}{9.85} \\ &= .10 \end{aligned}$$

We can read $Z_{\mathbf{r}}$ and Z_A from Table 14.1.

$$r = .60; \qquad Z_{\mathbf{r}} = .69$$
$$A = .80; \qquad Z_A = 1.10$$

Then

$$\begin{aligned} Z_{\mathbf{r}} - Z_A &= .69 - 1.10 \\ &= -.41 \end{aligned}$$

Our observed difference therefore is 4.1 standard deviations from its expected value of zero. It is larger than the value of 2.58—the boundary for our region of rejection; so we may reject our hypothesis. It is unlikely that this sample came from a population where $\mathbf{r} = .80$. Similar tests may be conducted whenever we have an hypothesis about some particular level of $\mathbf{r}$.

Other tests are also available. We can test the hypothesis that two observed measures of correlation, using the same variables sampled from different populations, are significantly different. In such a case the null hypothesis is that $\mathbf{r}_1 = \mathbf{r}_2$ or that $Z_{\mathbf{r}_1} - Z_{\mathbf{r}_2} = 0$. Problems of this sort sometimes arise in behavioral science research, but since they are essentially problems in multivariate analysis, they are beyond the scope of this book. Such tests are discussed in Hagood and Price (1952).

In general, when the sampling distribution of a statistic is known, great flexibility is possible. Many tests and estimates are available, and with some imagination extremely useful statistical inferences can be made.

Other Statistics. When our hypothesis leads us to use a coefficient of curvilinear correlation, it is obvious that the test of significance for a linear *r* is inappropriate. Then a procedure similar to the one discussed here may be used to test the significance of a curvilinear coefficient. See Ezekiel (1959) for a discussion of appropriate tests.

15 Testing Hypotheses about Nominal-Ordinal Combinations

In Chapter 10, θ was introduced to describe the degree of association in the nominal-ordinal case. But θ has one important limitation; its sampling distribution is unknown. When we have one nominal and one ordinal scale, we may use θ as a measure of association, but some other test of significance is necessary.

Several related tests may be used in this situation. Most of these, however, are variant forms of a test, called T, that was developed by Wilcoxon. This chapter will be concerned with the general Wilcoxon model and with a form of the T-test generally called the Mann-Whitney U-test.

The Wilcoxon Model and the *U*-test

Function. Association, in the nominal-ordinal case, is defined as the degree to which relative ranking on an ordinal scale can be guessed from a knowledge of nominal class membership. The rankings of cases classified into each nominal class are compared with the rankings of those in each of the other nominal classes. In this manner we determine the degree to which knowledge that an observation falls into a particular nominal class can help us in guessing its relative rank. When the members of the several classes all exhibit the same proportion of cases in each of the ranks, knowledge of class membership does not help in guessing relative rank and no association is present. But as the observations in one or more of the nominal classes tend to rank consistently higher or lower than those in the other classes, guessing is improved and association is present. The Wilcoxon model provides a test of the null hypothesis of no association against this alternative of systematic differences in ranking between subclasses. Specifically, the test determines the probability that any observed differences among subclass rankings are due to sampling variation from a population where no differences are present.

The Wilcoxon model provides a plan for testing the null hypothesis in the nominal-ordinal situation. Our concern in this chapter, however, will be restricted to the nominal scale containing only two subclasses. This particular version of Wilcoxon's test is generally called the *U*-test.

Rationale. The idea of consistent differences in ranking can perhaps be best introduced by an illustration. Suppose we rank two men and three women with respect to their musical ability (Table 15.1).

Table 15.1

	Rank in Musical Ability					
Sex	5	4	3	2	1	Number of Cases
Male	1	0	1	0	0	2
Female	0	1	0	1	1	3

The problem is to determine whether the members of either sex tend consistently to rank higher than members of the other sex. We can begin with either sex and count the number of members of the other sex that rank above and below each of its members. The highest ranking male (rank 5), ranks above three females (4, 2, and 1), and the other male (3) ranks above two females (2 and 1). Males therefore rank higher than females in $3 + 2 = 5$ comparisons. The top male (5) is below no females, and the other male (3) is below only one female (4). So the males rank lower in one comparison. There are $5 + 1 = 6$ comparisons in all.

We can, of course, begin with the other sex, but the result will be the same. If males rank higher than females in five out of six comparisons, females must rank higher in one and lower in five. The important result is simply that one group predominates in five of the six comparisons made.

This counting procedure defines U. U_i is simply the number of comparisons for which the members of one subclass rank higher than those in the other subclass. In any particular case, U_i has two values, U_1 and U_2. For our example males rank higher in five comparisons, so we can define U_1 equals 5. And females rank higher in one comparison, so U_2 equals 1. It makes no difference which value is called U_1 and which U_2. Whichever value is smaller, U_1 or U_2, is designated U and taken for our statistical test.

Let us assume a population where men and women are equal in musical ability. In such a population the men rank higher in half the comparisons, and the women rank higher in half. Therefore, for the entire population, $U_1 = U_2 = U$, and the expected value of U in any sample is the population value or one-half the number of comparisons made.

In our sample the ranks of 2 men are compared with those of 3 women;

this yields (2)(3) = 6 comparisons in all. If we assume that we have a random sample from a population where men and women are equal in musical ability, we should expect men to rank higher in one-half of these comparisons: $(\frac{1}{2})(6) = 3$. But we have observed that U_1 equals 5, U_2 equals 1, and therefore U equals 1. The job of the statistical test, then, is to determine the probability of getting a U as small as 1 in a sample of 5 from a population where men and women are equal in ranking. To do this we must find the sampling distribution of U when N equals 5 and there are no differences in population rankings.

We can divide the first five ranks into two classes—three to one class, two to the other—in ten ways (Table 15.2).

Table 15.2

Ranks	
Subclass *A*	Subclass *B*
5, 4	3, 2, 1
5, 3	4, 2, 1
5, 2	4, 3, 1
5, 1	4, 3, 2
4, 3	5, 2, 1
4, 2	5, 3, 1
4, 1	5, 3, 2
3, 2	5, 4, 1
3, 1	5, 4, 2
2, 1	5, 4, 3

U_1 and U_2 may be calculated for each of these possible outcomes, and the smaller value U can be found. Then, on the assumption that there are no differences in subclass rankings in the population from which we drew our sample, we can assign equal probabilities to each of these possible outcomes (see Table 15.4). From this table we also can, of course, determine the sampling distribution of U.

Table 15.3

U	Probability
0	.20
0–1	.40
0–2	.80
0–3	1.00

It turns out that our observed U equals 1 is a relatively likely outcome under the null hypothesis. Forty out of every hundred samples of this size from a population with no differences will produce a U as small as one or smaller. We should not be justified in rejecting the idea that men and women are equal in musical ability on the basis of these results.

This is the procedure that is used in determining the sampling distribution of U. Like the sampling distribution of G it is difficult to calculate when ties are present. Fortunately, however, U, again like G, is approximately

Table 15.4

Ranks		Number of Comparisons Where Subclass A Predominates	Number of Comparisons Where Subclass B Predominates	U_1 or U_2, the Smaller Value	
Subclass A	Subclass B	U_1	U_2	U	Probability
5, 4	3, 2, 1	6	0	0	$\frac{1}{10}$
5, 3	4, 2, 1	5	1	1	$\frac{1}{10}$
5, 2 4, 3	4, 3, 1 5, 2, 1	4	2	2	$\frac{2}{10}$
5, 1 4, 2	4, 3, 2 5, 3, 1	3	3	3	$\frac{2}{10}$
4, 1 3, 2	5, 3, 2 5, 4, 1	2	4	2	$\frac{2}{10}$
3, 1	5, 4, 2	1	5	1	$\frac{1}{10}$
2, 1	5, 4, 3	0	6	0	$\frac{1}{10}$

normally distributed when N is reasonably large. Whenever $N \geqslant 20$ the distribution of U is practically normal. In such cases the normal approximation may be used.

Procedure. In actual practice it is not necessary to compare each observation with each of the others. This is because the sum of the ranks in a class is related to the number of observations for which members of that class rank higher than those in another class.

$$U_i = R_i - \frac{n_i(n_i + 1)}{2} \tag{15.1}$$

where R_i = the sum of ranks in a subclass,
n_i = the number of observations in that same subclass.

For our data on musical ability, the sum of ranks for men is

$$5 + 3 = 8$$

and n_i for men is 2. We can put these values in our formula and we obtain

$$
\begin{aligned}
U_i &= R_i - \frac{n_i(n_i + 1)}{2} \\
&= 8 - \frac{(2)(3)}{2} \\
&= 8 - 3 \\
&= 5
\end{aligned}
$$

which is exactly the same result we obtained with our more involved comparing and counting procedure. Similarly, for women,

$$
\begin{aligned}
R_i &= 4 + 2 + 1 = 7 \\
n_i &= 3
\end{aligned}
$$

and

$$
\begin{aligned}
U_i &= R_i - \frac{n_i(n_i + 1)}{2} \\
&= 7 - \frac{(3)(4)}{2} \\
&= 7 - 6 \\
&= 1
\end{aligned}
$$

which is again the same result.

It is not necessary to calculate both values of U_i in this manner. If one value of U_i is calculated, the other may be determined by the following formula:

$$U_2 = n_1 n_2 - U_1 \tag{15.2}$$

U then is the smaller value; in our example it is 1.

When the number of observations in each subclass is less than 20, the significance of U may be read directly from Table G. In this example $n_1 = 2$ and $n_2 = 3$, so Table G is appropriate. Table G, however, has no entry for $n_1 = 2$ and $n_2 = 3$. This means that when we have only five observations we cannot make any decision at either $\alpha = .05$ or .01. This is consistent with our earlier tabulation of exact probabilities for this problem. There we found that the most extreme departure from expectation, U equals 0, had a two-tailed probability of .20. When N equals 5, therefore, we have too few observations for a test in the nominal-ordinal case.

If either n_1 or n_2 is greater than 20, the normal approximation may be used. As the sample size increases, the sampling distribution of U approaches the normal distribution. In such a case, the expected value of U is

$$\hat{U} = \frac{n_1 n_2}{2} \tag{15.3}$$

In other words, it is expected that in half of the comparisons one group will predominate and in half the other group will predominate. The standard deviation of U depends on the sample sizes and the number of ties.

$$s_U = \sqrt{\left(\frac{n_1 n_2}{N(N-1)}\right)\left(\frac{N^3 - N}{12} - \sum T_i\right)} \qquad (15.4)$$

where $N = n_1 + n_2$,
$T_i = (t_i^3 - t_i)/12$,
t_i = the number of observations tied for a given rank.

Use of Formula 15.4 requires that our data be tabulated in a special way. In this book ties have been handled simply by assigning the lowest possible rank to each of a set of tied observations. Suppose, for example, we have data on self-identification of social class for six people (Table 15.5).

Table 15.5

Person	Class Identification
A	Middle
B	Upper
C	Middle
D	Lower
E	Middle
F	Lower

To rank these observations we would typically assign 1 to the lower class, 2 to the middle, and 3 to the upper (Table 15.6).

Table 15.6

Person	Rank in Social Class
A	2
B	3
C	2
D	1
E	2
F	1

To use this formula, however, we must handle ties in a different way. *Each observation must be given the number of the mean of the rank for which it is tied.* In this case, there are two observations tied for lower class.

If they were not tied, they would rank 1 and 2. But, since they are, we must average their two ranks and assign them both the mean

$$\frac{1 + 2}{2} = 1.5$$

Then the three middle class observations are next. They should take ranks 3, 4, and 5; so again we must average them

$$\frac{3 + 4 + 5}{3} = 4$$

and rank each of these cases as 4. Then, since we already have used up the first five ranks, the highest observation receives 6. Thus, when mean ranks are assigned for ties, we obtain the array in Table 15.7.

Table 15.7

Person	Rank in Social Class (using mean ranks for ties)
A	4
B	6
C	4
D	1.5
E	4
F	1.5
Sum	21.0

All this is necessary in order to make the total sum of ranks agree with the value it would have had without ties. A good way to check the assignment of ranks to ties is provided by the fact that the sum of the first N whole numbers is $\frac{1}{2}N(N + 1)$. For $N = 6$, the sum is equal to 21. This agrees with the sum of our social class ranks with mean ranks for ties. This procedure must be used whenever we wish to compute U with tied observations.

Now the calculation of T may be specified. When we look down the mean rank array, we see two groups of ties; two people are tied at 1.5 and three tied at 4. For the first group,

$$\begin{aligned} T_i &= \frac{t_i^3 - t_i}{12} \\ &= \frac{2^3 - 2}{12} \\ &= \frac{6}{12} = .5 \end{aligned}$$

For the second,

$$T_i = \frac{t_i^3 - t_i}{12} = \frac{3^3 - 3}{12} = \frac{24}{12} = 2$$

$\sum T_i$ therefore equals 2.5.

To use the normal curve table to determine the significance of an observed value of U, we must calculate z,

$$z = \frac{U - \hat{U}}{s_U} \tag{15.5}$$

This is simply the departure of the observed U from its expected value expressed in standard deviation units. If the departure is large, it is likely that one group or the other predominates in the population; if it is small, we are unable to draw any such conclusion. The computed value may be compared with the values listed in Table G. Table G includes the normal curve z values necessary to reject the null hypothesis for a one-tailed or two-tailed test at $\alpha = .05$ or $.01$. For a two-tailed test at $\alpha = .05$, for example, the listed z is 1.960. If an observed z is equal to or greater than this value, the null hypothesis may be rejected.

Example

As one of a series of studies on the psychology of social class, Centers presented questionnaires to members of the student body in a high school in New Jersey.[1] Each student was asked to identify himself as a member of the upper, middle, working, or lower class.

Previous research had suggested that adult females have a slight tendency to identify with the higher social classes. So Centers set about to test the hypothesis that this same tendency would be observed for high school students. Various comparisons between males and females were made. In several of these, actual social class was held constant by examining only those students whose fathers' occupations tended to place them in some particular class position. Table 15.8 shows Center's results for 130 students from white-collar families.[1]

[1] Richard Centers, "Social Class Identification of American Youth," *Journal of Personality*, **18** (March, 1950), 290–302.

Table 15.8. *Sex Comparisons in Social Class Identification for Students from White-Collar Families*

	Number Affiliating with				
Sex	Upper Class	Middle Class	Working Class	Lower Class	Total
Male	0	41	22	1	64
Female	3	53	9	1	66

1. *Hypothesis.* H_1: Centers has proposed that females should rank higher than males in social class identification.

2. *Null Hypothesis.* H_0: Females rank lower than males or males and females do not differ in social class identification ranks.

3. *Test.* Social class may be viewed as an ordinal scale, and sex is a two-class nominal scale. The U-test therefore is appropriate as a test of H_0.

4. *Significance Level.* Let $\alpha = .01$.

5. *Sampling Distribution.* The number of observations in each subclass is greater than 20; so the significance of U may be determined by the normal approximation. Table G lists the z values for this test. Since H_1 specifies a direction of difference, a one-tailed test is appropriate.

6. *Rejection Region.* The region of rejection consists of all the one-tailed values of z which are so large that, under the null hypothesis, they would occur 1% of the time or less. Table G shows that for a one-tailed test at $\alpha = .01$, z must be at least 2.326 in order to reject the null hypothesis.

7. *Decision.* In order to compute z we must first rank the data in Table 15.8 according to the mean rank method. Two persons (a male and a female) both claim lower class membership. They share ranks 1 and 2, so their mean rank is $(1 + 2)/2 = 1.5$. Thirty-one people claim working class identification. The ranks they share are 3 to 33, and their mean is

$$\frac{3 + 4 + 5 + \cdots + 33}{31} = 18$$

Ninety-four identify themselves as middle class and take the average of ranks 34 through 127. Their average is

$$\frac{34 + 35 + \cdots + 127}{94} = 80.5$$

The remaining three are tied for ranks $128 - 130$. Their average, then, is

$$\frac{128 + 129 + 130}{3} = 129$$

Now we are prepared to calculate U using Formula 15.2 for tied observations. First we shall determine the values of R_i (Table 15.9).

Table 15.9

Class	Rank	Number of Males f	f_R Males	Number of Females f	f_R Females	t
Lower	1.5	1	1.5	1	1.5	2
Working	18	22	396.0	9	162.0	31
Middle	80.5	41	3300.5	53	4266.5	94
Upper	129	0	0	3	487.0	3
Total		64	3698	66	4817	130

Now two values of U_i may be calculated as

$$U_i = R_i - \frac{n_i(n_i + 1)}{2}$$

For males,

$$\begin{aligned} U_{\text{males}} &= 3698 - \frac{(64)(65)}{2} \\ &= 3698 - 2080 \\ &= 1618 \end{aligned}$$

For females,

$$\begin{aligned} U_{\text{females}} &= 4817 - \frac{(66)(67)}{2} \\ &= 4817 - 2211 \\ &= 2606 \end{aligned}$$

These calculations may be checked by means of Formula 15.2.

$$\begin{aligned} U_{\text{males}} &= n_1 n_2 - U_{\text{females}} \\ &= (64)(66) - 2606 \\ &= 4224 - 2606 \\ &= 1618 \end{aligned}$$

The results therefore do check.

Now $\hat{U}$, the expected value of U, may be calculated.

$$\begin{aligned} \hat{U} &= \frac{n_1 n_2}{2} \\ &= \frac{(64)(66)}{2} \\ &= 2112 \end{aligned}$$

We may now solve for the values of T.

$$T_i = \frac{t^3 - t}{12}$$

$$T_{\text{lower class}} = \frac{2^3 - 2}{12} = .5$$

$$T_{\text{working class}} = \frac{31^3 - 31}{12} = 2480.0$$

$$T_{\text{middle class}} = \frac{94^3 - 94}{12} = 69{,}207.5$$

$$T_{\text{upper class}} = \frac{3^3 - 3}{12} = 2.0$$

$$\sum T_i = 71{,}690.0$$

Now s_U may be calculated by means of Formula 15.4.

$$\begin{aligned} s_U &= \sqrt{\left(\frac{n_1 n_2}{N(N-1)}\right)\left(\frac{N^3 - N}{12} - \sum T_i\right)} \\ &= \sqrt{\left(\frac{(64)(66)}{(130)(129)}\right)\left(\frac{(130)^3 - 130}{12} - 71{,}690\right)} \\ &= \sqrt{\left(\frac{4224}{16{,}770}\right)\left(\frac{2196{,}870}{12} - 71{,}690\right)} \\ &= \sqrt{(.25188)(111{,}382)} \\ &= \sqrt{28{,}054.9} \\ &= 167.5 \end{aligned}$$

Finally we can determine z.

$$\begin{aligned} z &= \frac{U - \hat{U}}{s_U} \\ &= \frac{1618 - 2112}{167.5} \\ &= \frac{-494}{167.5} \\ &= -2.94 \end{aligned}$$

This value, $|-2.94|$, is larger than the 2.326 needed to reject the null hypothesis. We may conclude therefore that these students probably do come from a population where females rank themselves higher in social class. (The minus sign merely indicates that we took the smaller value of U_i.)

Summary of Procedure. These are the steps involved in the U-test.

1. Calculate U according to Formula 15.1. If there are ties, rank the observations according to the mean rank method.

2. If there are 20 or fewer observations in each subclass, determine the significance of U according to Table G.
3. If there are more than 20 observations in each of the subclasses, calculate z and read its significance from the bottom of Table G.

Other Statistics

Whitney's *U*-Test Extensions. Whitney has proposed two extensions of the U-test. Both are limited to the three subclass problems, and both test the null hypothesis against specific predictions of the rank order of the subclasses.

Runs Tests. Wald and Wolfowitz, Wallis, and Mood have all proposed runs tests. These tests depend on arranging a set of ranks in order and then counting the number of runs or sequences of each nominal class.

The runs tests represent a different and more general approach to the problem of distinguishing between subclasses. See Siegel (1956) and Tate and Clelland (1957) for discussion of these tests.

The Median Test. Westerberg, Mood, and Brown have described a test based on classifying observations as above or below the combined median. Siegel (1956) and Tate and Clelland (1957) also discuss the median test.

Other Statistics. Friedman has proposed χ_r^2, a multivariate ordinal test. Since it requires the simultaneous study of three variables, it is beyond the scope of this book.

Fisher and Yates have developed a normalized ranks procedure similar in rationale to the M discussed in Chapter 12. The use of this test requires the assumption of an underlying normal distribution.

Various other special-purpose tests have been proposed. However, they are not encountered very often in behavioral science research. To follow these up, see Siegel (1956), Tate and Clelland (1957), or Walker and Lev (1953).

16 Testing Hypotheses about Nominal-Interval Combinations

There are two ways of thinking about the nominal-interval problem. We can discuss as in Chapter 11, the amount of association between two variables—one nominal and one interval. Our concern here is with the degree to which interval-scale scores can be predicted from a knowledge of nominal-scale classes. From this point of view, the problem of this chapter is that of providing a test for the null hypothesis that the correlation in the population is zero.

The nature, however, of the nominal-interval measure of association provides us with an alternative way of looking at the problem. The measure rests on our ability to guess the interval-scale scores on the basis of the nominal-scale classes. The effectiveness of our guessing always depends on the size of the differences in scores between members of various classes. If men and women, for example, had the same average height, it would be impossible to distinguish the sexes on the basis of height—the correlation between sex and height would be zero. But if the sexes differed very greatly, they could be distinguished easily, and the correlation would be high. In the general case, as we saw in Chapter 11, the greater the difference in mean interval score between nominal classes, the greater the correlation. The correlation will be zero if all the subclasses have the same mean. Since this is the case, the null hypothesis may be stated in another form; we are concerned with a test of the hypothesis that the means of all of the subclasses are equal. This is exactly the same null hypothesis as the one previously stated; this is merely a new way of putting it.

This second statement form is particularly important from the viewpoint of the research scientist. Research workers are always faced with the problem of distinguishing between kinds of objects on the basis of some measured characteristic of these objects. Chemists, for example, distinguish various gases from one another on the basis of their molecular weights. And sociologists differentiate between occupations in terms of their average annual incomes. In both instances, the research worker is attempting to discriminate between kinds of things (nominal classes) on the basis of measurements (interval scores).

When the problem is one of describing association, η is the appropriate statistic; it reflects the degree to which observed classes may be distinguished on the basis of measurements. But in this case, the question is one of generalizing. We need a statistic that will tell us whether we can expect the observed class differences to hold up for the population. There is only one general procedure for making such a test, Fisher's F-test or analysis of variance.

Fisher's Analysis of Variance

Actually, analysis of variance is not one but a whole range of related procedures that may be used in the solution of many problems of statistical analysis. Many important applications of analysis of variance are concerned with multivariate analysis—where more than two variables are considered simultaneously—but these applications are beyond the scope of this book. Our attention will be confined to a discussion of the two variable cases: single classification or "one-way" analysis of variance.

Function. Single classification analysis of variance may be viewed as a test of the null hypothesis that any observed value of η arose by chance from a population in which there is no correlation. We can express this same idea in terms of mean differences by saying that the F-test evaluates the hypothesis that any observed differences in subclass means are due to sampling error, that all subclass means arose from a population with but a single grand mean. In any case, this evaluation is based on an analysis of the estimated population variance.

Rationale. Let us assume a population of individuals who are normally distributed along some interval scale. If we draw a random sample from such a population, we can estimate the variance of the population (we shall designate our variable Y).

$$\hat{\mathbf{s}}^2 = \frac{\sum_{i=1}^{N} y_i^2}{N-1}$$

where $\hat{\mathbf{s}}^2$ = the estimated population variance based on a sample of N observations.

With several random samples of equal size the estimated population variance is simply the mean of the several individual estimates

$$\hat{s}_W^2 = \frac{\sum_{j=1}^{k} \hat{s}_j^2}{k}$$

where $\hat{s}_j^2$ = the estimated population variance based on a particular sample.
$\hat{s}_W^2$ = the estimated population variance based upon the average variance within each of two or more samples of N observations,
k = the number of samples.

In this situation, where we have several samples, there is a second, independent way to estimate the population variance. This is based on the sample means. If we were to draw a series of two or more random samples from such a population, the mean of each of the samples would be a good estimate of the population mean. But we could hardly expect each of our sample means to hit the population value exactly. Instead, they would probably range around the true population value—some would overestimate the true mean and some underestimate it. The question is, how close would we expect these sample means to be to the true value? Should they all cluster quite closely around the population value or will they range rather widely in both directions?

Two factors must be considered in any attempt to answer a question about the range of variation of sample means: (1) the size of the successive samples and (2) the amount of variation, the variance, of scores in the population. In general, the smaller the samples and the larger the population variance, the more variation we should expect among the means of several samples.

It is fairly obvious that sample size must be a critical consideration for this or any other statistical test. By analogy we can think about proportions as we did in our earlier coin-tossing illustration. In a population of all possible tosses of a perfectly balanced coin, the proportion of heads is exactly .5. What, we may ask, is the probability of departing markedly from this proportion, say getting all heads, in samples of various sizes? For a sample of two tosses the probability is

$$(\tfrac{1}{2})^2 = \tfrac{1}{4}$$

For a sample of four tosses it is

$$(\tfrac{1}{2})^4 = \tfrac{1}{16}$$

Clearly, the larger the sample the smaller the probability of extreme departure from population values. This is true also for sample means.

As sample size increases, the observed means tend to be closer approximations of the true population value—extreme departures are less likely to occur.

The second consideration is population variance. On one hand, consider the number of meals eaten in a given day by the population of adult Americans. The mean is probably 3 and the range of variation quite small, say from 0 to 6 or 7. On the other hand, consider the number of cigarettes smoked that same day by that same population. Here, the mean might also be about 3, but the range of variation probably runs from 0 to 60 or 70. Now if we have a series of samples of equal size from these two distributions, we expect the means for cigarette smoking to vary more from sample to sample merely because of the sheer *possibility* of variation. We may occasionally hit a rare instance of a whole sample composed of heavy smokers with an average consumption of 25 cigarettes, but it is manifestly impossible to obtain a sample of eaters who consume an average of 25 meals in a day!

In evaluating the range of variation in the means of successive samples, we must therefore take both sample size and population variance into account. Formally, this can be expressed by means of an equality

$$s_{\bar{Y}}^2 = \frac{\mathbf{s}^2}{N_j}$$

where $s_{\bar{Y}}^2$ = the variance among sample means,
$\mathbf{s}^2$ = the true population variance,
N_j = the number of cases in each sample.

In short, the variance among means of successive samples drawn from the same normally distributed population increases with an increase in population variance and decreases with an increase in sample size.

In order to use this equation to estimate population variance on the basis of sample means we need only to turn it around:

$$\hat{\mathbf{s}}_B^2 = n_j s_{\bar{Y}}^2$$

where $\hat{\mathbf{s}}_B^2$ = an estimate of the variance in a normally distributed population based on the variance of means between samples,
n_j = the number of cases in each sample,
$s_{\bar{Y}}^2$ = the variance among sample means.

Thus, when we have two or more random samples from *a normally distributed population*, we have two independent estimates of the population variance, one based on the average variance *within* each of the samples and one based on the variance *between* the means of the samples. We should expect that usually these two estimates will be about equal. Both will, of course, vary from sample to sample, but since they are both estimates of the population variance they should be approximately equal.

Let us suppose that our several samples are from different populations with different means. In this case, the estimate based on the variance within samples is an estimate of the population variance. But the estimate based on differences between means is larger; it reflects not only the population variance, but also additional variation because of actual differences in the population means.

It is this fact that provides the basis for the *F*-test. *F* is simply a ratio between our two variance estimates.

$$F = \frac{\text{estimate of variance based on between mean differences}}{\text{estimate of variance based on within group variation}}$$

If the ratio is small, the two estimates agree closely. Then we must conclude that the observed mean differences reflect nothing but sampling variation from a single population with a single mean. If the ratio is large, we must at least entertain the notion that the observed means differ so much that they may represent actual differences in population values.

An example may help to clear up these concepts. Let us imagine an investigator with nothing better to do than to study the "post-sophomore slump" in college dating. He has, let us say, the notion that freshman and sophomore girls date more frequently than juniors and seniors, and he is anxious to test this hypothesis. His enthusiasm, however, is not unbounded, so he determines to take only two samples of ten girls each—one of freshmen and sophomores and one of juniors and seniors. He may obtain results like Table 16.1.

Table 16.1 *Number of Dates per Week*

	Freshmen and Sophomores	Juniors and Seniors	
	10	9	
	9	6	
	8	5	
	7	5	
	7	5	
	6	4	
	6	3	
	5	3	
	4	2	
	4	1	Both Groups
Total	66	43	109
Mean	6.6	4.3	5.45

Obviously, for the girls in the sample, the hypothesis of post-sophomore slump is supported. The difference in mean number of weekly dates between the lower and upper division students is 2.3, and $\eta = .49$. However, these samples are none too large, and we may be left with a question about how universally this conclusion may be applied. We want to know whether we may obtain an η of .49 from a population where there is no correlation or whether two means may vary as much as 2.3 when sampled from a population in which there is no difference in means. Let us assume that dating is normally distributed and compute an F-ratio.

First, we can estimate the population variance on the basis of the difference between the means of the two samples.

$$\hat{s}_B{}^2 = n_j s_{\bar{Y}}{}^2$$

In this case,

$$\bar{Y}_{\mathrm{F-So}} = 6.6$$
$$\bar{Y}_{\mathrm{J-Se}} = 4.3$$
$$\bar{Y} = 5.45$$

Then

$$s_{\bar{Y}}{}^2 = \frac{\sum_{j=1}^{k} (\bar{X}_j - \bar{X})^2}{k - 1}$$

and

$$\begin{aligned} s_{\bar{Y}}{}^2 &= \frac{(6.6 - 5.45)^2 + (4.3 - 5.45)^2}{2 - 1} \\ &= \frac{(1.15)^2 + (-1.15)^2}{1} \\ &= 2.644 \end{aligned}$$

So

$$\begin{aligned} \hat{s}_B{}^2 &= n_j s_{\bar{Y}}{}^2 \\ &= (10)(2.644) \\ &= 26.44 \end{aligned}$$

This estimate is based solely on differences in means. Its size may be due either to population variance or to a real difference in population means. To determine which it is we must calculate our other estimate of population variance

$$\hat{s}_W = \frac{\sum_{j=1}^{k} \hat{s}_j{}^2}{k}$$

Here we need to know the variance of each of the samples in order to calculate their average. For freshmen and sophomores,

$$\hat{s}^2_{F-So} = \frac{\sum_{i=1}^{N} y_i^2}{n_{F-S_o} - 1}$$
$$= \frac{36.36}{9}$$
$$= 4.04$$

And for juniors and seniors,

$$\hat{s}^2_{J-Se} = \frac{\sum_{i=1}^{N} y_i^2}{n_{J-S_s} - 1}$$
$$= \frac{46.08}{9}$$
$$= 5.12$$

Then

$$\hat{s}_W = \frac{\sum_{s=1}^{k} \hat{s}_j^2}{k}$$
$$= \frac{4.04 + 5.12}{2}$$
$$= 4.58$$

We now have two estimates of the variance in the population, one based on the differences in means and one derived from the variance within samples. We can now compute their ratio in order to determine the likelihood that means as different as these could have arisen by chance from a population with a single mean.

$$F = \frac{\hat{s}_B^2}{\hat{s}_W^2}$$
$$= \frac{26.44}{4.58}$$
$$= 5.77$$

In order to evaluate the significance of this ratio we must know its distribution under the null hypothesis. This distribution is known; it is listed in Table H. Its form, however, is somewhat different from the earlier tables, so some comments on its use are in order.

In the first place, no distinction between one-tailed and two-tailed tests is indicated. The analysis of variance is *always* a one-tailed test. This is because the F-test is concerned with departures in only one direction from its expected value. F takes its expected value of one when the numerator ($\hat{s}_B^2$) and the denominator ($\hat{s}_W^2$) are equal. If the denominator is larger, F is less than one and we fail to reject the null hypothesis. Only when the numerator is larger do we suspect a difference in population means. F therefore is a one-tailed test.

Second, since F is a ratio of two estimates, we enter the table with two values for degrees of freedom. One value expresses the number of degrees of freedom for the numerator and one for the denominator. The number of degrees of freedom for the numerator is always determined on the basis of the number of means which go into calculating $\hat{s}_B^2$. It is equal to

$$\text{df}_B = k - 1 \tag{16.1}$$

or the number of samples minus one. For the denominator,

$$\begin{aligned} \text{df}_W &= (n_1 - 1) + (n_2 - 1) + \cdots + (n_k - 1) \\ &= N - k \end{aligned} \tag{16.2}$$

In other words, it is equal to the sum of the degrees of freedom for each of the samples.

A convenient check of df_B and df_W is provided by the following equality:

$$\text{df} = \text{df}_B + \text{df}_W$$

where df = the total number of cases in all subsamples minus one.

In this example,

$$\begin{aligned} \text{df}_B &= 2 - 1 = 1 \\ \text{df}_W &= (10 - 1) + (10 - 1) = 18 \\ \text{df} &= 18 + 1 = 19 \end{aligned}$$

This checks since the total number of observations is 20, and $20 - 1 = 19$.

We can now evaluate the null hypothesis with degrees of freedom equal to 1 and 18. We read df_B across the top of the table and df_W down the side. For 1 and 18 we find two values listed in Table H: 4.41 and 8.28. The smaller value is the F required to reject H_0 at $\alpha = .05$, and the larger value is the F required at $\alpha = .01$. Our investigator, let us say, decides that with a total sample as small as twenty he should set α equal to .05. Hence an F of 4.41 or larger will lead him to reject the null hypothesis. The calculated F is 5.77, so he will reject H_0 and conclude that dating patterns for freshmen and sophomores as compared to juniors and seniors really do differ in the population.

Procedure. When the samples are all equal in size, the F-ratio might actually be calculated on the basis of the estimates previously described.

When η is used as a measure of association, however, a simpler method can be derived directly from the computing procedure used for η. This formula may be used in all cases with or without equal N's.

$$F = \left(\frac{\eta^2}{1 - \eta^2}\right)\left(\frac{N - k}{k - 1}\right) \tag{16.3}$$

where N = the number of cases in the total sample,
k = the number of samples.

If we apply Formula 16.3 to the data of our earlier example, we obtain the following results:

$$F = \left(\frac{\eta^2}{1 - \eta^2}\right)\left(\frac{N - k}{k - 1}\right)$$

$$\eta = .49$$

Thus

$$\begin{aligned} F &= \left(\frac{.2427}{1 - .2427}\right)\left(\frac{20 - 2}{2 - 1}\right) \\ &= \left(\frac{.2427}{.7573}\right) \\ &= 5.769 \end{aligned}$$

This is the same result we produced earlier with a more involved computing procedure. Note also that in this case we have already determined the degrees of freedom in the second term of our equation. The numerator is equal to df_W (18) and the denominator is df_B (1). This formula may be used whenever we wish to compute F.

Example

As part of a larger study in preventive psychiatry, Muuss examined the relationship between a causal-learning program and manifest anxiety for a sample of sixth grade students.[1] The basic hypothesis of the study was that children who are trained to understand "the multiple, complex, interacting nature of the factors that operate in human behavior" will exhibit signs of better mental health than others. One index of mental health examined was the degree to which a child is willing to be punitive or punishing, rather than understanding, in dealing with others.

Three samples of students were selected and matched according to age, sex, and I.Q. One group of 25 was trained in causal-learning for two

[1] Rolf E. Muuss, "The Effects of a One- and Two-Year Causal-Learning Program," *Journal of Personality*, **28** (December, 1960), 470–491.

years, one group for one year, and the third group received no training. All 75 were then given a standard test of punitiveness, the problem situation test. Results are shown in Table 16.2.

Table 16.2. *Punitiveness Levels of Students according to Training in Causality*

	Training in Causality			
	A None	*B* One Year	*C* Two Years	Total Group
$\bar{Y}_j$	4.12	5.00	2.04	3.72
$\bar{Y}_j - \bar{Y}$	−.40	−1.28	1.68	
$(\bar{Y}_j - \bar{Y})^2$	.16	1.63	2.82	
n_j	25	25	25	
$n_j(\bar{Y}_j - \bar{Y})^2$	4.00	40.75	78.50	
$(Y_i - \bar{Y})^2$				607.12

1. *Hypothesis.* H_1: Muuss' hypothesis is that mean levels of punitiveness differ significantly according to training in causality.

2. *Null Hypothesis.* H_0: There are no differences in the population values of the means from which these three samples were drawn.

3. *Test.* Since these test results are normalized and the individuals were randomly assigned to training groups, the F-test is appropriate.

4. *Significance Level.* Let $\alpha = .01$.

5. *Sampling Distribution.* F is distributed according to Table H in the Appendix.

6. *Rejection Region.* The region of rejection consists of all one-tailed values of F which are so large that they are likely to occur less than one time in one hundred samples when H_0 is true. Table H has no entry for degrees of freedom, $\text{df}_B = 3 - 1 = 2$ and $\text{df}_W = (25)(3) - 3 = 72$. The closest value is $\text{df}_B = 2$ and $\text{df}_W = 60$. Here, with $\alpha = .01$, an F value of 4.98 is necessary to reject the null hypothesis.

7. *Decision.* Table 16.2 shows the results of Muuss' research. We can use those results to compute η^2 and F.

$$\eta^2 = \frac{\sum_{j=1}^{k} n_j(\bar{Y}_j - \bar{Y})^2}{\sum_{i=1}^{N} (Y_i - \bar{Y})^2}$$

$$= \frac{4.00 + 40.75 + 70.50}{607.12}$$

$$= .19$$

Then

$$\begin{aligned} F &= \left(\frac{\eta^2}{1 - \eta^2}\right)\left(\frac{N - k}{k - 1}\right) \\ &= \left(\frac{.19}{.81}\right)\left(\frac{72}{2}\right) \\ &= (.234)(36) \\ &= 8.4 \end{aligned}$$

We can therefore reject the null hypothesis and conclude that these samples did arise from populations with different means; there is a relationship between causal training and punitiveness. It should be noted, however, that the order of magnitude of the means differs from the prediction. Students with two years' training are markedly less punitive, but those with one year's training are slightly more punitive than untrained persons!

Summary of Procedure. The following steps must be followed to use the *F*-test:

1. Calculate η^2 according to Formula 11.1.
2. Determine F according to Formula 16.3.
3. Calculate the two values of df and evaluate F according to Table H.

Other Statistics. The only other statistic appropriate for use as a test in the nominal-interval setting is Student's *t*-test. The *t*-test, however, may be applied only when the number of samples (or classes in the nominal scale) is two. And even in that case $t^2 = F$, so t is not really a different test. When you see references to *t*-tests in the literature you may understand them as a special case of F.

17 Testing Hypotheses about Ordinal-Interval Combinations

In Chapter 12 the coefficient of multiserial correlation M was introduced to describe the degree of association between an ordinal and an interval scale. This chapter will be concerned with a general test of significance for M.

Test of Significance of M

Function. It is possible, of course, that any observed value of M might arise due to sampling variation from a population where there is no association. The purpose of this test is to evaluate the null hypothesis that the population value of the correlation is zero.

Rationale. M was defined as a special case of Pearson's r. It is special in two respects: (1) it requires that observations on the ordinally scaled variable be transformed into a normal distribution form and (2) the final coefficient of correlation must be corrected for the broad categories of classification inherent in the ordinal variable. The transformation has no effect on the calculation of r or on its significance; it demands only that the final coefficient be interpreted in a language filled with "ifs." To interpret M we must say that this is the amount of correlation we should expect to observe *if* we were able to measure our ordinal variable on an interval level and *if* it were really normally distributed. But the important point to note here is, that without the correction for broad categories, M *is* Pearson's r.

The correction for broad categories, however, is quite a different matter. Although a multiserial coefficient which is not corrected is a form of Pearson's r, such a statistic cannot be readily interpreted. Without correction it is not a good estimate of what Pearson's r would be if it were calculated on the basis of a set of regular interval-scale values. The correction for broad categories therefore is necessary in order to produce a statistic which can be interpreted as an estimate of r under the if-conditions just listed.

In effect, then, we have two statistics, or at least two forms of the same statistic. One is an uncorrected coefficient r and the other is a corrected coefficient M. M is important since it provides a measure of association which can be interpreted; r is important in providing a test of significance.

In the uncorrected coefficient of correlation, we are dealing with a statistic which has a known distribution. Our test of significance therefore is quite simple: we can use this uncorrected value and test r by means of Table F in the Appendix. Such a test differs in no way from the test of any other Pearson's coefficient of correlation.

Procedure. If M has already been calculated, it includes the correction for broad categories. In order to determine its significance we must uncorrect M—convert it back to r. Since the original correction was accomplished by dividing r by the standard deviation of the broadly classed variable, we can uncorrect M by multiplying it by the standard deviation of that variable.

$$r = Ms_z$$

where s_z is the standard deviation of the broadly classed ordinal scale. For computing purposes this formula becomes

$$r = M\left(\sqrt{\sum \frac{(o_b - o_a)^2}{p}}\right) \tag{17.1}$$

This is actually quite simple to compute since the quantity

$$\sum \frac{(o_b - o_a)^2}{p}$$

has already been used as a component in the denominator of M.

Example

In a study of social stratification Haer examined the relationships among a set of indices to class position.[1] Amount of education is well established as such an index, and certain earlier work had suggested that amount of travel might be related to social class. So Haer was concerned with the degree to which amount of travel was positively related to a well-established class variable—education. Haer took a sample of 320 white adults from

[1] John L. Haer, "Predictive Utility of Five Indices of Social Stratification," *American Sociological Review*, **22** (October, 1957), 542–546.

the population of Tallahassee, Florida. Education was measured by recording the number of years of school completed. Amount of travel was indexed crudely by recording for each person whether he had traveled outside the United States. Haer's data are shown in Table 17.1.

It is not unreasonable to assume that the amount people travel is normally distributed. So if we take their foreign travel as a rough index to this variable, we can determine the degree of association between educational level and travel by means of M.

$$
\begin{aligned}
M &= \frac{\sum \bar{Y}(o_b - o_a)}{s_Y \sum \dfrac{(o_b - o_a)^2}{p}} \\
&= \frac{(13.97)(.3928) + (11.70)(-.3928)}{(.354)\left(\dfrac{.1543}{.57} + \dfrac{.1543}{.43}\right)} \\
&= \frac{.89}{(3.54)(.63)} \\
&= \frac{.89}{2.23} \\
&= .40
\end{aligned}
$$

This, then, is what we should expect the correlation between education and travel to be if we could measure travel in an interval scale and if it were normally distributed.

Now in order to test the significance of our observed correlation we must convert it to a value of r.

1. *Hypothesis.* H_1: This test is based on the hypothesis that education and travel are positively related.

2. *Null Hypothesis.* H_0: The correlation between education and travel is negative or zero in the population from which this sample is drawn.

3. *Test.* Since this is a random sample, and since the assumption that both variables are normally distributed is not unreasonable, the r-test may be used.

4. *Significance Level.* Let $\alpha = .01$.

5. *Sampling Distribution.* r is distributed according to Table F.

6. *Rejection Region.* Since H_1 specifies a direction of association, a one-tailed test is appropriate. The region of rejection consists of all one-tailed values of r which are so large that, when H_0 is true, they are likely to occur less than one time in 100 on the basis of sampling variation. We have degrees of freedom, $\text{df} = N - 2 = 320 - 2 = 318$. The largest entry in Table F shows that for $\text{df} = 100$ the one-tailed test with $\alpha = .01$, r must be equal to, or greater than, .230 in order to reject H_0.

Table 17.1. *Relationship between Educational Level and Travel*

Years of School	Travel outside United States	No travel outside United States
24		1
23	1	
22	1	
21		1
20	8	
19	2	
18	4	4
17	8	5
16	31	11
15	9	6
14	14	15
13	10	9
12	27	63
11	6	11
10	6	17
9	3	10
8	2	15
7	3	2
6	1	7
5		3
4		1
3		1
2		
1		
0	2	
Totals	138	182

7. *Decision.* M has already been calculated. We must modify this value in order to compute r.

$$
\begin{aligned}
r &= M\sqrt{\sum\frac{(o_b - o_a)^2}{p}} \\
&= .40\sqrt{.63} \\
&= (.40)(.79) \\
&= .316
\end{aligned}
$$

Therefore we may reject the null hypothesis and conclude that, among white adults in Tallahassee, travel and education are related. It is wise to remember, however, that this conclusion depends on the assumption that both travel and education are normally distributed in the population in question.

Summary of Procedure. The r-test may be computed by following these steps:

1. Calculate M according to Formula 12.1.
2. Calculate r according to Formula 17.1.
3. Determine df and evaluate r on the basis of Table F.

Other Statistics. The only other statistic appropriate as a test in the ordinal-interval situation is the standard error of biserial r. This test, however, may be used only when the ordinal scale is limited to two categories, and then it will yield exactly the same results as the r-test described earlier.

18 Testing Hypotheses about Two Nominal Scales

Since many behavioral science data are expressed in the form of nominal scales, techniques for testing hypotheses about these scales are extremely important. There are a great many such techniques, but the most generally useful is Pearson's *chi-square* (χ^2) *test.*

Pearson's Chi-Square Test

Function. In Chapter 7 we saw that the degree of association between two nominal scales could be described by means of λ. The sampling distribution of λ, however, is quite complex. Furthermore, λ is sensitive to only one of many forms that association might take in nominal scales. In this chapter, therefore, we shall not discuss the distribution of λ. Instead we shall examine a statistic that is sensitive to *any* systematic departure from independence or total nonpredictability. Chi-square is such a statistic. Specifically, χ^2 allows us to test the hypothesis that any association we observe is the result of sampling variation from a population in which the association is zero.

Rationale. We can begin by defining what is meant by independence or lack of association in the nominal-nominal case. Suppose, for example, that we have a sample of 100 students who have had a class in statistics. And suppose we have the hypothesis there is some relationship between sex and performance in statistics. We can report our results in a contingency table as in Table 18.1.

Table 18.1

Sex	Passing	Failing	Total
Male	52	8	60
Female	28	12	40
Total	80	20	100

A glance at Table 18.1 shows that a larger proportion of males than females passed the course. There is therefore some observed association between sex and final grade ($\lambda = .07$). What we want to know, however, is how this table would look if there were no association between these two variables.

The reason underlying independence runs as follows: 20 of the 100 students failed; this amounts to 20%. If there were no association between sex and final grade, there should be no difference between males and females when it comes to failing. Therefore 20% of the males should have failed—20% of the 60 males is 12 who should have failed—and 20% of the 40 females or 8 should have failed. By the same reasoning, 80% of the males, 48, should have passed, and 80% of the females, 32, should have passed. Table 18.2 shows then the frequencies we should expect to observe if there were no association at all between sex and final grade.

Table 18.2

	Final Grade		
Sex	Passing	Failing	Total
Male	48	12	60
Female	32	8	40
Total	80	20	100

Obviously, our observed frequencies are not identical with these expectations. So our next question is: What are the chances of getting differences from our expectations as great as or greater than these we have observed if there is really no association between sex and final grade in the population? Clearly, we would not expect to get *exactly* 20% of the males and 20% of the females failing every test, but what, we may ask, are the chances of failing as few and passing as many males and failing as many and passing as few females as our sample shows?

Here χ^2 comes into play, for χ^2 is a test of the significance of the discrepancy between observed and expected frequencies. In this example there are four observed values (f_o).

	f_o
Males passing	52
Males failing	8
Females passing	28
Females failing	12

In addition, there are, of course, four corresponding expected values (f_e).

	f_e
Males passing	48
Males failing	12
Females passing	32
Females failing	8

There are therefore four discrepancy values, $(f_o - f_e)$ as shown in Table 18.3.

Table 18.3

	f_o	f_e	$(f_o - f_e)$ Difference
Males passing	52	48	4
Males failing	8	12	−4
Females passing	28	32	−4
Females failing	12	8	4

According to our hypothesis of no relationship, then, four too many males passed and four too few failed, whereas four too few females passed and four too many failed. Note that if we add these differences, their sum is zero. Since, if our hypothesis is to make sense at all, the total of observed frequencies must be equal to the total of expectations, the sum of their discrepancies must always equal zero.

The sum of the differences therefore between observed and expected frequencies cannot be used directly as an index of discrepancy. However, if each of these differences is squared, $(f_o - f_e)^2$, they all become positive and they may be added together to provide such an index.

We still have not taken the size of the expected values into account. Suppose we had a sample of 1000 students instead of 100. And suppose there were still four too many boys passing, four too many girls failing, and so on. Here a difference of 4 from an expected frequency of 480 would seem far less important than our observed difference of 4 from an expected 48. In the new case, the divergence between observation and expectation is only 1 in 120, whereas in our sample it is 1 in 12. Therefore each squared deviation is divided by its corresponding expected frequency in order to evaluate the importance of its deviation in terms of the degree to which it may possibly deviate.

Here we must be careful that none of our expected frequencies is less than 5. When an expected frequency is very small, tiny differences in discrepancy are weighted very heavily. Thus, when any expected frequency is below 5, χ^2 becomes unstable—it is not a fair test of our hypothesis. Later we shall discuss techniques for dealing with problems involving very small expected frequencies.

χ^2, then, is equal to the sum of the squares of all differences, each divided by its corresponding expected frequency. Thus

$$\chi^2 = \sum \frac{(f_o - f_e)^2}{f_e}$$

where f_o is an observed frequency and f_e is the corresponding expected frequency. Table 18.4 gives the data for the example.

Table 18.4

Cell	f_o	f_e	$f_o - f_e$	$(f_o - f_e)^2$	$(f_o - f_e)^2/f_e$
Boys passing	52	48	4	16	.33
Boys failing	8	12	−4	16	1.33
Girls passing	28	32	−4	16	.50
Girls failing	12	8	4	16	2.00
Total	100	100	0		$\chi^2 = 4.16$

Note that the computed value of χ^2 would have been zero if the observed frequencies were identical with the expected frequencies. As the differences increase, χ^2 becomes larger. Thus, if each of our observed frequencies had differed from its expected value by 6, χ^2 would have been equal to 9.38.

We have calculated a value of χ^2 for our example; now we must evaluate its significance. Since our observed frequencies differ from their expected values, χ^2 differs from zero. Our question is whether differences as great as these could be expected to occur as a result of sampling variation from a population with no association. We must determine the sampling distribution of χ^2 when $\boldsymbol{\chi}^2 = 0$.

The sampling distribution of χ^2 depends on the number of degrees of freedom or independent differences that enter into the computation. A difference may be considered to be independent if its expected frequency can be arbitrarily set. In setting our expected frequencies in the preceding problem, we were constrained by the restriction that they had to total to 100 students, 60 males and 40 females, 80 passing and 20 failing. Therefore, as soon as we set one expected frequency in any cell all the other values were fixed. Let us label the cells as in Table 18.5.

When we give cell (*a*) the value of, say, 50, cell (*b*) must be 10, since (*a*) + (*b*) must total to 60. And cell (*c*) must be 30, since (*a*) + (*c*) must

Table 18.5

Sex	Final Grade Passing	Failing	Total
Males	(*a*)	(*b*)	60
Females	(*c*)	(*d*)	40
Total	80	20	100

equal 80. Cell (*d*) then must be 10, since (*c*) + (*d*) must equal 40 and (*b*) + (*d*) must equal 20. No matter where we begin or how we set its value, only one of these cells may be freely established. All the others are then determined. In our example, then, we have one degree of freedom (df = 1).

Now we are ready to evaluate the significance of our computed value of χ^2. This may be done simply by comparing our calculated value with those listed in Table D. Since this problem has one degree of freedom, however, we are faced with an additional problem. The table of χ^2 is constructed in such a manner that tabulated values are only approximations of the values we calculate. These approximations are close enough—they introduce no serious bias—except for one degree of freedom. Therefore, whenever χ^2 is computed with one degree of freedom, it is necessary to calculate an adjusted value of the statistic. This adjustment is called Yates' correction; it consists of changing each of the observed frequencies in the direction of the expected frequency by .5. If we apply this correction to this case, we must recompute χ^2 (Table 18.6).

Table 18.6

Cell	f_o	f_e	Adjusted f_e	$(f_o - \text{adj.} f_e)$	$(f_o - \text{adj.} f_e)^2$	$(f_o - \text{adj.} f_e)^2/\text{adj.} f_e$
Boys passing	52	48	48.5	3.5	12.25	.29
Boys failing	8	12	11.5	−3.5	12.25	1.07
Girls passing	28	32	31.5	−3.5	12.25	.39
Girls failing	12	8	8.5	3.5	12.25	1.44
Total	100	100	100.0	0		$\chi^2 = 3.19$

So, in this case our adjusted value of χ^2 is equal to 3.19 and df = 1. We can enter the χ^2 table and test the hypothesis that $\boldsymbol{\chi}^2 = 0$. Let $\alpha = .05$. According to Table D, with one degree of freedom, it is necessary that χ^2

be greater than or equal to 3.84 in order to reject the hypothesis of no association. Our computed value of χ^2 is 3.19, so it falls below the 5% level of significance. Divergences as great as or greater than these would occur by chance more than five in every 100 samples. Therefore we cannot reject our null hypothesis; hence we must conclude that we have insufficient evidence to generalize the observed association between sex and final grade to the population.

Procedure. We have already seen that with one degree of freedom it is necessary to compute a corrected value of χ^2. Furthermore, a simplified formula may be used in all cases of four cell—one degree of freedom—tables. Hence, we shall examine separately procedures for computing χ^2 with one and with more than one degree of freedom.

COMPUTING χ^2 WITH ONE DEGREE OF FREEDOM. All four cell or 2 × 2 contingency tables (like Table 18.5) have one degree of freedom. If we label the cells in the following way, a very short formula for χ^2 may be used.

a	b	$a + b$
c	d	$c + d$
$a + c$	$b + d$	N

Then

$$\chi_y^2 = \frac{N\left(|ad - bc| - \frac{N}{2}\right)^2}{(a + b)(c + d)(a + c)(b + d)} \tag{18.1}$$

The subscript y in this formula indicates that it incorporates Yates' correction for one degree of freedom. And the vertical lines | | around the difference, $ad - bc$, indicate that this difference is to be taken without regard to its sign.

By way of illustration we shall apply this formula to the data of our earlier example (Table 18.7).

$$\begin{aligned}\chi_y^2 &= \frac{N\left(|ad - bc| - \frac{N}{2}\right)^2}{(a + b)(c + d)(a + c)(b + d)} \\ &= \frac{100\left(|624 - 224| - \frac{100}{2}\right)^2}{(60)(40)(80)(20)} \\ &= \frac{12{,}250{,}000}{3{,}840{,}000} \\ &= 3.19\end{aligned}$$

Table 18.7

Sex	Final Grade		
	Passing	Failing	Total
M	52_a	8_b	60_{a+b}
F	28_c	12_d	40_{c+d}
Total	80_{a+c}	20_{b+d}	100_N

Example

Gould has made a study of medical practices in a village in North India.[1] He collected information on illnesses and on the types of therapy undertaken to deal with them. He discovered that a clear distinction is made between "village medicine" and "doctor medicine." The former is a complex of common sense and supernatural ritual, the traditional folk medicine of village India. And the latter is the therapy offered by the physicians in a modern medical unit nearby. Either kind of service is available to any villager who is ill. But Gould hypothesized that members of the various castes differ in their tendency to utilize the services of the modern medical unit. He collected data on 30 cases of illness in order to test this hypothesis. These data are reported in Table 18.8.

Table 18.8. *Therapy Utilized for Reported Illnesses in Relation to Socioeconomic Status of Castes*

Caste Status	"Village Medicine"	"Doctor Medicine"	Total
Upper Castes	7	10	17
Lower Castes	10	3	13
Total	17	13	30

1. *Hypothesis.* H_1: There is a relationship between caste status and type of therapy utilized for illness.

2. *Null Hypothesis.* H_0: There is no association between caste status and type of therapy employed.

3. *Test.* The χ_y^2 test may be employed; this is a problem with a set of independent frequencies and one degree of freedom, and no expected frequencies are below five.

[1] Harold A. Gould, "The Implications of Technological Change for Folk and Scientific Medicine," *American Anthropologist*, **59** (June, 1957), 507–516.

4. *Significance Level.* Let $\alpha = .05$.

5. *Sampling Distribution.* χ_y^2 as computed from Formula 18.1 approximates the distribution listed in Table D with df = 1.

6. *Rejection Region.* The region of rejection consists of all values of χ^2 which are so large that the probability associated with their occurrence under the null hypothesis is equal to or less than 5 in 100. Table D shows that when df = 1, a χ^2 of 3.84 or larger will occur no more than 5 times in 100 as a result of sampling variation. Hence we shall reject the null hypothesis if χ^2 is equal to or greater than 3.84.

$$\begin{aligned}\chi_y^2 &= \frac{N(|ad - bc| - N/2)^2}{(a + b)(c + d)(a + c)(b + d)} \\ &= \frac{30(|21 - 100| - 30/2)^2}{(17)(13)(17)(13)} \\ &= \frac{30(79 - 15)^2}{48{,}841} \\ &= \frac{122{,}880}{48{,}841} \\ &= 2.52\end{aligned}$$

Our computed value of χ^2 is less than the critical value of 3.84, so association as great as this would result from sampling variation more than 5 times in every 100 samples. We cannot reject the null hypothesis; we must conclude that we have been unable to demonstrate any association between caste status and type of therapy employed in the population from which Gould's sample was drawn.

COMPUTING χ^2 WITH MORE THAN ONE DEGREE OF FREEDOM. In order to compute χ^2 for larger tables, problems with more than one degree of freedom, we must go back to our general formula. Thus

$$\chi^2 = \sum \frac{(f_o - f_e)^2}{f_e} \tag{18.2}$$

where f_o = the observed frequency in a cell,
f_e = the corresponding expected frequency.

Unlike our formula for χ_y^2 this one provides no shortcut for introducing expected frequencies directly into the problem. It is necessary to compute them from the data.

It is not necessary, however, to go through the process of computing the relative proportions for each and every cell. Suppose we are interested in the relationship between two nominal scales. One we shall call X is distributed in three classes, and the other, Y, has two classes. They might be represented as in Table 18.9.

Table 18.9

		Variable X			
		X_1	X_2	X_3	Total
Variable Y	Y_1	(a)	(b)	(c)	$a+b+c$
	Y_2	(d)	(e)	(f)	$d+e+f$
	Total	$a+d$	$b+e$	$c+f$	N

If we begin with the marginal totals, we can establish the expected frequencies for each cell. The expected frequency for cell (a) in the table is determined by the following operation:

$$f_{e(a)} = \frac{(a+b+c)(a+d)}{N}$$

and cell (e)

$$f_{e(e)} = \frac{(d+e+f)(b+e)}{N}$$

After some expected frequencies have been calculated, the rest may, of course, be obtained by subtraction from the marginal totals.

In order to evaluate the departure of χ^2 from its expected value, it is again necessary to determine the appropriate number of degrees of freedom. In this case establishing one expected frequency does not fix the others. Suppose the marginal totals were as in Table 18.10.

Table 18.10

	X_1	X_2	X_3	Total
Y_1	(a)	(b)	(c)	150
Y_2	(d)	(e)	(f)	150
Total	100	100	100	300

If cell (a) were set at 50, cell (d) would have to be 50 since together they must total to 100, but cells (b), (c), (e), and (f) would still be free to vary without violating the requirement that the appropriate totals be reached. However, as soon as one more cell was filled, all the remaining values would be fixed. Only two cells may be arbitrarily filled and all the others are then determined. This problem, then, has two degrees of freedom.

A simple method of determining the degrees of freedom in χ^2 tests is to subtract one from the number of rows and multiply this difference by the number of columns minus one. This is shown by the following formula:

$$\text{df}\,\chi^2 = (R - 1)(C - 1) \tag{18.3}$$

where R = the number of rows in the table,
C = the number of columns.

Example

Roe has reported a series of studies in which she attempted to uncover some of the factors underlying success in science. In one of these studies she was concerned with the degree to which various ways of thinking characterize scientists in various fields.[1] Forty-one eminent scientists in the fields of physics, biology, psychology, and anthropology were studied. Each of these subjects was asked a series of questions concerning the form of his thoughts. Their responses were roughly classified into one of two types: (1) visual—these scientists tend to organize their thoughts in terms of pictures, diagrams, images, and models and (2) verbal—these scientists organize their thoughts in terms of words, and frequently describe themselves as talking to themselves.

Roe had the hypothesis that there might be some relationship between a man's field of study and the type of imagery he employed. Her data are summarized in Table 18.11.

Table 18.11. *Type of Imagery Exhibited by Scientists Specializing in Various Fields*

	Imagery		
Field of Study	Verbal	Visual	Total
Biology	4	10	14
Physics	4	10	14
Psychology and anthropology	11	2	13
Total	19	22	41

Note that Roe combined the categories of psychology and anthropology. This was done in order to avoid small expected frequencies in these cells. This combination would seem justified since members of both these

[1] Anne Roe, "A Study of Imagery in Research Scientists," *Journal of Personality*, **19** (June, 1951), 459–470.

categories are social rather than natural scientists; they could be expected to be similar. In general, combining categories in order to avoid expected frequencies below 5 is acceptable if there is some rationale for the combination made. *In no case may categories be combined in order to maximize or minimize* χ^2.

1. *Hypothesis.* H_1: Roe has provided the general hypothesis that field of study and mode of imagery are related.

2. *Null Hypothesis.* H_0: There is no association between field of scientific specialization and type of imagery.

3. *Test.* The χ^2 test may be employed; this is a problem involving a set of independent frequencies, more than one degree of freedom, and no expected frequencies below 5.

4. *Significance Level.* Let $\alpha = .05$.

5. *Sampling Distribution.* χ^2 as computed from Formula 18.2 approximates the distribution listed in Table D with df $= (R - 1)(C - 1) = (3 - 1)(2 - 1) = 2$.

6. *Rejection Region.* The region of rejection consists of all values of χ^2 which are so large that the probability associated with their occurrence under the null hypothesis is equal to or less than 5 in 100. Table D shows that when df $= 2$, a χ^2 of 5.99 or larger will occur 5 times in 100 as a result of sampling variation in a population where no association is present. We shall therefore reject the null hypothesis if χ^2 is equal to or greater than 5.99.

7. *Decision.* Table 18.11 shows the results of Roe's research. We must first compute our expected frequencies for that table; then we can proceed to calculate χ^2.

$$f_{e(a)} = \frac{(a + b)(a + c + e)}{N} = \frac{(14)(19)}{41} = 6.49$$

$$f_{e(b)} = \frac{(a + b)(b + d + f)}{N} = \frac{(14)(22)}{41} = 7.51$$

$$f_{e(c)} = \frac{(c + d)(a + c + e)}{N} = \frac{(14)(19)}{41} = 6.49$$

$$f_{e(d)} = \frac{(c + d)(b + d + f)}{N} = \frac{(14)(22)}{41} = 7.51$$

$$f_{e(e)} = \frac{(e + f)(a + c + e)}{N} = \frac{(13)(19)}{41} = 6.02$$

$$f_{e(f)} = \frac{(e + f)(b + d + f)}{N} = \frac{(13)(22)}{41} = 6.98$$

Now we may proceed to compute χ^2.

$$\chi^2 = \sum \frac{(f_o - f_e)^2}{f_e}$$

Cell	f_o	f_e	$f_o - f_e$	$(f_o - f_e)^2$	$(f_o - f_e)^2/f_e$
a	4	6.49	−2.49	6.20	.96
b	10	7.51	2.49	6.20	.82
c	4	6.49	−2.49	6.20	.96
d	10	7.51	2.49	6.20	.82
e	11	6.02	4.98	24.80	4.12
f	2	6.98	−4.98	24.80	3.55
Total	41	41	0		$\chi^2 = 11.23$

Our observed value of χ^2 then is 11.23. Since this value is larger than the 5.99 shown in Table D, we can reject the null hypothesis. Our conclusion must be that we should hardly expect to observe as much association between field of study and type of imagery as we have if there were no association in the population. We can therefore use these data as evidence for the presence of such association.

Summary of Procedure. The following steps must be performed in applying χ^2 to test the hypothesis of no association.

1. Place the observed frequencies in an $R \times C$ contingency table.
2. Determine the number of degrees of freedom (df).
3. If there is one degree of freedom, compute $\chi_y{}^2$ using Formula 18.1.
4. If there is more than one degree of freedom, determine the expected frequency for each cell and compute χ^2 using Formula 18.2.
5. Determine the significance of the computed χ^2 by reference to Table D. If χ^2 is equal to or greater than the tabulated value for the appropriate df and α, reject H_0.

Other Statistics. We have seen that χ^2 can be used only when the expected frequency in any cell is greater than 5. If we are dealing with a set of variables distributed in more than two classes, we can sometimes collapse two or more categories in order to raise our expected frequencies. However, in the case of a 2×2 table there is no way to collapse categories even when we have an expected value of less than 5. In view of this limitation, we sometimes need other statistics that can be used to test hypotheses when our expected frequencies are small. Then, too, certain other statistics are sometimes used to test hypotheses in conditions where χ^2 might be employed. A discussion of several of these statistics follows.

FISHER'S EXACT PROBABILITY TEST. This is a test which places no restriction on the minimum size of expected frequencies. It may be employed in all one degree of freedom problems where expected frequencies are small. This test is discussed in Siegel (1956) and Walker and Lev (1953).

STANDARD ERROR OF YULE'S Q. Here we must compute Q, a coefficient of association in a 2×2 table, before we can test our hypothesis. This statistic therefore may be used only in problems with one degree of freedom. The standard error of Q is discussed in Moroney (1953).

STANDARD ERROR OF YULE'S Y. The standard error of Y involves the same restriction as the standard error of Q discussed above. This statistic is described by Moroney (1953).

Postscript

Now that you have completed this book, it is hoped that you have a general overview of the field of statistics. You know what statistics is up to—as a field—and you have learned some of the basic thinking which underlies the application of statistics to research in behavioral science.

All this may leave you with the question, "Where do I go from here?" You are not, on the basis of this book, prepared to "do statistics." But you do know enough to do some reading and learn some more. A great many special techniques have been left out entirely—tests for other hypotheses, alternative measures of association, and the like. Then, too, your exposure to the principles of both sampling and estimation has been slight. However, you are now prepared to read in these areas; you should have no trouble with Parten (1950) for sampling or Walker and Lev (1953) or Hagood and Price (1952) for estimation. By now you certainly are not afraid, so go to it.

Most important, however, this introduction has not even touched on the problems of multivariate analysis—analysis of variables taken more than two at a time. But since the principles are the same as those for one and two variable analysis, you are ready to explore these areas. You can study multiple and partial correlation, factor analysis, and multiple classification analysis of variance. Try any of the books on these topics in the following list, and chances are you will be enthusiastic too.

1. Blalock (1960)
2. Cattell (1952)
3. Edwards (1958)
4. Ezekiel and Fox (1959)
5. McNemar (1955)
6. Peters and Van Voorhis (1940)
7. Siegel (1956)
8. Snedecor (1956)
9. Yule and Kendall (1958)

Bibliography

Blalock, Hubert M. (1960), *Social Statistics*, New York: McGraw-Hill Book Company.

Cattell, Raymond B. (1952), *Factor Analysis: An Introduction and Manual for the Psychologist and Social Scientist*, New York: Harper and Brothers.

Croxton, Frederick E., and Dudley J. Cowden (1956), *Applied General Statistics*, Second edition, Englewood Cliffs, New Jersey: Prentice-Hall.

Cureton, Edward E. (n.d.), "Correlational Methods and Non-parametric Tests Based on Ranks," University of Tennessee (unpublished).

Dornbusch, Sanford M., and Calvin F. Schmid (1955), *A Primer of Social Statistics*, New York: McGraw-Hill Book Company.

Edwards, Allen (1958), *Experimental Design*, New York: Rinehart and Company.

Ezekiel, Mordecai, and Karl A. Fox (1959), *Methods of Correlation and Regression*, Third edition, New York: John Wiley and Sons.

Freeman, Linton, and Douglas M. More (1956), "Teaching Introductory Statistics in the Liberal Arts Curriculum," *The American Statistician*, **10**, pp. 20–22.

Garret, Henry E. (1947), *Statistics in Psychology and Education*, New York: Longmans, Green.

Goodman, Leo, and William Kruskall (1954), "Measures of Association for Cross Classifications," *Journal of the American Statistical Association*, **49**, pp. 733–764.

Guttman, L. (1941), "The Quantification of a Class of Attributes: A Theory and Method of Scale Construction," in P. Horst et al., *The Prediction of Personal Adjustment*, New York: Bulletin No. 48, Social Science Research Council, pp. 319–348.

Hagood, Margaret Jarman, and Daniel O. Price (1952), *Statistics for Sociologists*, Revised edition, New York: Henry Holt and Co.

Huff, Darrell (1954), *How to Lie with Statistics*, New York: W. W. Norton and Company.

Kelley, T. L. (1947), *Fundamentals of Statistics*, Cambridge, Massachusetts: Harvard University Press.

Kendall, M. G. (1948), *Rank Correlation Methods*, London: Griffin.

McCormick, Thomas C. (1941), *Elementary Social Statistics*, New York: McGraw-Hill Book Company.

McNemar, Quinn (1955), *Psychological Statistics*, Second edition, New York: John Wiley and Sons.

Moroney, M. J. (1953), *Facts from Figures*, Baltimore: Penguin Books.

Mueller, John H. and Karl F. Schuessler (1961), *Statistical Reasoning in Sociology*, Boston: Houghton Mifflin Company.

Parten, Mildred (1950), *Surveys, Polls and Samples: Practical Procedures*, New York: Harper and Brothers.

Peatman, John Gray (1947), *Descriptive and Sampling Statistics*, New York: Harper and Brothers.

Peters, Charles C., and Walter R. Van Voorhis (1940), *Statistical Procedures and Their Mathematical Bases*, New York: McGraw-Hill Book Company.

Senders, Virginia L. (1958), *Measurement and Statistics*, New York: Oxford University Press.

Siegel, Sidney (1956), *Nonparametric Statistics for the Behavioral Sciences*, New York: McGraw-Hill Book Company.

Snedecor, G. W. (1956), *Statistical Methods Applied to Experiments in Agriculture and Biology*, Ames, Iowa: Collegiate Press.

Stevens, S. S. (1946, 1951), "Mathematics, Measurements, and Psychophysics," in S. S. Stevens, Ed., *Handbook of Experimental Psychology*, New York: John Wiley and Sons, pp. 1–49.

Tate, Merle W., and Richard C. Clelland (1957), *Non-parametric and Shortcut Statistics*, Danville, Illinois: Interstate Printers and Publishers.

Walker, Helen (1929), *Studies in the History of Statistical Method*, Baltimore: Williams and Wilkins.

Walker, Helen (1951), *Mathematics Essential for Elementary Statistics*, Second edition, New York: Henry Holt and Co.

Walker, Helen, and Joseph Lev (1953), *Statistical Inference*, New York: Henry Holt and Co.

Wallis, W. Allen, and Harry V. Roberts (1956), *Statistics, A New Approach*, Glencoe, Illinois: The Free Press.

Wert, James, Charles Neidt, and J. Stanley Ahmann (1954), *Statistical Methods in Educational and Psychological Research*, New York: Appleton-Century-Crofts.

Yule, G. Udney, and M. G. Kendall (1958), *An Introduction to the Theory of Statistics*, New York: Hafner Publishing Co.

Appendix A

Table of Statistical Symbols

Class and Symbol	Meaning
Variables	
X	Any variable
Y	Any other variable
Constants	
X_i	A score on the variable X in a given problem
Y_i	A score on the variable Y in a given problem
R	The number of rows in a given statistical table
C	The number of columns in a given statistical table
N	The number of cases or observations studied
A	An arbitary constant
α	The selected level of significance
Instructions—Operators	
$+, \sum$	Add
$-$	Subtract
$\times, \cdot, ()()$	Multiply
$\div, /, \text{——}$	Divide
$()^2$	Square
$\sqrt{\ }$	Extract the square root
Statistics—Results	
General	
f	Frequency
Proportion	Proportion
%	Percentage
Ratio	Ratio

Class and Symbol	Meaning
Averages	
Mode	Mode
Median	Median
$\bar{X}$	Mean
Indexes of Variation	
v	Variation ratio
d	Decile range
s^2	Variance
s	Standard deviation
Measures of Association	
λ	Guttman's coefficient of association
G	Goodman and Kruskal's coefficient of rank association
r	Pearson's correlation coefficient
θ	Coefficient of nominal-ordinal association
η	Correlation ratio
M	Coefficient of multiserial correlation
Statistics used in Testing Significance	
χ^2	Chi-square
S	Test for Goodman and Kruskal's coefficient of rank correlation
r	Pearson's coefficient of correlation
U	Wilcoxon-Mann-Whitney U-test
F	Fisher's analysis of variance
Equality and Inequality	
$=$	Is equal to
$>$	Is greater than
$<$	Is less than
$\geqslant$	Is greater than or equal to
$\leqslant$	Is less than or equal to

Appendix B

Statistical Tables

Table A. *Square Roots of Numbers* 1–1000

Number	Square Root	Number	Square Root
1	1.0000	31	5.5678
2	1.4142	32	5.6569
3	1.7321	33	5.7446
4	2.0000	34	5.8310
5	2.2361	35	5.9161
6	2.4495	36	6.0000
7	2.6458	37	6.0828
8	2.8284	38	6.1644
9	3.0000	39	6.2450
10	3.1623	40	6.3246
11	3.3166	41	6.4031
12	3.4641	42	6.4807
13	3.6056	43	6.5574
14	3.7417	44	6.6332
15	3.8730	45	6.7082
16	4.0000	46	6.7823
17	4.1231	47	6.8557
18	4.2426	48	6.9282
19	4.3589	49	7.0000
20	4.4721	50	7.0711
21	4.5826	51	7.1414
22	4.6094	52	7.2111
23	4.7958	53	7.2081
24	4.8990	54	7.3485
25	5.0000	55	7.4162
26	5.0990	56	7.4833
27	5.1962	57	7.5498
28	5.2915	58	7.6158
29	5.3852	59	7.6811
30	5.4772	60	7.7460

Table A (*continued*)

Number	Square Root	Number	Square Root
61	7.8012	101	10.0499
62	7.8740	102	10.0995
63	7.9373	103	10.1489
64	8.0000	104	10.1980
65	8.0623	105	10.2470
66	8.1240	106	10.2956
67	8.1854	107	10.3441
68	8.2462	108	10.3923
69	8.3066	109	10.4403
70	8.3666	110	10.4881
71	8.4261	111	10.5357
72	8.4853	112	10.5830
73	8.5440	113	10.6301
74	8.6023	114	10.6771
75	8.6603	115	10.7238
76	8.7178	116	10.7703
77	8.7750	117	10.8167
78	8.8318	118	10.8628
79	8.8882	119	10.9087
80	8.9443	120	10.9545
81	9.0000	121	11.0000
82	9.0554	122	11.0454
83	9.1104	123	11.0905
84	9.1652	124	11.1355
85	9.2195	125	11.1803
86	9.2736	126	11.2250
87	9.3274	127	11.2694
88	9.3808	128	11.3137
89	9.4340	129	11.3578
90	9.4868	130	11.4018
91	9.5394	131	11.4455
92	9.5917	132	11.4891
93	9.6437	133	11.5326
94	9.6954	134	11.5758
95	9.7468	135	11.6190
96	9.7980	136	11.6619
97	9.8489	137	11.7047
98	9.8995	138	11.7473
99	9.9499	139	11.7898
100	10.0000	140	11.8322

Table A (*continued*)

Number	Square Root	Number	Square Root
141	11.8743	181	13.4536
142	11.9164	182	13.4907
143	11.9583	183	13.5277
144	12.0000	184	13.5647
145	12.0416	185	13.6051
146	12.0830	186	13.6382
147	12.1244	187	13.6748
148	12.1655	188	13.7113
149	12.2066	189	13.7477
150	12.2474	190	13.7840
151	12.2882	191	13.8203
152	12.3288	192	13.8564
153	12.3693	193	13.8924
154	12.4097	194	13.9284
155	12.4499	195	13.9642
156	12.4900	196	14.0000
157	12.5300	197	14.0357
158	12.5698	198	14.0712
159	12.6095	199	14.1067
160	12.6491	200	14.1421
161	12.6886	201	14.1774
162	12.7279	202	14.2127
163	12.7671	203	14.2478
164	12.8062	204	14.2829
165	12.8452	205	14.3178
166	12.8841	206	14.3527
167	12.9228	207	14.3875
168	12.9615	208	14.4222
169	13.0000	209	14.4568
170	13.0384	210	14.4914
171	13.0767	211	14.5258
172	13.1149	212	14.5602
173	13.1529	213	14.5945
174	13.1909	214	14.6287
175	13.2288	215	14.6629
176	13.2665	216	14.6969
177	13.3041	217	14.7309
178	13.3417	218	14.7648
179	13.3791	219	14.7986
180	13.4164	220	14.8324

Table A (*continued*)

Number	Square Root	Number	Square Root
221	14.8661	261	16.1555
222	14.8997	262	16.1864
223	14.9332	263	16.2173
224	14.9666	264	16.2481
225	15.0000	265	16.2788
226	15.0333	266	16.3095
227	15.0665	267	16.3401
228	15.0997	268	16.3707
229	15.1327	269	16.4012
230	15.1658	270	16.4317
231	15.1987	271	16.4621
232	15.2315	272	16.4924
233	15.2643	273	16.5227
234	15.2971	274	16.5529
235	15.3297	275	16.5831
236	15.3623	276	16.6132
237	15.3948	277	16.6433
238	15.4272	278	16.6733
239	15.4596	279	16.7033
240	15.4919	280	16.7332
241	15.5242	281	16.7361
242	15.5563	282	16.7929
243	15.5885	283	16.8226
244	15.6205	284	16.8523
245	15.6525	285	16.8819
246	15.6844	286	16.9115
247	15.7162	287	16.9411
248	15.7480	288	16.9706
249	15.7797	289	17.0000
250	15.8114	290	17.0294
251	15.8430	291	17.0587
252	15.8745	292	17.0880
253	15.9060	293	17.1172
254	15.9374	294	17.1464
255	15.9687	295	17.1756
256	16.0000	296	17.2047
257	16.0312	297	17.2337
258	16.0624	298	17.2627
259	16.0935	299	17.2916
260	16.1245	300	17.3205

Table A (*continued*)

Number	Square Root	Number	Square Root
301	17.3494	341	18.4662
302	17.3781	342	18.4932
303	17.4069	343	18.5203
304	17.4356	344	18.5472
305	17.4642	345	18.5742
306	17.4929	346	18.6011
307	17.5214	347	18.6279
308	17.5499	348	18.6548
309	17.5784	349	18.6815
310	17.6068	350	18.7083
311	17.6352	351	18.7350
312	17.6635	352	18.7617
313	17.6918	353	18.7883
314	17.7200	354	18.8149
315	17.7482	355	18.8414
316	17.7764	356	18.8680
317	17.8045	357	18.8944
318	17.8326	358	18.9209
319	17.8606	359	18.9473
320	17.8885	360	18.9737
321	17.9165	361	19.0000
322	17.9444	362	19.0263
323	17.9722	363	19.0526
324	18.0000	364	19.0788
325	18.0278	365	19.1050
326	18.0555	366	19.1311
327	18.0831	367	19.1572
328	18.1108	368	19.1883
329	18.1384	369	19.2094
330	18.1659	370	19.2354
331	18.1934	371	19.2614
332	18.2209	372	19.2873
333	18.2483	373	19.3132
334	18.2757	374	19.3391
335	18.3030	375	19.3649
336	18.3303	376	19.3907
337	18.3576	377	19.4165
338	18.3848	378	19.4422
339	18.4120	379	19.4679
340	18.4391	380	19.4936

Table A (*continued*)

Number	Square Root	Number	Square Root
381	19.5192	421	20.5183
382	19.5448	422	20.5426
383	19.5704	423	20.5670
384	19.5959	424	20.5913
385	19.6214	425	20.6155
386	19.6469	426	20.6398
387	19.6723	427	20.6640
388	19.6977	428	20.6882
389	19.7231	429	20.7123
390	19.7484	430	20.7364
391	19.7737	431	20.7605
392	19.7990	432	20.7846
393	19.8242	433	20.8087
394	19.8494	434	20.8327
395	19.8746	435	20.8567
396	19.8997	436	20.8806
397	19.9249	437	20.9045
398	19.9499	438	20.9284
399	19.9750	439	20.9523
400	20.0000	440	20.9762
401	20.0250	441	21.0000
402	20.0499	442	21.0238
403	20.0749	443	21.0476
404	20.0998	444	21.0713
405	20.1246	445	21.0950
406	20.1494	446	21.1187
407	20.1742	447	21.1424
408	20.1990	448	21.1660
409	20.2237	449	21.1896
410	20.2485	450	21.2132
411	20.2731	451	21.2368
412	20.2978	452	21.2603
413	20.3224	453	21.2838
414	20.3470	454	21.3073
415	20.3715	455	21.3307
416	20.3961	456	21.3542
417	20.4206	457	21.3776
418	20.4450	458	21.4009
419	20.4695	459	21.4243
420	20.4939	460	21.4476

Table A (*continued*)

Number	Square Root	Number	Square Root
461	21.4709	501	22.3830
462	21.4942	502	22.4054
463	21.5174	503	22.4277
464	21.5407	504	22.4499
465	21.5639	505	22.4722
466	21.5870	506	22.4944
467	21.6102	507	22.5167
468	21.6333	508	22.5389
469	21.6564	509	22.5610
470	21.6795	510	22.5832
471	21.7025	511	22.6053
472	21.7256	512	22.6274
473	21.7486	513	22.6495
474	21.7715	514	22.6716
475	21.7945	515	22.6936
476	21.8174	516	22.7156
477	21.8403	517	22.7376
478	21.8632	518	22.7596
479	21.8861	519	22.7816
480	21.9089	520	22.8035
481	21.9317	521	22.8254
482	21.9545	522	22.8473
483	21.9773	523	22.8692
484	22.0000	524	22.8910
485	22.0227	525	22.9129
486	22.0454	526	22.9347
487	22.0681	527	22.9565
488	22.0907	528	22.9783
489	22.1133	529	23.0000
490	22.1359	530	23.0217
491	22.1585	531	23.0434
492	22.1811	532	23.0651
493	22.2036	533	23.0868
494	22.2261	534	23.1084
495	22.2486	535	23.1301
496	22.2711	536	23.1517
497	22.2935	537	23.1733
498	22.3159	538	23.1948
499	22.3383	539	23.2164
500	22.3607	540	23.2379

Table A (*continued*)

Number	Square Root	Number	Square Root
541	23.2594	581	24.1039
542	23.2809	582	24.1247
543	23.3024	583	24.1454
544	23.3238	584	24.1661
545	23.3452	585	24.1868
546	23.3666	586	24.2074
547	23.3880	587	24.2281
548	23.4094	588	24.2487
549	23.4307	589	24.2693
550	23.4521	590	24.2899
551	23.4734	591	24.3105
552	23.4947	592	24.3311
553	23.5160	593	24.3516
554	23.5372	594	24.3721
555	23.5584	595	24.3926
556	23.5797	596	24.4131
557	23.6008	597	24.4336
558	23.6220	598	24.4540
559	23.6432	599	24.4745
560	23.6643	600	24.4949
561	23.6854	601	24.5153
562	23.7065	602	24.5357
563	23.7276	603	24.5561
564	23.7487	604	24.5764
565	23.7697	605	24.5967
566	23.7908	606	24.6171
567	23.8118	607	24.6374
568	23.8328	608	24.6577
569	23.8537	609	24.6779
570	23.8747	610	24.6982
571	23.8956	611	24.7184
572	23.9165	612	24.7385
573	23.9374	613	24.7588
574	23.9583	614	24.7790
575	23.9792	615	24.7992
576	24.0000	616	24.8193
577	24.0208	617	24.8395
578	24.0416	618	24.8596
579	24.0624	619	24.8797
580	24.0832	620	24.8998

Table A (*continued*)

Number	Square Root	Number	Square Root
621	24.9199	661	25.7099
622	24.9399	662	25.7294
623	24.9600	663	25.7488
624	24.9800	664	25.7682
625	25.0000	665	25.7876
626	25.0200	666	25.8070
627	25.0400	667	25.8263
628	25.0599	668	25.8457
629	25.0799	669	25.8650
630	25.0998	670	25.8844
631	25.1197	671	25.9037
632	25.1396	672	25.9230
633	25.1595	673	25.9422
634	25.1794	674	25.9615
635	25.1992	675	25.9808
636	25.2190	676	26.0000
637	25.2389	677	26.0192
638	25.2587	678	26.0384
639	25.2784	679	26.0576
640	25.2982	680	26.0768
641	25.3180	681	26.0960
642	25.3377	682	26.1151
643	25.3574	683	26.1343
644	25.3772	684	26.1534
645	25.3969	685	26.1725
646	25.4165	686	26.1916
647	25.4362	687	26.2107
648	25.4558	688	26.2298
649	25.4755	689	26.2488
650	25.4951	690	26.2679
651	25.5147	691	26.2869
652	25.5343	692	26.3059
653	25.5539	693	26.3249
654	25.5734	694	26.3439
655	25.5930	695	26.3629
656	25.6125	696	26.3818
657	25.6320	697	26.4008
658	25.6515	698	26.4197
659	25.6710	699	26.4386
660	25.6905	700	26.4575

Table A (*continued*)

Number	Square Root	Number	Square Root
701	26.4764	741	27.2213
702	26.4953	742	27.2397
703	26.5141	743	27.2580
704	26.5330	744	27.2764
705	26.5518	745	27.2947
706	26.5707	746	27.3130
707	26.5895	747	27.3313
708	26.6083	748	27.3496
709	26.6271	749	27.3679
710	26.6458	750	27.3861
711	26.6646	751	27.4044
712	26.6833	752	27.4226
713	26.7021	753	27.4408
714	26.7208	754	27.4591
715	26.7395	755	27.4773
716	26.7582	756	27.4955
717	26.7769	757	27.5136
718	26.7955	758	27.5318
719	26.8142	759	27.5500
720	26.8328	760	27.5681
721	26.8514	761	27.5862
722	26.8701	762	27.6043
723	26.8887	763	27.6225
724	26.9072	764	27.6405
725	26.9258	765	27.6586
726	26.9444	766	27.6767
727	26.9629	767	27.6948
728	26.9815	768	27.7128
729	27.0000	769	27.7308
730	27.0185	770	27.7489
731	27.0370	771	27.7669
732	27.0555	772	27.7849
733	27.0740	773	27.8029
734	27.0924	774	27.8209
735	27.1109	775	27.8388
736	27.1293	776	27.8568
737	27.1477	777	27.8747
738	27.1662	778	27.8927
739	27.1846	779	27.9106
740	27.2029	780	27.9285

Table A (*continued*)

Number	Square Root	Number	Square Root
781	27.9464	821	28.6531
782	27.9643	822	28.6705
783	27.9821	823	28.6880
784	28.0000	824	28.7054
785	28.0179	825	28.7228
786	28.0357	826	28.7402
787	28.0535	827	28.7576
788	28.0713	828	28.7750
789	28.0891	829	28.7924
790	28.1069	830	28.8097
791	28.1247	831	28.8271
792	28.1425	832	28.8444
793	28.1603	833	28.8617
794	28.1780	834	28.8791
795	28.1957	835	28.8964
796	28.2135	836	28.9137
797	28.2312	837	28.9310
798	28.2489	838	28.9482
799	28.2666	839	28.9655
800	28.2843	840	28.9828
801	28.3019	841	29.0000
802	28.3196	842	29.0172
803	28.3373	843	29.0345
804	28.3049	844	29.0517
805	28.3725	845	29.0689
806	28.3901	846	29.0861
807	28.4077	847	29.1033
808	28.4253	848	29.1204
809	28.4429	849	29.1376
810	28.4605	850	29.1548
811	28.4781	851	29.1719
812	28.4956	852	29.1890
813	28.5132	853	29.2062
814	28.5307	854	29.2233
815	28.5482	855	29.2404
816	28.5657	856	29.2575
817	28.5832	857	29.2746
818	28.6007	858	29.2916
819	28.6082	859	29.3087
820	28.6356	860	29.3258

Table A (*continued*)

Number	Square Root	Number	Square Root
861	29.3428	901	30.0167
862	29.3598	902	30.0333
863	29.3769	903	30.0500
864	29.3939	904	30.0666
865	29.4109	905	30.0832
866	29.4279	906	30.0998
867	29.4449	907	30.1164
868	29.4618	908	30.1330
869	29.4788	909	30.1496
870	29.4958	910	30.1662
871	29.5127	911	30.1828
872	29.5296	912	30.1993
873	29.5466	913	30.2159
874	29.5635	914	30.2324
875	29.5804	915	30.2490
876	29.5973	916	30.2655
877	29.6142	917	30.2820
878	29.6311	918	30.2985
879	29.6479	919	30.3150
880	29.6648	920	30.3315
881	29.6816	921	30.3480
882	29.6985	922	30.3645
883	29.7153	923	30.3809
884	29.7321	924	30.3974
885	29.7489	925	30.4138
886	29.7658	926	30.4302
887	29.7825	927	30.4467
888	29.7993	928	30.4631
889	29.8161	929	30.4795
890	29.8329	930	30.4959
891	29.8496	931	30.5123
892	29.8664	932	30.5287
893	29.8831	933	30.5450
894	29.8998	934	30.5614
895	29.9166	935	30.5778
896	29.9333	936	30.5941
897	29.9500	937	30.6105
898	29.9666	938	30.6268
899	29.9833	939	30.6431
900	30.0000	940	30.6594

Table A (*continued*)

Number	Square Root	Number	Square Root
941	30.6757	971	31.1609
942	30.6920	972	31.1769
943	30.7083	973	31.1929
944	30.7246	974	31.2090
945	30.7409	975	31.2250
946	30.7571	976	31.2410
947	30.7734	977	31.2570
948	30.7896	978	31.2730
949	30.8058	979	31.2890
950	30.8221	980	31.3050
951	30.8383	981	31.3209
952	30.8545	982	31.3369
953	30.8707	983	31.3528
954	30.8869	984	31.3688
955	30.9031	985	31.3847
956	30.9192	986	31.4006
957	30.9354	987	31.4166
958	30.9516	988	31.4325
959	30.9677	989	31.4484
960	30.9839	990	31.4643
961	31.0000	991	31.4802
962	31.0161	992	31.4960
963	31.0322	993	31.5119
964	31.0483	994	31.5278
965	31.0644	995	31.5436
966	31.0805	996	31.5595
967	31.0966	997	31.5753
968	31.1127	998	31.5911
969	31.1288	999	31.6070
970	31.1448	1000	31.6228

Table B. *Areas of the Normal Curve*

	Area from $\bar{X}$ to z	Area in the larger portion	Area in the smaller portion
	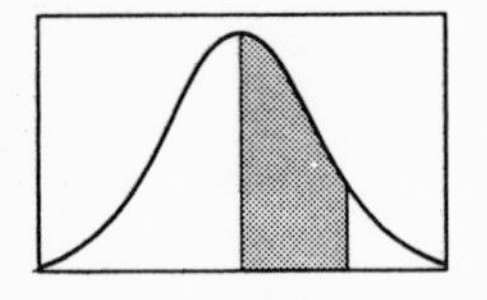	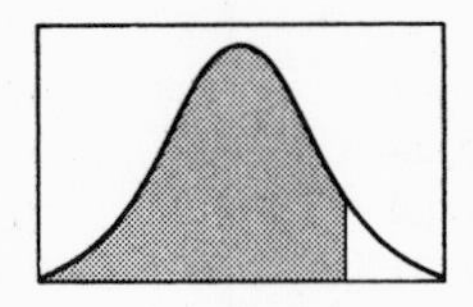	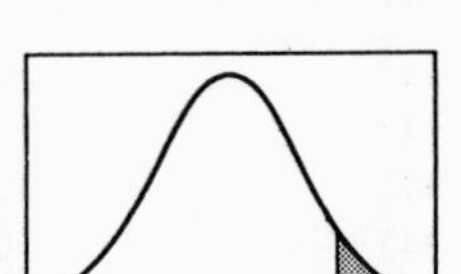
z			
0.0	.0000	.5000	.5000
0.1	.0398	.5398	.4602
0.2	.0793	.5793	.4207
0.3	.1179	.6179	.3821
0.4	.1554	.6554	.3446
0.5	.1915	.6915	.3085
0.6	.2257	.7257	.2743
0.7	.2580	.7580	.2420
0.8	.2881	.7881	.2119
0.9	.3159	.8159	.1841
1.0	.3413	.8413	.1587
1.1	.3643	.8643	.1357
1.2	.3849	.8849	.1151
1.3	.4032	.9032	.0968
1.4	.4192	.9192	.0808
1.5	.4332	.9332	.0668
1.6	.4452	.9452	.0548
1.7	.4554	.9554	.0446
1.8	.4641	.9641	.0359
1.9	.4713	.9713	.0287
2.0	.4772	.9772	.0228
2.1	.4821	.9821	.0179
2.2	.4861	.9861	.0139
2.3	.4893	.9893	.0107
2.4	.4918	.9918	.00820
2.5	.4938	.9938	.00621
2.6	.4953	.9953	.00466
2.7	.4965	.9965	.00347
2.8	.4974	.9974	.00256
2.9	.4981	.9981	.00187
3.0	.49865	.99865	.00135

Table C. Deviates and Ordinates of the Unit Normal Distribution

Proportion in the Tail of the Distribution	Deviate z	Ordinate o	Proportion in the Tail of the Distribution	Deviate z	Ordinate o
.500	0.0000	.3989	.295	0.5388	.3450
.495	0.0125	.3989	.290	0.5534	.3423
.490	0.0251	.3988	.285	0.5681	.3395
.485	0.0376	.3987	.280	0.5828	.3366
.480	0.0502	.3984	.275	0.5978	.3337
.475	0.0627	.3982	.270	0.6128	.3306
.470	0.0753	.3978	.265	0.6280	.3275
.465	0.0878	.3974	.260	0.6433	.3244
.460	0.1004	.3969	.255	0.6588	.3211
.455	0.1130	.3964	.250	0.6745	.3178
.450	0.1257	.3958	.245	0.6903	.3144
.445	0.1383	.3951	.240	0.7063	.3109
.440	0.1510	.3944	.235	0.7225	.3073
.435	0.1637	.3936	.230	0.7388	.3036
.430	0.1764	.3928	.225	0.7554	.2999
.425	0.1891	.3919	.220	0.7722	.2961
.420	0.2019	.3909	.215	0.7892	.2922
.415	0.2147	.3899	.210	0.8064	.2882
.410	0.2275	.3887	.205	0.8239	.2841
.405	0.2404	.3876	.200	0.8416	.2800
.400	0.2533	.3863	.195	0.8596	.2757
.395	0.2663	.3850	.190	0.8779	.2714
.390	0.2793	.3837	.185	0.8965	.2669
.385	0.2924	.3823	.180	0.9154	.2624
.380	0.3055	.3808	.175	0.9346	.2578
.375	0.3186	.3792	.170	0.9542	.2531
.370	0.3319	.3776	.165	0.9741	.2482
.365	0.3451	.3759	.160	0.9945	.2433
.360	0.3585	.3741	.155	1.0152	.2383
.355	0.3719	.3723	.150	1.0364	.2332
.350	0.3853	.3704	.145	1.0581	.2279
.345	0.3989	.3684	.140	1.0803	.2226
.340	0.4125	.3664	.135	1.1031	.2171
.335	0.4261	.3643	.130	1.1264	.2115
.330	0.4399	.3621	.125	1.1503	.2059
.325	0.4538	.3599	.120	1.1750	.2000
.320	0.4677	.3576	.115	1.2004	.1941
.315	0.4817	.3552	.110	1.2265	.1880
.310	0.4959	.3528	.105	1.2536	.1818
.305	0.5101	.3503	.100	1.2816	.1755
.300	0.5244	.3477	.095	1.3106	.1690

Table C (*continued*)

Proportion in the Tail of the Distribution	Deviate z	Ordinate o	Proportion in the Tail of the Distribution	Deviate z	Ordinate o
.090	1.3408	.1624	.045	1.6954	.0948
.085	1.3722	.1556	.040	1.7507	.0862
.080	1.4051	.1487	.035	1.8119	.0773
.075	1.4395	.1416	.030	1.8808	.0680
.070	1.4758	.1343	.025	1.9600	.0584
.065	1.5141	.1268	.020	2.0537	.0484
.060	1.5548	.1191	.015	2.1701	.0379
.055	1.5982	.1112	.010	2.3263	.0267
.050	1.6449	.1031	.005	2.5758	.0145

Table D. *Significant Values of* χ^2 *for Testing* H_0.

df	$\alpha = .05$	$\alpha = .01$	df	$\alpha = .05$	$\alpha = .01$
1	3.84	6.64	20	31.41	37.57
2	5.99	9.21			
3	7.82	11.34	21	32.67	38.93
4	9.49	13.28	22	33.92	40.29
5	11.07	15.09	23	35.17	41.64
			24	36.42	42.98
6	12.59	16.81	25	37.65	44.31
7	14.07	18.48			
8	15.51	20.09	26	38.88	45.64
9	16.92	21.07	27	40.11	46.96
10	18.31	23.21	28	41.34	48.28
			29	42.56	49.59
11	19.68	24.72	30	43.77	50.89
12	21.03	26.22			
13	22.36	27.69	40	55.76	63.69
14	23.68	29.14	50	67.50	76.15
15	25.00	30.58	60	78.08	88.38
			70	90.53	100.42
16	26.30	32.00	80	101.88	112.33
17	27.59	33.41			
18	28.87	34.80	90	113.14	124.12
19	30.14	36.19	100	124.34	135.81

Table E. *Significant Values of G for Testing* H_0.

	One-Tailed Test		Two-Tailed Test	
N	$\alpha = .01$	$\alpha = .05$	$\alpha = .01$	$\alpha = .05$
4			1.000	
5	1.000		0.800	1.000
6	0.867	1.000	0.733	0.867
7	0.714	0.905	0.619	0.810
8	0.643	0.786	0.571	0.714
9	0.556	0.722	0.500	0.667
10	0.511	0.644	0.467	0.600
11	0.491	0.600	0.418	0.564
12	0.455	0.576	0.394	0.545
13	0.436	0.564	0.359	0.513
14	0.407	0.516	0.363	0.473
15	0.390	0.505	0.333	0.467
16	0.383	0.483	0.317	0.433
17	0.368	0.471	0.309	0.426
18	0.346	0.451	0.294	0.412
19	0.333	0.439	0.287	0.392
20	0.326	0.421	0.274	0.379
21	0.314	0.410	0.267	0.371
22	0.307	0.394	0.264	0.359
23	0.296	0.391	0.257	0.352
24	0.290	0.377	0.246	0.341
25	0.287	0.367	0.240	0.333
26	0.280	0.360	0.237	0.329
27	0.271	0.356	0.231	0.322
28	0.265	0.344	0.228	0.312
29	0.261	0.340	0.222	0.310
30	0.255	0.333	0.218	0.301
31	0.252	0.325	0.213	0.295
32	0.246	0.323	0.210	0.290
33	0.242	0.314	0.205	0.288
34	0.237	0.312	0.201	0.280
35	0.234	0.304	0.197	0.277
36	0.232	0.302	0.194	0.273
37	0.228	0.297	0.192	0.267
38	0.223	0.292	0.189	0.263
39	0.220	0.287	0.188	0.260
40	0.218	0.285	0.185	0.256
z	1.960	2.576	1.812	2.326

Table F. *Significant Values of r for Testing H_0.*

	Two-Tailed Test		One-Tailed Test	
df	$\alpha = .05$	$\alpha = .01$	$\alpha = .05$	$\alpha = .01$
1	.997	.9999	.988	.9995
2	.950	.990	.900	.980
3	.878	.959	.805	.934
4	.811	.917	.729	.882
5	.754	.874	.669	.833
6	.707	.834	.622	.789
7	.666	.798	.582	.750
8	.632	.765	.549	.716
9	.602	.735	.521	.685
10	.576	.708	.497	.658
11	.553	.684	.476	.634
12	.532	.661	.458	.612
13	.514	.641	.441	.592
14	.497	.623	.426	.574
15	.482	.606	.412	.558
16	.468	.590	.400	.542
17	.456	.575	.389	.528
18	.444	.561	.378	.516
19	.433	.549	.369	.503
20	.423	.537	.360	.492
21	.413	.526	.352	.482
22	.404	.515	.344	.472
23	.396	.505	.337	.462
24	.388	.496	.330	.453
25	.381	.487	.323	.445
26	.374	.479	.317	.437
27	.367	.471	.311	.430
28	.361	.463	.306	.423
29	.355	.456	.301	.416
30	.349	.449	.296	.409
35	.325	.418	.275	.381
40	.304	.393	.257	.358
45	.288	.372	.243	.338
50	.273	.354	.231	.322
60	.250	.325	.211	.295
70	.232	.303	.195	.274
80	.217	.283	.183	.256
90	.205	.267	.173	.242
100	.195	.254	.164	.230

Table G. *Significant Values of U for Testing* H_0.

Two-Tailed Test, $\alpha = .05$

N_2

N_1	3	4	5	6	7	8	9	10	11	12	13	14	15	16	17	18	19	20
1	–	–	–	–	–	–	–	–	–	–	–	–	–	–	–	–	–	–
2	–	–	–	–	–	0	0	0	0	1	1	1	1	1	2	2	2	2
3	–	–	0	1	1	2	2	3	3	4	4	5	5	6	6	7	7	8
4		0	1	2	3	4	4	5	6	7	8	9	10	11	11	12	13	13
5			2	3	5	6	7	8	9	11	12	13	14	15	17	18	19	20
6				5	6	8	10	11	13	14	16	17	19	21	22	24	25	27
7					8	10	12	14	16	18	20	22	24	26	28	30	32	34
8						13	15	17	19	22	24	26	29	31	34	36	38	41
9							17	20	23	26	28	31	34	37	39	42	45	48
10								23	26	29	33	36	39	42	45	48	52	55
11									30	33	37	40	44	47	51	55	58	62
12										37	41	45	49	53	57	61	65	69
13											45	50	54	59	63	67	72	76
14												55	59	64	67	74	78	83
15													64	70	75	80	85	90
16														75	81	86	92	98
17															87	93	99	105
18																99	106	112
19																	113	119
20																		127

$z = 1.960$

Two-Tailed Test, $\alpha = .01$

N_2

N_1	3	4	5	6	7	8	9	10	11	12	13	14	15	16	17	18	19	20
1	–	–	–	–	–	–	–	–	–	–	–	–	–	–	–	–	–	–
2	–	–	–	–	–	–	–	–	–	–	–	–	–	–	–	–	0	0
3	–	–	–	–	–	–	0	0	0	1	1	1	2	2	2	2	3	3
4		–	–	0	0	1	1	2	2	3	4	4	5	5	6	6	7	8
5			0	1	2	3	3	4	5	6	7	7	8	9	10	11	12	13
6				2	3	4	5	6	7	9	10	11	12	13	15	16	17	18
7					4	6	7	9	10	12	13	15	16	18	19	21	22	24
8						8	10	12	14	16	18	19	21	23	25	27	29	31
9							11	13	16	18	20	22	24	27	29	31	33	36
10								16	18	21	24	26	29	31	34	37	39	42
11									21	24	27	30	33	36	39	42	45	48
12										27	31	34	37	41	44	47	51	54
13											34	38	42	45	49	53	56	60
14												42	46	50	54	58	63	67
15													51	55	60	64	69	73
16														60	65	70	74	79
17															70	75	81	86
18																81	87	92
19																	93	99
20																		105

$z = 2.576$

Table G (*continued*)

One-Tailed Test, $\alpha = .05$

N_2

N_1	3	4	5	6	7	8	9	10	11	12	13	14	15	16	17	18	19	20
1	–	–	–	–	–	–	–	–	–	–	–	–	–	–	–	–	0	0
2	–	–	0	0	0	1	1	1	1	2	2	2	3	3	3	4	4	4
3	0	0	1	2	2	3	3	4	5	5	6	7	7	8	9	9	10	11
4		1	2	3	4	5	6	7	8	9	10	11	12	14	15	16	17	18
5			4	5	6	8	9	11	12	13	15	16	18	19	20	22	23	25
6				7	8	10	12	14	16	17	19	21	23	25	26	28	30	32
7					11	13	15	17	19	21	24	26	28	30	33	35	37	39
8						15	18	20	23	26	28	31	33	36	39	41	44	47
9							21	24	27	30	33	36	39	42	45	48	51	54
10								27	31	34	37	41	44	48	51	55	58	62
11									34	38	42	46	50	54	57	61	65	69
12										42	47	51	55	60	64	68	72	77
13											51	56	61	65	70	75	80	84
14												61	66	71	77	82	87	92
15													72	77	83	88	94	100
16														83	89	95	101	107
17															96	102	109	115
18																109	116	123
19																	123	130
20																		138

$z = 1.812$

One-Tailed Test, $\alpha = .01$

N_2

N_1	3	4	5	6	7	8	9	10	11	12	13	14	15	16	17	18	19	20
1	–	–	–	–	–	–	–	–	–	–	–	–	–	–	–	–	–	–
2	–	–	–	–	–	–	–	–	–	–	0	0	0	0	0	0	1	1
3	–	–	–	–	0	0	1	1	1	2	2	2	3	3	4	4	4	5
4		–	0	1	1	2	3	3	4	5	5	6	7	7	8	9	9	10
5			1	2	3	4	5	6	7	8	9	10	11	12	13	14	15	16
6				3	4	6	7	8	9	11	12	13	15	16	18	19	20	22
7					6	8	9	11	12	14	16	17	19	21	23	24	26	28
8						10	11	13	15	17	20	22	24	26	28	30	32	34
9							14	16	18	21	23	26	28	31	33	36	38	40
10								19	22	24	27	30	33	36	38	41	44	47
11									25	28	31	34	37	41	44	47	50	53
12										31	35	38	42	46	49	53	56	60
13											39	43	47	51	55	59	63	67
14												47	51	56	60	65	69	73
15													56	61	66	70	75	80
16														66	71	76	82	87
17															77	82	88	93
18																88	94	100
19																	101	107
20																		114

$z = 2.326$

Table H. *Significant Values of F for Testing H_0.**

$\alpha = .05$

df_W \ df_B	1	2	3	4	5	6	8	12	24	∞
1	161.4	199.5	215.7	224.6	230.2	234.0	238.9	243.9	249.0	254.3
2	18.51	19.00	19.16	19.25	19.30	19.33	19.37	19.41	19.45	19.50
3	10.13	9.55	9.28	9.12	9.01	8.94	8.84	8.74	8.64	8.53
4	7.71	6.94	6.59	6.39	6.26	6.16	6.04	5.91	5.77	5.63
5	6.61	5.79	5.41	5.19	5.05	4.95	4.82	4.68	4.53	4.36
6	5.99	5.14	4.76	4.53	4.39	4.28	4.15	4.00	3.84	3.67
7	5.59	4.74	4.35	4.12	3.97	3.87	3.73	3.57	3.41	3.23
8	5.32	4.46	4.07	3.84	3.69	3.58	3.44	3.28	3.12	2.93
9	5.12	4.26	3.86	3.63	3.48	3.37	3.23	3.07	2.90	2.71
10	4.96	4.10	3.71	3.48	3.33	3.22	3.07	2.91	2.74	2.54
11	4.84	3.98	3.59	3.36	3.20	3.09	2.95	2.79	2.61	2.40
12	4.75	3.88	3.49	3.26	3.11	3.00	2.85	2.69	2.50	2.30
13	4.67	3.80	3.41	3.18	3.02	2.92	2.77	2.60	2.42	2.21
14	4.60	3.74	3.34	3.11	2.96	2.85	2.70	2.53	2.35	2.13
15	4.54	3.68	3.29	3.06	2.90	2.79	2.64	2.48	2.29	2.07
16	4.49	3.63	3.24	3.01	2.85	2.74	2.59	2.42	2.24	2.01
17	4.45	3.59	3.20	2.96	2.81	2.70	2.55	2.38	2.19	1.96
18	4.41	3.55	3.16	2.93	2.77	2.66	2.51	2.34	2.15	1.92
19	4.38	3.52	3.13	2.90	2.74	2.63	2.48	2.31	2.11	1.88
20	4.35	3.49	3.10	2.87	2.71	2.60	2.45	2.28	2.08	1.84
21	4.32	3.47	3.07	2.84	2.68	2.57	2.42	2.25	2.05	1.81
22	4.30	3.44	3.05	2.82	2.66	2.55	2.40	2.23	2.03	1.78
23	4.28	3.42	3.03	2.80	2.64	2.53	2.38	2.20	2.00	1.76
24	4.26	3.40	3.01	2.78	2.62	2.51	2.36	2.18	1.98	1.73
25	4.24	3.38	2.99	2.76	2.60	2.49	2.34	2.16	1.96	1.71
26	4.22	3.37	2.98	2.74	2.59	2.47	2.32	2.15	1.95	1.69
27	4.21	3.35	2.96	2.73	2.57	2.46	2.30	2.13	1.93	1.67
28	4.20	3.34	2.95	2.71	2.56	2.44	2.29	2.12	1.91	1.65
29	4.18	3.33	2.93	2.70	2.54	2.43	2.28	2.10	1.90	1.64
30	4.17	3.32	2.92	2.69	2.53	2.42	2.27	2.09	1.89	1.62
40	4.08	3.23	2.84	2.61	2.45	2.34	2.18	2.00	1.79	1.51
60	4.00	3.15	2.76	2.52	2.37	2.25	2.10	1.92	1.70	1.39
120	3.92	3.07	2.68	2.45	2.29	2.17	2.02	1.83	1.61	1.25
∞	3.84	2.99	2.60	2.37	2.21	2.09	1.94	1.75	1.52	1.00

* This table is abridged from Table V of R. A. Fisher and F. Yates, *Statistical Tables for Biological, Agricultural, and Medical Research* (1948 ed.), published by Oliver & Boyd, Ltd., Edinburgh and London.

Table H (*continued*)

$\alpha = .01$

df_W \ df_B	1	2	3	4	5	6	8	12	24	∞
1	4052	4999	5403	5625	5764	5859	5981	6106	6234	6366
2	98.49	99.01	99.17	99.25	99.30	99.33	99.36	99.42	99.46	99.50
3	34.12	30.81	29.46	28.71	28.24	27.91	27.49	27.05	26.60	26.12
4	21.20	18.00	16.69	15.98	15.52	15.21	14.80	14.37	13.93	13.46
5	16.26	13.27	12.06	11.39	10.97	10.67	10.27	9.89	9.47	9.02
6	13.74	10.92	9.78	9.15	8.75	8.47	8.10	7.72	7.31	6.88
7	12.25	9.55	8.45	7.85	7.46	7.19	6.84	6.47	6.07	5.65
8	11.26	8.65	7.59	7.01	6.63	6.37	6.03	5.67	5.28	4.86
9	10.56	8.02	6.99	6.42	6.06	5.80	5.47	5.11	4.73	4.31
10	10.04	7.56	6.55	5.99	5.64	5.39	5.06	4.71	4.33	3.91
11	9.65	7.20	6.22	5.67	5.32	5.07	4.74	4.40	4.02	3.60
12	9.33	6.93	5.95	5.41	5.06	4.82	4.50	4.16	3.78	3.36
13	9.07	6.70	5.74	5.20	4.86	4.62	4.30	3.96	3.59	3.16
14	8.86	6.51	5.56	5.03	4.69	4.46	4.14	3.80	3.43	3.00
15	8.68	6.36	5.42	4.89	4.56	4.32	4.00	3.67	3.29	2.87
16	8.53	6.23	5.29	4.77	4.44	4.20	3.89	3.55	3.18	2.75
17	8.40	6.11	5.18	4.67	4.34	4.10	3.79	3.45	3.08	2.65
18	8.28	6.01	5.09	4.58	4.25	4.01	3.71	3.37	3.00	2.57
19	8.18	5.93	5.01	4.50	4.17	3.94	3.63	3.30	2.92	2.49
20	8.10	5.85	4.94	4.43	4.10	3.87	3.56	3.23	2.86	2.42
21	8.02	5.78	4.87	4.37	4.04	3.81	3.51	3.17	2.80	2.36
22	7.94	5.72	4.82	4.31	3.99	3.76	3.45	3.12	2.75	2.31
23	7.88	5.66	4.76	4.26	3.94	3.71	3.41	3.07	2.70	2.26
24	7.82	5.61	4.72	4.22	3.90	3.67	3.36	3.03	2.66	2.21
25	7.77	5.57	4.68	4.18	3.86	3.63	3.32	2.99	2.62	2.17
26	7.72	5.53	4.64	4.14	3.82	3.59	3.29	2.96	2.58	2.13
27	7.68	5.49	4.60	4.11	3.78	3.56	3.26	2.93	2.55	2.10
28	7.64	5.45	4.57	4.07	3.75	3.53	3.23	2.90	2.52	2.06
29	7.60	5.42	4.54	4.04	3.73	3.50	3.20	2.87	2.49	2.03
30	7.56	5.39	4.51	4.02	3.70	3.47	3.17	2.84	2.47	2.01
40	7.31	5.18	4.31	3.83	3.51	3.29	2.99	2.66	2.29	1.80
60	7.08	4.98	4.13	3.65	3.34	3.12	2.82	2.50	2.12	1.60
120	6.85	4.79	3.95	3.48	3.17	2.96	2.66	2.34	1.95	1.38
∞	6.64	4.60	3.78	3.32	3.02	2.80	2.51	2.18	1.79	1.00

Table I. *One Thousand Random Digits*

2	4	6	7	9	0	1	9	8	1
5	6	0	9	0	0	9	8	6	2
1	3	8	5	9	8	9	5	5	7
4	5	7	8	8	9	2	7	3	6
6	2	5	4	5	7	3	8	6	8
0	7	4	4	1	9	2	5	4	9
9	1	0	1	6	6	4	1	8	8
8	6	7	5	2	8	7	6	4	0
8	9	2	4	6	6	6	6	1	7
2	9	2	7	8	9	0	9	1	4

8	1	4	5	5	6	9	8	7	3
2	7	9	6	5	4	6	4	8	3
0	0	0	5	5	8	9	7	6	9
7	8	3	4	7	0	7	7	5	2
8	5	8	6	3	5	4	2	2	2
7	3	5	3	6	8	0	7	3	3
1	8	6	0	1	0	7	4	4	7
7	9	5	3	0	1	5	5	5	1
5	6	6	7	8	5	8	1	1	9
3	0	3	3	9	1	9	9	1	9

9	7	4	7	8	4	7	1	0	9
5	6	4	5	1	4	5	4	1	1
5	7	4	0	4	2	5	9	6	7
8	6	0	5	6	9	4	4	3	2
6	7	6	7	3	3	7	1	8	9
2	6	0	6	7	3	3	0	6	9
6	7	5	5	1	4	7	4	1	2
6	3	0	9	9	9	5	3	8	0
0	3	7	3	0	3	0	6	8	6
7	1	6	8	2	0	5	3	2	1

9	8	7	8	2	4	9	1	7	1
9	7	7	2	0	4	3	0	7	6
1	2	7	5	4	9	3	9	5	0
2	0	9	2	4	5	2	7	3	5
2	2	7	7	1	3	3	7	2	6
7	2	9	8	3	6	0	5	4	1
5	4	3	4	3	2	2	5	6	7
9	2	2	1	9	7	6	9	4	3
8	6	3	5	3	1	9	2	6	4
1	6	9	2	0	7	0	2	7	5

4	4	8	5	4	4	6	3	5	1
4	5	6	4	7	8	1	1	8	1
4	3	4	6	0	9	6	1	2	4
2	2	0	9	8	1	5	4	2	4
4	9	1	1	3	2	7	9	9	3
8	1	9	9	5	8	7	0	9	0
9	6	1	4	3	6	8	0	0	6
8	9	2	7	4	9	3	6	6	7
0	4	8	3	1	5	7	6	0	7
3	7	2	6	3	3	2	0	0	5

Table I (*continued*)

9	3	3	9	1	2	2	6	2	3
3	7	2	1	2	0	8	6	9	3
1	4	7	4	7	4	3	8	5	5
8	4	1	3	7	7	7	4	4	3
1	2	5	6	3	1	1	3	3	0
6	5	5	0	8	7	3	2	2	7
8	5	8	2	3	1	0	8	4	7
4	2	3	9	5	6	7	0	8	6
0	7	2	3	4	3	6	7	0	7
9	2	6	3	5	0	5	3	4	0
2	0	7	2	2	0	3	1	0	3
7	4	8	0	6	6	5	4	9	3
7	7	6	4	5	2	1	1	4	2
1	2	9	7	1	1	0	0	9	2
5	3	9	1	4	6	8	2	6	9
2	2	9	9	2	7	1	0	7	9
5	6	4	7	1	6	6	4	0	3
6	2	9	4	3	2	2	6	5	2
6	1	2	8	0	8	1	6	9	4
5	4	4	6	2	9	4	5	8	9
8	1	4	3	8	0	9	4	9	2
1	1	7	1	8	9	6	9	7	9
1	9	6	2	7	2	8	0	8	2
2	1	8	7	0	7	1	2	5	8
1	7	5	0	9	6	4	5	9	2
8	7	7	1	8	2	9	8	0	2
5	4	9	1	3	2	5	1	7	6
8	4	7	5	9	2	1	0	3	2
5	0	8	0	2	4	3	5	8	6
6	1	4	1	9	4	2	9	1	0
8	5	2	3	4	1	0	7	7	8
8	3	6	5	1	3	4	3	2	9
7	1	3	3	2	2	1	4	9	8
1	7	4	8	6	0	5	1	2	4
6	9	7	5	7	6	0	0	0	4
7	7	9	7	8	0	0	6	6	8
9	1	7	3	2	6	9	1	9	7
7	9	0	5	6	3	9	9	8	4
2	3	3	4	9	9	9	4	6	6
2	4	5	5	0	3	1	6	5	1
3	6	3	5	4	9	4	0	9	5
0	3	6	7	1	5	8	5	4	0
7	6	2	2	8	1	2	3	0	5
9	8	0	0	5	5	3	4	8	5
3	9	4	8	4	0	3	7	4	8
8	9	8	1	5	0	7	8	4	0
1	0	4	6	4	5	3	7	5	2
4	8	5	2	8	0	6	0	5	7
5	7	3	3	2	2	3	2	1	6
1	2	5	9	1	6	7	2	8	2

Appendix C

Data for Problems

This appendix contains data that were collected in the course of an actual research project.[1] They are included in this book in order to allow the student to practice thinking about statistical topics in the context of realistic problems. The problems and exercises associated with the chapters in this text call for analysis of these data. It is to be hoped, however, that interested students will find problems of their own that can be solved in terms of the materials presented here.

The data were collected by random sampling of the adult populations of three suburban communities (here called I, II, and III) in upstate New York in 1962. Data on 15 selected variables for each individual in each sample are included in this appendix. Individuals are identified by case number and the scale of each variable is assigned a code. These codes are listed.

Variable	Code Name	Scale	Code Categories
Case number	CASE	Arbitrary observation identification number	000–294
Age	AGE	Years, as of last birthday	00–99
Sex	SEX	Female	0
		Male	1
Education	EDUC	Years of school completed	00–17
Occupational Prestige	OCUP	Private household and laborers (except farm and mines)	0
		Farmers and farm laborers	1
		Operatives and service workers (except private household)	2

[1] They are printed here as a result of the generous cooperation of Warner Bloomberg, Jr., and Morris H. Sunshine. See their book, *Suburban Power Structures and Public Education*, Syracuse, New York: Syracuse Univ. Press, 1963.

Variable	Code Name	Scale	Code Categories
Occupational Prestige	OCUP	Craftsmen, foremen, and kindred workers	3
		Clerical and sales	4
		Professional, managerial, technical, proprietors (except farm)	5
Annual Income of Head of Household	INCO	Under $2999	0
		$3000–$4999	1
		$5000–$7499	2
		$7500–$9999	3
		$10,000–$19,999	4
		$20,000–$29,999	5
		$30,000–$49,999	6
		Over $50,000	7
Marital Status	MARTL	Single	0
		Married	1
		Separated	2
		Widowed	3
		Divorced	4
Religion	RELIG	Protestant	0
		Catholic	1
		Jewish	2
		None or other	3
Political Party Preference	POLIT	None or other	0
		Liberal	1
		Democrat	2
		Republican	3
Voting Behavior	VOTE	Response to the question, "Did you vote in the last presidential election?"	
		No	0
		Yes	1
Activity Index	ACTIV	Number of memberships in clubs and voluntary organizations	00–99
Children	CHLDN	Number of school-age children	0–9
Father's Education	FAED	Years of school completed by respondent's father	00–17
Father's Occupational Prestige	FOCUP	Private household and laborers (except farm and mines)	0

Variable	Code Name	Scale	Code Categories
Father's Occupational Prestige	FOCUP	Farmers and farm laborers	1
		Operatives and service workers (except private household)	2
		Craftsmen, foremen, and kindred workers	3
		Clerical and sales	4
		Professional, managerial, technical, proprietors (except farm)	5
Neighboring	NBR	Response to the question, "Would you say that this is (*a*) very much a neighboring area, (*b*) somewhat a neighboring area, or (*c*) not a neighboring area?"	
		Not	0
		Somewhat	1
		Very much	2
Visiting	VISIT	Response to the question, "How often do you visit with your neighbors?"	
		Never	0
		Perhaps a few times a year	1
		About once a month	2
		Less than four times a month	3
		At least once a week	4
		Every day	5

The codes on page 260 may be read in a straightforward manner. Females, for example, are coded "0" and males, "1" on SEX. To find the males, therefore, merely run down the column marked SEX in the Data Table and every "1" entry indicates a male. Similarly, if you find an entry of "3" under CHLDN this means that that family had 3 schoolage children at the time of the interview.

Since the data are authentic, you will not only have a chance to try out your statistical skills, but you may also learn a little about some suburban communities.

Data Table

Community I

CASE	AGE	SEX	EDUC	OCUP	INCO	MARTL	RELIG	POLIT	VOTE	ACTIV	CHLDN	FAED	FOCUP	NBR	VISIT
1	42	0	12	3	4	1	0	0	1	2	3	5	3	1	4
2	30	0	12		2	1	0	0	1	2	3	8	3	1	5
3	45	0	8		2	1	0	3	1	0	0	6	2	1	4
4	45	1	14	3	3	1	1	3	1	2	1	4	1	1	2
5	21	0	15		1	0	1	2	0	4	0	8	3	2	4
6	31	1	8	3	3	1	1	0	1	4	2	9	3	0	1
7	55	1	11	3	4	1	0	3	1	7	1	8	3	1	3
8	33	0	10		2	1	1	2	1	0	4		2	1	1
9	52	1	5	5	1	1	0	2	1	3	0		1	2	5
10	31	0	12	4	2	1	0	3	1	1	2	5	1	2	5
11	35	0	17		1	1	1	3	1	3	1	16	5	1	4
12	66	0	12		0	1	0	3	1	1	0	9	5	2	5
13	21	0	12	4	4	0	1	0	0	2	2	10	4	1	3
14	56	1	8	3	2	1	1	3	1	3	0		3	0	4
15	55	0	12	4	2	1	1	3	1	5	0	8	3	2	3
16	53	0	13	2	3	1	1	3	1	0	0	9	3	1	4
17	41	0	12		3	1	1	3	1	0	2	4	3	1	4
18	56	0	13	4	1	4	0	0	0	1	0	12	5	0	0
19	58	1	4	3	2	4	1	2	1	2	1	4	3	1	4
20	54	0	8	4	1	3	1	3	1	5	1	7	3	1	3

21	28	1	16	5	2	1	0	3	1	2	0	10	5	2	4
22	64	0	12		0	3	0	2	1	2	0	12	3	2	5
23	45	1	10	5	1	1	1	3	1	3	3	4	5	0	4
24	75	0	9		0	3	0	3	0		0		1	2	4
25	35	1	16	5	4	1	1	3	1	8	5	12	5	1	1
26	41	1	10	5	2	1	0	3	1	1	3	12	3	1	2
27	75	0	9		0	3	0	3	0	1	0	5	1	2	4
28	65	1	8	5	5	1	0	3	1	2	0		1	2	0
29	44	1	7	3	3	1	1	2	1	2	3	0	5	1	4
30	40	0	12		3	1	0	3	1	1	0	7	3	0	4
31	47	0	12	2	3	1	0	3	1	4	1	8	5	1	4
32	30	0	16		3	1	0	3	1	4	0	16	5	1	5
33	41	1	12	3	2	1	1	2	1	3	2		2	1	3
34	38	0	12	2	3	1	1	3	1	1	5		3	1	4
35	37	1	11	3	3	1	0	2	1	3	4	5	1	1	1
36	39	1	17	5	3	1	3	2	1	0	0	6	4	0	4
37	63	1	10	5	2	3	0	3	1	3	0		3	2	5
38	46	0	13		3	1	0	3	1	2	1	8	3	1	4
39	75	0	0		2	3	1	3	0	0	1		2	2	5
40	36	0	12		2	1	1	2	1	2	3	14	5	1	4
41	56	1	17	5	3	1	0	2	0	3	2	17	5	0	2
42	39	1	12	5	2	1	0	3	1	1	1	8	3	1	4
43	73	0	9		0	3	0	3	1	7	0		3	2	1
44	35	0	12	4	3	1	0	3	0	1	1		5	0	1
45	77	1	11	3	0	1	0	3	1	1	0		1	1	4
46	40	0	16	5	4	1	0	2	1	2	2	6	5	1	0
47	34	1	9	2	2	1	0	3	1	3	2	6	2	2	4
48	34	1	14	5	2	1	0	2	0	2	1	17	5	1	5
49	24	0	12		4	1	1	3	1	1	1	15	3	1	5
50	33	1	16	5	4	1	0	3	1	6	2	8	3	1	2

Community I

CASE	AGE	SEX	EDUC	OCUP	INCO	MARTL	RELIG	POLIT	VOTE	ACTIV	CHLDN	FAED	FOCUP	NBR	VISIT
51	49	0	16	5	4	1	0	3	1	5	1	10	5	1	4
52	53	1	12	5	4	1	1	2	1	3	1	12	2	1	3
53	37	0	9	3	2	1	1	0	1	4	1		0	2	5
54	37	0	12		2	1	0	2	1	3	2	6	3	1	4
55	33	0	12		4	1	0	0	0	2	2	8	0	0	4
56	43	1	12	2	1	1	1	2	1	2	0	5	2	2	5
57	39	1	14	5	4	1	0	2	0	4	3	8	1	1	5
58	37	0	12	4	3	1	1	2	1	1	4	8	3	1	5
59	22	0	16	5	3	0	1	2	1	3	1	8	3	1	5
60	25	0	13		2	1	1	0	1	2	1	12	3	2	5
61	36	1	10	3	3	1	0	0	0	2	3	6	3	1	0
62	37	1	12	5	2	1	1	2	1	1	1	7	3	0	4
63	43	1	8	3	3	1	0	3	1	1	1		3	0	1
64	28	0	13		3	1	1	3	1	2	2	8	2	1	4
65	50	1	14	5	3	1	0	3	1	3	1	14	5	1	4
66	40	1	10	3	2	1	1	2	1	5	4	5	3	1	2
67	36	1	12	5	3	1	1	3	1	6	4	12	2	1	4
68	26	0	12		2	1	0	3	1	0	0		3	2	4
69	27	0	13		2	1	1	3	1	2	0	12	5	1	5
70	33	1	17	5	4	1	1	3	1	6	2	9	2	2	4
71	37	0	11		2	1	0	3	1	3	1	4	1	2	5
72	41	0	12	4	4	1	0	3	1	2	0	8	2	1	1
73	35	1	7	2	1	1	0	2	0	0	3		1	1	0
74	61	1	12	3	2	1	0	3	1	1	0		1	1	5
75	48	1	9	3	1	1	1	2	0	1	1	5	3	2	4

76	28	1	15	5	4	1	0	2	1	1	0	14	3	2	4
77	21	1	15		4	0	0	0	0	3	1	12	5	2	4
78	60	1	14	5	4	1	1	3	1	1	0		5	1	4
79	49	1	13	3	3	1	1	2	1	6	2	12	3	1	5
80	25	0	12		2	1	1	0	0	0	0	14	4	1	4
81	37	1	16	5	3	1	1	0	1	4	0	6	3	2	4
82	57	0	16	5	1	3	0	3	1	2	0	6	1	1	4
83	49	0	16	5	3	1	0	3	1	4	0	6	1	2	5
84	39	1	8	3	1	1	1	2	1	2	0	1	2	1	2
85	67	0	8	4	1	3	0	3	1	3	1	8	1	2	4
86	43	0	8	0	2	1	0	2	1	0	0		3	2	4
87	58	1	8	3	4	4	0	3	1	2	0		0	1	5
88	46	0	11	3	1	1	0	3	1	2	0	4	3	1	2
89	33	1	10	3	3	1	1	2	1	3	3	0	3	2	4
90	33	1	12	3	4	1	0	3	1	2	1	10	5	1	4
91	37	1	10	4	2	1	1	2	1	4	1	6	4	1	3
92	42	0	17	5	2	3	0	3	1	6	2	6	1	1	2
93	39	0	10		1	1	1	3	1	1	0	9	2	0	4
94	47	0	16	5	3	1	0	1	1	4	0	3	3	0	4
95	29	0	7		2	1	0	2	0	1	0	8	3	0	0
96	44	1	10	3	3	1	0	0	1	2	1	12	2	2	4
97	45	0	9	2	2	1	1	2	1	8	1			0	4
98	45	0	12	5	3	1	1	3	1	2	0	8	5	1	4
99	38	0	14	5	1	1	0	2	1	2	0	8	1	1	4
100	44	0	17	5	4	1	0	3	1	4	0	6	1	2	1
101	37	1	15	5	3	1	0	3	1	3	0	11	3	0	3
102	32	0	14		4	1	0	3	1	3	1	12	5	1	5
103	33	0	14		3	1	1	0	1	6	2	14	4	1	4
104	28	0	16	4	4	1	0	3	1	3	0	16	1	2	3
105	25	0	12		4	1	1	3	1	3	0	10	5	1	5

Community I

CASE	AGE	SEX	EDUC	OCUP	INCO	MARTL	RELIG	POLIT	VOTE	ACTIV	CHLDN	FAED	FOCUP	NBR	VISIT
106	34	0	12		2	1	1	3	1	4	2	12	5	2	5
107	41	0	14		3	1	1	3	1	7	2	14	3	2	5
108	39	1	8	3	2	1	1	2	1	2	9	8	0	1	4
109	30	1	14	5	3	1	0	3	1	1	0	12	3	1	4
110	44	1	8	3	3	1	0	3	1	2	0	8	1	1	4
111	59	0	9		1	4	0	3	1	3	0	12	5	0	4
112	33	1	16	5	4	1	1	3	1	4	0	8	3	0	3
113	32	1	17	5	2	1	0	3	1	9	0	17	5	2	5
114	71	0	8		1	1	0	3	1	1	0	6	3	1	1
115	29	1	10	2	2	1	0	3	1	3	2	12	3	1	4
116	59	1	6		0	1	0	0	0	0	3	3	0	1	4
117	25	1	13	3	4	0	1	2	1	2	1	5	3	2	3

Community II

CASE	AGE	SEX	EDUC	OCUP	INCO	MARTL	RELIG	POLIT	VOTE	ACTIV	CHLDN	FAED	FOCUP	NBR	VISIT
118	32	0	15	5	2	1	0	3	1	1	2	6	5	2	4
119	48	0	12	3	2	3	0	2	1	1	0	5	5	1	4
120	68	1	10	1	0	1	0	3	1	1	0		1	2	2
121	83	0	10	2	0	0	0	2	1	1	0		3	2	1
122	60	0	11	1	6	1	0	3	1	2	0		3	2	4
123	29	0	14	5	1	1	1	2	1	3	3	17	5	0	3
124	68	1	12	5	1	1	0	3	1	5	0	12	5	1	2
125	56	0	16			1	0	3	1	0	0	17	5	0	1
126	54	0	12	5	2	1	0	3	1	0	0	0	1	1	4
127	22	0	9		2	1	1	0	1	0	1	8	5	1	5
128	72	1	16	1	1	1	0	3	1	0	0	10	5	0	1
129	25	0	12		0	1	0	3	1	2	0		3	1	5
130	58	0	9		1	1	0	3	1	3	1	8	3	0	1
131	48	0	8	2	0	1	0	2	1	1	0		3	1	0
132	43	0	15	5	3	1	0	3	1	5	2	11	3	1	4
133	23	0	11		2	1	0	3	1	1	0	8	1	2	4
134	43	1	10	3	2	1	1	3	1	1	0		1	1	4
135	52	1	8	3	1	1	0	3	1	1	0		3	1	4
136	32	1	12	5	3	1	0	3	1	1	2	7	3	1	4
137	76	1	4	2	0	3	3	2	1	1	0	1	2	1	5
138	33	0	12		3	1	0	1	1	3	1	8	2	1	3
139	43	1	12	0	3	1	0	3	1	2	2	8	0	1	1
140	30	0	12	4	1	1	1	3	1	1	0	6	5	2	4
141	27	1	17	5	2	1	0	3	1	6	0	13	0	1	3
142	86	1	8		0	2	3	2	1	0	0		1	1	1

Community II

CASE	AGE	SEX	EDUC	OCUP	INCO	MARTL	RELIG	POLIT	VOTE	ACTIV	CHLDN	FAED	FOCUP	NBR	VISIT
143	49	0	12		2	1	0	3	1	3	0	10	0	1	5
144	44	1	11	5	2	1	0	2	1	3	1	8	0	2	4
145	42	1	12	3	2	1	1	2	1	1	1	8	3	2	5
146	50	1	12	5	4	1	0	2	1	0	0		1	1	4
147	30	0	8		2	1	0	0	1	1	1		3	2	5
148	44	0	10	4	4	1	1	3	1	2	0	4	0	2	5
149	64	1	6	0	1	1	0	3	1	1	0	5	1	0	1
150	28	1	17	5	3	1	0	3	1	2	0	13	1	2	2
151	44	1	8	3	2	1	0	2	1	1	5		0	0	1
152	26	0	9	2	2	1	1	3	0	0	0	6	2	1	4
153	19	1	11	2	1	1	0	3	0	2	0	15	5	1	3
154	51	1	10	0	2	1	0	3	1	3	2	8	1	1	3
155	40	0	16		2	4	0	0	1	6	4	17	5	2	4
156	36	1	12	5	3	1	1	2	1	3	0	8	2	0	2
157	38	0	12		2	1	0	2	1	1	4	16	5	1	4
158	66	0	12		4	1	1	2	1	1	0	8	1	1	4
159	56	0	9		2	1	1	2	1	2	0		0	0	3
160	71	0			0	3	0	3	1	0	0		1	0	0
161	34	0	11		3	1	0	3	1	1	5	8	0	1	5
162	59	1	8	5	4	1	0	3	1	6	0	12	3	2	4
163	27	0	10		2	1	0	3	1	0	0	12	3	0	0
164	29	0	12		1	1	1	2	0	0	0	8	3	2	4
165	30	0	12		2	1	0	3	0	0	0	8	1	2	5
166	45	1	12	5	2	1	1	3	1	2	2	12	4	2	3
167	36	0	11		2	1	0	3	1	5	1	9	4	1	0

168	64	1	9	2	2	1	0	0	0	1	0			2	0
169	39	1	12	5		0	1	3	1	1	0	6	0	1	4
170	36	0	12		2	1	0	3	1	1	4	12	5	1	4
171	66	1	12		1	2	0	3	1	0	1	5	1	1	5
172	43	1	12	1	4	1	0	0	0	1	3	7	1	2	4
173	56	0	13		0	3	0	2	0	0	0		5	2	5
174	58	1	11	3	2	1	1	2	1	2	1	8	4	1	2
175	35	0	9	4	0	2	0	0	1	0	3		1	1	5
176	63	1	9	5	2	1	3	3	1	1	0	17	5	1	1
177	41	1	10	0	3	1	0	3	1	0	3	12	0	2	5
178	82	0	13		0	3	0	3	1	3	0	12	1	1	1
179	45	1	9	4	2	1	1	0	1	4	2	8	0	2	5
180	43	1	11	3	3	1	0	2	1	0	0	8	0	0	0
181	23	0	12		1	1	3	2	0	0	0	7	2	1	4
182	27	0	13	3	1	2	1	2	0	0	1	12	3	2	5
183	42	1	12	3	3	1	1	2	1	2	2	8	0	0	4
184	36	0	10	0	2	1	0	0	0	0	1		3	0	1
185	24	0	12		2	1	0	2	0	0	0	10	0	1	4
186	33	0	12		2	1	0	3	1	2	2	8	3	1	2
187	37	0	13		3	1	0	3	1	5	5	11	4	2	4
188	57	1	9	5	3	1	1	3	1	4	1	8	5	2	4
189	38	0	13		1	1	1	2	1	6	3	8	1	2	5
190	39	0	12	4	1	4	0	3	1	0	0	12	1	1	1
191	29	0	12		2	1	0	3	1	5	1	14	3	2	5
192	53	0	10		3	1	1	0	1	0	0	8	0	1	4
193	58	0	11	2	0	1	0	2	1	7	0	8	0	2	5
194	50	1	12	4	4	1	0	3	1	1	1	8	1	2	4
195	41	0	11	5		1	3	2	1	2	1	8	0	1	4
196	45	0	8		4	1	1	2	0	1	2	4	1	2	4
197	38	1	12	2	2	1	1	2	1	4	2	9	0	1	4

Community III

CASE	AGE	SEX	EDUC	OCUP	INCO	MARTL	RELIG	POLIT	VOTE	ACTIV	CHLDN	FAED	FOCUP	NBR	VISIT
198	48	0	17	4	3	1	0	3	1	6	3	13	4	0	0
199	30	1	12		1	1	0	3	1	2	0	8	0	1	4
200	51	1	11	3	2	1	1	0	1	6	2	3	3	2	5
201	26	0	16		2	1	0	3	1	8	0	10	5	1	4
202	32	1	14	3		1	1	3	1	0	0	12	3	1	3
203	41	1	14	5	4	1	1	2	1	11	5	14	4	1	5
204	40	1	16	5	4	1	2	0	1	2	1	12	5	0	4
205	62	1	7	0	0	0	0	3	1	3	0	0	1	0	4
206	35	0	16	5	3	1	0	3	1	5	2	12	4	1	5
207	39	1	14	4	2	1	1	3	1	4	3	12	2	0	1
208	72	1	10	4	4	1	1	3	1	3	0	14	5	1	5
209	69	1	4	3	3	1	0	3	1	2	0	4	1	1	5
210	47	0	12	4	7	0	0	3	1	2	0	8	5	2	2
211	45	1	12	3	4	1	1	3	1	3	0	8	2	1	5
212	43	0	16	5	4	1	0	2	1	7	5	16	5	0	4
213	56	0	8		3	1	0	3	0	1	0	6	2	2	0
214	35	1	16	5	4	0	3	0	0	0	0	4	2	0	2
215	77	1	8	0	0	3	1	0	1	3	0	7	1	2	5
216	71	0	12	2	0	0	3	0	0	1	0	8	2	1	1
217	47	1	13	4	2	1	0	2	1	7	2	16	4	1	4
218	39	1	12	5	2	1	0	3	1	4	1	6	3	1	4
219	59	0	12		3	1	0	2	1	6	0	17	5	2	4
220	66	1	9	2	1	1	0	3	1	2	0	14	3	1	5
221	25	1	12		2	1	1	2	1	2	0	8	5	0	4
222	40	1	12	5	4	1	1	3	1	4	0	8	4	1	4

223	72	0	9		2	3	0	3	1	0	2		1	2	5
224	44	1	16	5	3	1	0	3	1	2	2	8	4	0	4
225	54	1	12		3	1	0	3	1	1	0	8	5	1	4
226	54	0	15	5	2	3	0	3	1	4	2	16	3	1	1
227	62	0	14		4	1	0	3	1	5	0	7	1	1	2
228	48	1	16	5	4	1	0	3	1	7	2	14	4	1	4
229	39	1	17	5	3	1	1	2	1	2	2	14	4	2	4
230	86	1	10		2	3	0	2	1	4	0	1	1	1	0
231	43	0	17	5	4	1	0	3	1	3	2	12	4	1	4
232	57	0	15		4	1	0	3	1	0	0	14	4	0	4
233	69	1	12	3	2	1	0	3	1	1	0		3	1	5
234	42	0	14	5	3	1	0	0	0	2	0	9	5	0	0
235	33	1	12	2	2	1	1	0	0	4	1	9	3	1	4
236	45	0		5	5	1	0	3	1	0	1		3	0	4
237	52	1	8	3	2	1	0	3	1	1	1	8	4	1	4
238	28	0	12		2	1	1	2	1	2	0	16	5	2	4
239	50	0	14	4	2	1	0	3	1	0	0	16	5	1	1
240	65	0	8		0	1	1	3	1	2	0	8	3	2	5
241	58	0	15	5	2	1	1	3	1	5	0	0	2	1	4
242	28	1	15	3	2	1	0	2	1	4	1	11	2	1	4
243	39	1	10	3	3	1	1	2	1	0	2	5	2	1	4
244	42	0	12		3	1	1	2	1	4	3	9	3	1	5
235	31	1	16	4	3	1	1	3	1	2	0	16	5	1	4
246	62	0	12		5	1	1	3	1	5	0	8	5	1	1
247	56	1	12	5	4	1	1	0	1	9	0	14	5	1	2
248	31	0	16		4	1	0	3	1	4	1	10	3	1	4
249	57	1	14	5	6	1	1	3	1	11	3	8		1	4
250	21	1	17	0	5	0	0	3	1	2	1	17	5	1	2
251	46	1	17	4	4	1	0	3	1	14	1	12	5	1	4
252	38	0	12		4	1	0	3	0	0	3	7	3	1	2

Community III

CASE	AGE	SEX	EDUC	OCUP	INCO	MARTL	RELIG	POLIT	VOTE	ACTIV	CHLDN	FAED	FOCUP	NBR	VISIT
253	30	1	14	4	3	1	0	3	1	9	0	16	5	1	3
254	31	1	17	5	3	1	0	3	1	5	0	12	2	0	3
255	65	0	15		1	1	0	3	1	4	0	6	1	1	1
256	47	1	12	3	3	1	0	2	1	4	2	8	2	1	1
257	31	0	16		4	1	1	3	1	5	5	12	3	1	4
258	25	0	16		3	1	1	2	1	0	0	12	5	1	4
259	20	0	16	2	3	0	1	2	0	5	0	10	3	0	0
260	43	1	10	2	3	1	1	3	1	5	7	8	1	2	4
261	32	0	12		2	1	1	3	1	3	3	7	1	2	5
262	37	1	12	3	4	1	1	2	1	6	5		1	1	4
263	35	0	12	4	2	1	0	3	1	0	3	12	3	1	0
264	49	1	10	2	1	1	0	3	1	0	0	6	2	1	0
265	55	1	6	3	2	1	0	3	0	1	0		1	1	3
266	30	1	16	5	2	1	0	3	1	5	0	8	3	2	4
267	39	1	9	3	2	1	1	3	1	5	1	6	1	1	4
268	60	0	7	0	1	1	1	3	0	0	0		2	2	0
269	44	1	8	3	2	1	1	2	1	3	2	4	1	2	2
270	60	0	12	5	4	1	1	0	1	3	0	11		2	4
271	42	1	16	5	2	1	1	2	1	0	0	4	0	0	2
272	27	1	15	5	4	1	2	0	1	7	0	11	5	1	4
273	33	0	15	5	3	1	1	2	1	5	0	6	0	1	4
274	29	0	12		4	1	2	0	1	2	0	12	4	1	5
275	41	0	12		4	1	1	3	1	2	0	6	5	1	2
276	35	0	17	5	3	0	1	2	1	7	0	6	3	0	0
277	66	0	13		2	3	1	3	1	5	0	6	5	1	3

278	40	1	12		6	1	0	3	1	4	3	5	2	1	3
279	63	1	16		4	1	0	3	1	5	0	9	3	1	4
280	43	0	16	5	6	1	0	3	1	3	3	17	5	2	5
281	38	0	16		4	1	0	3	1	4	3	15	5	0	0
282	24	0	12	4	4	1	0	0	0	1	0	16	5	1	5
283	40	0	12	4	3	1	2	2	1	1	2		2	0	5
284	43	0	14		4	1	1	3	1	5	2	10	5	1	5
285	32	1	16	5	3	1	2	3	1	10	0	12	2	1	4
286	32	1	14	5	2	1	0	3	1	8	3	6	4	2	5
287	36	0	12		3	1	2	2	1	0	0	3	2	1	3
288	36	0	10		1	1	0	0	1	1	4	12	3	1	0
289	45	0	12		4	1	1	2	1	2	0	3	3	2	4
290	52	1	10	2	3	1	0	2	0	3	1		3	1	1
291	53	0	12		4	1	1	3	1	3	0	8	0	0	4
292	32	1	14	5	3	1	0	0	0	1	0	4	2	1	4
293	58	1	8	5	2	1	0	2	1	4	0	5	1	1	5
294	51	1	17	5	4	1	0	2	1	5	1	12	3	1	3

Problems and Exercises

Throughout this book it is stressed that statistics is a special language. And, in order to be useful, all languages require practice. Statistics is no exception to this rule; anyone who wants to use the language of statistics must practice thinking and talking in that language until its concepts become part of his regular vocabulary.

These problems and exercises are designed to help the student get the practice he needs to be able to think and talk in statistical terms. The problems are arranged by chapters, and the student is encouraged to complete all the problems for one chapter before proceeding to the next.

Answers are provided for odd-numbered exercises. It is often useful to check your work and correct your errors before moving on to the next problem.

Here, as in the rest of the book, the emphasis is on understanding concepts. Understanding, however, is often enhanced through solving numerical problems—and the more realistic the problems, the deeper the understanding. Appendix C, therefore, includes a set of observations taken from random samples of actual communities in a real study. Problems that require computation will refer to Appendix C. By means of this reference to actual data it is hoped that the student will develop a realistic view of the use of statistical procedures in the solution of problems of data analysis.

Section A

1. What is the aim of the statistical method?
2. Why should a student in social or behavioral science study statistics?

Chapter 1

1. What are the minimal requirements for scaling a variable?
2. What additional requirement is necessary to establish a nominal scale?
3. What additional requirement is necessary to establish an ordinal scale?
4. What additional requirement is necessary to establish an interval scale?

5. Here are five variables. Indicate the usual kind of scale that is applied to each.
   (*a*) Time.
   (*b*) Species.
   (*c*) Social class.
   (*d*) Birth order.
   (*e*) Social security number.
6. Refer to the data in Appendix C. For each of the variables indicate whether it is scaled as nominal, ordinal, or interval.
7. Each of these variables is coded numerically. For which variables may we legitimately add up the numerical codes of different cases?
8. For which variables may we compare two cases and decide whether they are equal or not equal to each other?

Chapter 2

1. Explain each of the following in your own words:
   (*a*) Average.
   (*b*) Index of variation.
   (*c*) Degree of association.
2. Distinguish between two types of inference.
3. Explain what is meant when it is said that two variables are "highly associated."
4. An anthropologist reports that in a society he studied no woman is taller than the shortest man. Are sex and age for these people unassociated, moderately associated, or strongly associated?
5. "Men usually weigh more than 150 pounds." Does this sentence convey a measure of association? Explain.
6. An investigator wants to know if a coin he has is "fair." He tossed it 100 times and got 80 heads. Is this problem one which requires an average, a measure of association, or a test of significance?
7. Sometimes people say, "Women are more emotional than men." Is this a problem requiring an average, a measure of association, or a test of significance?
8. Distinguish between a sample and a population.
9. Define the population or populations described in Appendix C.
10. Pick one pair of variables in Appendix C which you would expect to be highly associated. Explain the reasons for your choice.

Chapter 3

1. Examine every "word" in the following and see if you can classify it as an operator, variable, constant, connective, or statistic.
   (*a*) $1 + 2 = 3$.
   (*b*) $X + Y = t$.
   (*c*) $X > Y$.

2. In what way is Appendix A similar to an ordinary dictionary?
3. Write the symbol which shows the average for some unspecified group.
4. By means of a concrete illustration of your own show that $\sum X^2 \neq (\sum X)^2$.
5. Can you find one instance where that statement does not hold?
6. In ordinary words, what does this equation say? $a + b = b + a$.
7. In ordinary words, what does this equation say? $(a)(-b) = (-a)(b)$.
8. Round the following numbers to two places:

   (*a*) 4.5950. (*c*) 4.5944.
   (*b*) 4.5850. (*d*) 4.5856.

9. If the ratio of males to females is 10/1, what percentage of the population is male? Show your work.
10. These data are from Appendix C:

    Males = 141 Protestant = 170
    Females = 153 Nonprotestant = 124

    Compute the ratio of males to females and the proportion of Protestants.

Section B

1. What is the difference between an *array* and a *frequency distribution*?
2. Construct a frequency distribution for the variable age in Community II in Appendix C.
3. Draw a frequency polygon for this variable.
4. Construct a frequency distribution for marital status for Community II.
5. Draw a histogram for this variable.

Chapter 4

1. In what way is the mode an "average"?
2. Under what circumstances might the mode take a numerical value?
3. Can v ever take as its value the name of a category?
4. If, for a given set of observations, there are 50 males and 50 females, then what is the mode for this distribution?
5. In a ten class nominal scale, what is the largest value v could take?
6. Calculate the mode for the variable defined in Exercise 2, Section B.
7. Calculate the variation ratio for this variable.
8. In which community in Appendix C is the mode the best summary for the distribution of sex?

Chapter 5

1. What is the relation between the 5th decile and the median?
2. The median is to the mode as d is to

   (*a*) The proportion.
   (*b*) The percentage.
   (*c*) The ratio.
   (*d*) The variation ratio.

3. Define the following:
   (*a*) The first quartile.
   (*b*) The third quintile.
   (*c*) The top centile.
   (*d*) The top percentile.
   (*e*) The first quantile.
4. For the data on education in Community II in Appendix C, calculate the median.
5. Calculate d for this distribution.
6. On the average do these people have about the same amount of education as their fathers? Explain.
7. In Community II is the median a better summary of respondent's education or father's education?
8. Choose three variables from Appendix C for which the median should not be used as an average.

Chapter 6

1. Suppose you were to calculate the mean, the median, and the mode for a distribution of interval scale scores. What information would each reveal?
2. (*a*) Might the three statistics in Problem 1 all yield the same values?
   (*b*) Name one set of circumstances in which such a result would occur.
   (*c*) Might they all differ?
   (*d*) Name a set of circumstances in which this would occur.
   (*e*) Construct an hypothetical distribution ($N = 10$) in which $\bar{X} \neq$ median $\neq$ mode.
3. If two distributions have identical standard deviations, may we assume that they are quite similar in other respects? Explain.
4. For a distribution of age in years, what is the unit of measurement of each of the following:
   (*a*) $\bar{X}$. (*b*) s. (*c*) z.
5. Take the first 25 individuals from the sample of Community I in Appendix C. Calculate their mean age.
6. What is the value of s for age for these 25 people?
7. The mean age for all persons in all three samples is 44 and $s = 14$. Assume that this distribution is normal.
   (*a*) What proportion of these people are older than 72?
   (*b*) $N = 294$; how many are younger than 58?
   (*c*) What is the age above which 50% fall?
   (*d*) What is the age below which the youngest 47 persons fall?
8. Given the information in Problem 7, what is the median for this distribution?
9. What is the mode?

Section C

1. Check an introductory text in sociology, psychology, political science, or anthropology, and copy three illustrative statements which imply the need for a coefficient of association.
2. State each of these illustrations in at least four different forms (refer to association, guessing, differences, relatedness, and the like).

Chapter 7

1. Construct a table such that $\lambda = 1$.
2. Suppose Table 7.1 had yielded $\lambda = 1$. What would this mean?
3. Can you construct a table whose λ value is such that it implies that knowledge of the second variable actually increases our original error?
4. For Community I in Appendix C, are men more active in politics than women? What is the association (λ) between sex and voting in the last presidential election for these people?
5. Do the same for Community II.
6. (*a*) On the basis of intuition would you expect a strong association between religion and political party affiliation? Using the data table, compute λ for these variables in Community III.
   (*b*) Was your intuition sound?

Chapter 8

1. If $G = -1$, does this indicate a small degree of association? Explain.
2. Given the following table of frequencies:

	1	2	3
1	10	0	0
2	0	10	0
3	0	0	10

   (*a*) What is the value of G?
   (*b*) What is the value of λ for this table?
   (*c*) Now let us forget the order of the columns; let us reverse columns 2 and 3. Now what is the value of λ?
   (*d*) What is G?
   (*e*) Explain what happened.
3. Consider Table 8.7. Would you like to live in a society where this G is 0? Is -1? Is 1? Explain.
4. Let us see what one American suburb looks like in this connection. Refer to the data for Community I. Using only the male cases, record their occupation and their father's occupation. In this manner, you can replicate Table 8.7. Compute G. What conclusions can you draw?

5. Take the following five cases from Community I: 9, 16, 45, 86, 104. Calculate the relationship between occupation and income. What do you make of this?
6. Now calculate the relationship between occupation and income for all cases in Community I. Were you right in your answer to Question 5?

Chapter 9

1. The mean is the "best" guess for any interval scale. Why?
2. Examine these distributions:

X:	0	1	2	3	4	5
Y:	0	2	1	4	3	5

   (*a*) By simple inspection, does it appear that the points, X and Y, will fall on a straight line? Explain.
   (*b*) Make a free-hand diagram to verify your answer to Problem 2*a*.
3. Pearson's r describes the degree of linear association between two interval scales. Explain "linear association" using the concepts ΔX and ΔY.
4. (*a*) What is the "line of regression?"
   (*b*) In what way is it similar to a mean?
5. In Table 9.11 what do these symbols stand for:
   (*a*) X; (*b*) Y; (*c*) Y'; (*d*) $Y - Y'$; (*e*) Y^2; (*f*) $s_{y'}^2$?
6. True–False:
   (*a*) If $s_y^2 = s_{y'}^2$ then $r^2 = 1$.
   (*b*) If $s_{y'}^2 = 0$, then $r = 1$.
   (*c*) $r_{xy} = r_{yx}$.
   (*d*) If b is minus, r is minus.
   (*e*) $s^2_{y'} > s_y^2$.
7. Using the data in Appendix C, compute the correlation coefficient between respondent's education and respondent's father's education in Community III. (Arrange your work as in Table 9.14.) Interpret your finding.
8. For Community II in Appendix C, take the following cases: 118, 123, 128, 133, 138, 143, 148, 153, 158, 163. Calculate a, b, $s_{y'}^2$ and r between education (X) and father's education (Y). Compare your results with those you got on Problem 6, assignment 5; what new statements can you make?
9. For all cases in this community on which both education and father's education is known, we obtain the following summary data:

$$\begin{aligned} \sum X \text{ (education)} &= 731 \\ \sum Y \text{ (father's education)} &= 578 \\ \sum X^2 &= 8{,}811 \\ \sum Y^2 &= 6{,}106 \\ \sum XY &= 6{,}935 \\ N &= 63 \end{aligned}$$

   Compute r and compare your results with those above.

10. For Community I, the data on education and father's education yield the following summary data:

$$\begin{aligned} \sum X &= 1{,}187 \\ \sum Y &= 834 \\ \sum X^2 &= 15{,}481 \\ \sum Y^2 &= 8{,}640 \\ \sum XY &= 10{,}733 \\ N &= 96 \end{aligned}$$

Compute r and compare with the previous results.

Chapter 10

1. Compare Table 10.1 and Table 10.2. In what critical way do these tables differ?
2. In what way is θ a better measure of association than λ for this problem?
3. (*a*) In what way is θ like λ_a, as opposed to λ, G, and r? (*Hint:* think of r_{xy} and r_{yx}.)
   (*b*) In what way is θ like λ and λ_a as opposed to G and r?
4. Given the following empty table:

	4	3	2	1	Σ
A					10
B					10
Σ	5	5	5	5	20

   and the information that no case in Class *A* is tied for any rank with a case in Class *B*:
   (*a*) Is it possible to calculate λ_a to guess ranks from classes, given this information? Explain.
   (*b*) Is it possible to calculate θ? Explain.
5. Under what conditions will θ take its maximum value?
6. Using the data on Community III in Appendix C, determine the relationship between sex and visiting. Explain your results.
7. In Community II is there any systematic tendency for Democrats to have higher or lower occupational prestige than Republicans?
8. How about Liberals as compared with Republicans?
9. How about all three—Democrats, Liberals, Republicans—all compared at once. Explain your results.

Chapter 11

1. What other statistic determines error in the same way as η?
2. Suppose η in the problem in sex and cigarette purchase had equalled .84. What does .84 mean?

3. The mean cigarette purchase for men was 9, and for women it was 5. Had these means been identical what value would η have taken?
4. $-1 \leqslant r \leqslant 1$. $0 \leqslant \eta \leqslant 1$. Explain.
5. $r_{xy} = r_{yx}$. $\eta_{xy} \neq \eta_{yx}$. Explain.
6. For the data in Appendix C, name five pairs of variables for which η is an appropriate measure of association.
7. In Community II, what is the association between sex and activity?
8. In the problems in Chapter 9 you determined the relation between education and father's education for Community I. Suppose we treat father's education as a three class variable:

   (*a*) 8 years or less.
   (*b*) 9 through 12 years.
   (*c*) 13 years or more.

   In this case we can calculate η between the variables. These data are from Appendix C:

Class according to FAED	N	$\bar{Y}$	$\sum y^2$
$\leqslant$ 8 years	56	11.71	
9–12 years	27	12.63	
$\geqslant$ 13 years	13	14.62	
Total	96	12.36	804.24

   What is η? How does it compare with r? Explain the difference.

Chapter 12

1. What assumptions must be made in order to use M as a measure of association?
2. How does the interpretation of M differ from that of r?
3. How is M like r?
4. (*a*) What range of values can M take?
   (*b*) May M take a negative sign?
5. Assume that the variable neighboring in Community II in Appendix C is normally distributed. Transform this variable into normal deviates.
6. Calculate r between these $\bar{z}$ values and number of school-age children; correct for broad categories.
7. Give a full statement describing your results.
8. Suppose that the tendency to vote is normally distributed and that it is crudely classified by the dichotomy: vote, no vote. Calculate M for voting and activity for individuals in Community II.

Section D

1. Define the following terms:
   (*a*) Population.
   (*b*) Random sample.
   (*c*) Alternative events.
   (*d*) Independent events.
   (*e*) Sampling error.
   (*f*) Null hypothesis.
   (*g*) Sampling distribution.
   (*h*) Region of rejection.
   (*i*) One-tailed test.
   (*j*) Type I error.
   (*k*) Biased estimator.
   (*l*) Efficient estimator.
   (*m*) Confidence coefficient.
   (*n*) Confidence limits.
   (*o*) Confidence interval.
   (*p*) Parameter.
   (*q*) Estimate.
2. If you know the actual value of a parameter, what is the probability of (*a*) Making a Type I error? (*b*) Making a Type II error?
3. Complete the following table for two dice:

Sum of Values Shown on the Faces	Probability
2	$(\frac{1}{6})(\frac{1}{6}) = \frac{1}{36}$
3	$(\frac{1}{6})(\frac{1}{6}) + (\frac{1}{6})(\frac{1}{6}) = \frac{2}{36}$
4	$(\frac{1}{6})(\frac{1}{6}) + (\frac{1}{6})(\frac{1}{6}) + (\frac{1}{6})(\frac{1}{6}) = \frac{3}{36}$
5	
6	
7	
8	
9	
10	
11	
12	

   (*a*) What is this table called?
   (*b*) Under what hypotheses are the probabilities calculated?
   (*c*) What is the probability of rolling either 7 or 11?
   (*d*) If one rolls a 3, then what is the probability of rolling a 7?
   (*e*) What is the probability of rolling three sevens in a row?
   (*f*) Given that you have rolled three sevens in a row, what is the probability of not rolling a 7?

4. For the data in Appendix C, state three research questions that call for: (*a*) estimates, (*b*) tests of significance.

Chapter 13

1. What, specifically, is the hypothesis discussed in this chapter?
2. If we sample from a population, but do not conduct a statistical test of significance, what can we say about our sample value of G?
3. Refer to Table 13.4. Is it *possible* to get $G = 1.0$ with a random sample of 10 from a population where $\mathbf{G} = 0$? Explain.
4. Write a title for Table 13.3.
5. (*a*) Is it possible to calculate a test of significance for a statistic with an unknown sampling distribution?
   (*b*) Would it be reasonable to calculate the exact sampling distribution for G when $\mathbf{G} = 0$ and $N = 1000$? Explain.
   (*c*) How is this problem, in fact, handled?
6. Specify the confidence limits for an observed $G = 0$ with a confidence coefficient of .90 and $N = 4$ (use Table 13.3).
7. In Exercise 5, Chapter 8 you calculated G between occupation and income for five cases in Community I. Can you test the significance of this statistic?
8. In Exercise 6, Chapter 8 you calculated G between occupation and income for the whole of Community I. For this problem $\hat{S} = 434$ and $s_{\hat{s}} = 216$. Let $\alpha = .05$ and do a two-tailed test of significance. Interpret your results.
9. On the same problem, let $\alpha = .01$; now what are your conclusions?

Chapter 14

1. Given the following bivariate distribution:

Person	X	Y	Person	X	Y
A	14	1	H	14	1
B	12	3	I	12	4
C	10	2	J	11	3
D	10	2	K	11	4
E	11	2	L	10	3
F	11	3	M	37	84
G	15	2	N	48	3

If r were calculated for this random sample, would you advise that a test of significance be conducted? Explain.

2. What is meant by the expression, "the standard error" of r?
3. (*a*) Make up two cases on two variables such that $r = 1$.
   (*b*) Make up two cases such that $r = -1$.
   (*c*) Are any other values of r possible when $N = 2$? Why?
4. (*a*) If you want to run a minimum risk of making a Type I error, but do not particularly care about the Type II risk, what would you do?
   (*b*) Suppose Type II errors are to be avoided at all costs, then what?
5. (*a*) Using the variables in Appendix C, state an hypothesis that would require a one-tailed test of r.
   (*b*) State an hypothesis that would lead to a two-tailed test.
6. Assume a normal population and test the significance of each of the r's you computed in the assignment for Chapter 9 at $\alpha = .01$ with a one-tailed test. State each step in the test of significance and interpret your results.
7. Comment on the assumption of normalcy in Problem 6.
8. Assume a normal population and estimate $\mathbf{r}$ between education and father's education in Community II.
9. Do the same for Community I, only in this case establish a confidence interval with a confidence coefficient of .95. Express your interval in terms of z-scores; do not try to convert them to r's.
10. Test the hypothesis that this sample (Community II) came from a population where $\mathbf{r} = .50$. Let $\alpha = .01$.

Chapter 15

1. What is the purpose of the U-test?
2. Is U an alternative to θ? Explain.
3. Write a title for Table 15.4.
4. What is there about Table 15.8 that suggests that behavior of females is different from behavior of males?
5. (*a*) What is the range of variation of U?
   (*b*) Of θ?
6. The cases listed in Appendix C are in random order. This means that you can choose from the beginning of the list in order to obtain a random sample. Take the first ten Democrats in Community II and compare them with the first ten Republicans. Did they come from the same population with respect to occupational prestige? Let $\alpha = .05$ and conduct a two-tailed test.
7. Using the first five men and the first five women in Community III, test the hypothesis that females visit more than males at $\alpha = .05$.

Chapter 16

1. What is the relationship between η and F?
2. When successive random samples are drawn from a normally distributed population,
   (*a*) How many estimates of the population variance may we calculate?
   (*b*) How many of these are independent of each other?
3. What assumptions must be made in order to use the F-test?
4. (*a*) What is the expected value of F under the null hypothesis?
   (*b*) What is the corresponding value of η?
5. Assume that you have random samples of I.Q.'s for each sex.
   (*a*) Construct two frequency polygons that would reflect a large value of F (let the horizontal axis be I.Q. and the vertical axis be frequency; use a dotted line for males and a solid line for females).
   (*b*) Repeat the drawing showing a small value of F.
6. Explain how each of the following results might be obtained:
   (*a*) F significant—η small.
   (*b*) F insignificant—η large.
7. Is the association between sex and activity in Community II significant at $\alpha = .05$?
8. Test the hypothesis that the result you obtained in Problem 8, Chapter 11 reflects a difference in the population in Community I. Describe all steps in your test.

Chapter 17

1. What is measured by M?
2. What is the relationship between M and r?
3. What facts in Table 17.1 would you discover by means of simple inspection that might lead you to conclude that
   (*a*) M is positive?
   (*b*) M is not at or near zero?
4. Suppose that Haer had merely hypothesized that travel and education are related. With $\alpha = .01$ would you reject H_0?
5. Would it be possible to construct a table for the sampling distribution of M like the one for r? Explain.
6. Test the significance at $\alpha = .05$ of the result obtained in problem 12–8.

Chapter 18

1. What does the χ^2 test determine?
2. What is the relationship between χ^2 and λ?
3. Does Yates' correction always reduce the value of χ^2? Explain.

4. (*a*) What is independence?

   (*b*) Have we studied any other tests of independence?

5. How many degrees of freedom are there in each of the following tables?

   (*a*) 2×2.

   (*b*) 10×2.

   (*c*) 10×10.

   (*d*) 100×2.

6. Let $\alpha = .05$ and test the significance of the departure from independence for the data described in Problem 5, Chapter 7.

7. Do the same for Problem 6, Chapter 7.

8. Define any problem where χ^2 would be an appropriate test using the data in Appendix C. State your problem and conduct a test showing all the steps in your work.

Answers to Odd-Numbered Problems

Section A

1. To enhance rigorous thought and precise communication.

Chapter 1

1. Being able to decide whether two observations are equal or unequal.
3. If two observations are unequal, being able to decide which is the larger.
5. (*a*) Interval.
   (*b*) Nominal.
   (*c*) Ordinal.
   (*d*) Ordinal.
   (*e*) Nominal.
7. Age, education, activity, father's education, children.

Chapter 2

1. (*a*) *Average.* Typical observation which represents a distribution.
   (*b*) *Index of variation.* A measure of the tendency of observations to differ from the average.
   (*c*) *Degree of association.* The extent to which it is possible to guess values of one variable given values of a second variable.
3. Knowledge of the values taken by one variable enables one to guess the values of the second variable with greater accuracy than that possible without such knowledge.
5. Only if one can safely assume that women usually weigh less than 150 pounds.
7. A measure of association.
9. The three populations in Appendix C consist of all adults residing in three New York suburbs in 1963.

Chapter 3

ant) + (operator) 2(constant) = (connective) 3(constant).
ble) + (operator) Y(variable) = (connective) t(statistic).
ble) > (connective) Y(variable).

3. $\bar{X}$.
5. Yes, for example, when $X = 0$ or $X = 1$.
7. In multiplication, the product of quantities with unlike signs is always negative.
9. Ratio $= \frac{10}{1}$

$$\text{Proportion} = \frac{10}{10 + 1} = \frac{10}{11} = .909$$

$$\text{Percentage} = (100)(.909) = 90.9\%$$

Section B

1. An *array* is an ordered listing of all observations; a *frequency distribution* is an ordered listing of categories showing the frequencies of observed events in each category.
3.

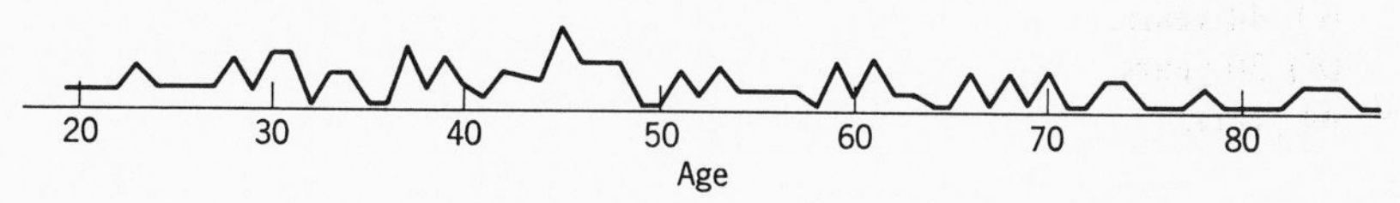

5.

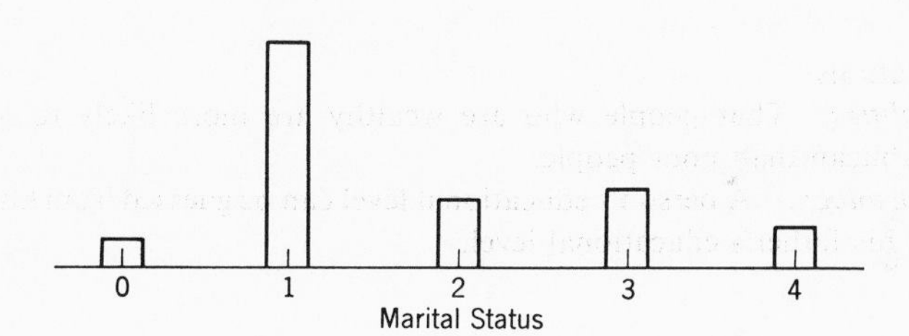

Chapter 4

1. It is the typical observation in the sense that it occurs most often.
3. No.
5. About 89.99%.
7. .16.

Chapter 5

1. d_5 = median.
3. (*a*) That point in a distribution below which 25% of the cases fall.
   (*b*) That point below which 60% of the cases fall.

(*c*) That point below which 99% of the cases fall.
(*d*) Same as (*c*).
(*e*) That point in a distribution below which some specified proportion of cases fall.

5. d = 5.5 years.
7. Respondent's education; for father's education d = 7 years.

Chapter 6

1. They are all averages in that they attempt to describe the typical score in a distribution. They are different in that they define "typical" in three distinct senses: the mode is the common score; the median is the center of the distribution; and the mean is a weighted balance point.
3. No, they could have different means.
5. 45.08.
7. (*a*) .02.
   (*b*) 247 people.
   (*c*) 44 years.
   (*d*) 30 years.
9. 44 years.

Section C

1. Illustrations:
   (*a*) *Politics.* That people who are wealthy are more likely to vote Republican than poor people.
   (*b*) *Sociology.* A person's educational level can be guessed from knowledge of his father's educational level.

Chapter 7

1. 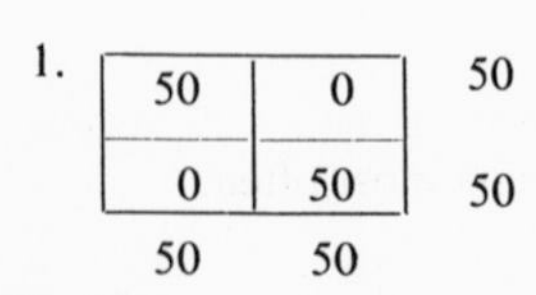

50	0	50
0	50	50
50	50	

3. No.
   $\lambda = 0$.

...dictability is perfect; the minus sign merely means that the ...ased on inversions.

3. If G were -1, your family's advantages become obstacles to your occupational success; if G were $+1$ your family's advantages guarantee your occupational success; and if G were 0 then everyone has the same chance for success whatever their family background.
5. $G = 0$; knowledge of the order of one of these variables does not reduce error in guessing order on the other. It seems unlikely that occupational prestige and income are totally unrelated in Community I. These five cases were deliberately chosen to generate a value of 0.

Chapter 9

1. Since we use the standard deviation as an estimate of error in guessing interval scale scores, and since the $\bar{X}$ guess yields the smallest variance, the $\bar{X}$ is the "best" guess.
3. $\Delta Y/\Delta X$ is constant.
5. (*a*) Number of hours studied.
   (*b*) Number of A's.
   (*c*) Guessed values of Y.
   (*d*) Deviation of observed values of Y from guessed values of Y.
   (*e*) Squared deviations.
7. $r = .42$.
9. $r = .44$.

Chapter 10

1. In Table 10.2 members of class A invariably have Y ranks superior to members of class B; this is not the case in Table 10.1.
3. (*a*) θ and λ_a are asymmetrical, that is, values taken by one variable are guessed from values taken by the other, but the reverse is not implied. But λ, G, and r are all symmetrical, that is, values taken by each variable are guessed on the basis of knowledge of values taken by the other.
   (*b*) θ, λ, and λ_a all involve at least one nominal scale; hence the idea of order of the relationship between the variables is meaningless, and consequently θ, λ, and λ_a vary between 0 and 1. G and r, of course, vary between -1 and $+1$.
5. When every member of each class ranks consistently above (or below) all the members of each of the other classes.
7. $\theta = .06$.
9. $\theta = .16$.

Chapter 11

1. r.
3. Zero.

5. r is a symmetrical measure of association; η predicts only from classes to interval scale scores; hence it is asymmetrical.
7. $\eta = .14$.

Chapter 12

1. That the ordinally scaled variable would be normally distributed if you were able to measure it by means of an interval scale.
3. *M is r* if the assumptions involved in normalizing are true. These assumptions are shown in Exercise 1.
5. $\bar{z}_2 = 1.03$.
   $\bar{z}_1 = -.27$.
   $\bar{z}_0 = -1.51$.
7. Had we been able to measure the attitude toward the neighborhood in an interval scale, and if that attitude is normally distributed, about 6% of the variance in the attitude should be shared with number of school-age children.

Section D

1. (*a*) *Population.* The name of the class of cases to which we wish to generalize.
   (*b*) *Random sample.* A set of observations from a selected population chosen such that every set of that size has an equal probability of being chosen.
   (*c*) *Alternative events.* Events which cannot both occur at the same time.
   (*d*) *Independent events.* Two events are independent if the occurrence of one does not affect the probability of occurrence of the second.
   (*e*) *Sampling error.* The chance variation in the value of some observation from sample to sample.
   (*f*) *Null hypothesis.* The negation of a research hypothesis—usually the hypothesis of no difference or no association.
   (*g*) *Sampling distribution.* The list of possible outcomes with their associated probabilities under some hypothetical state of affairs.
   (*h*) *Region of rejection.* A specified section of the sampling distribution which includes all the outcomes that are so unlikely that we agree to reject the null hypothesis if such outcomes are observed.
   (*i*) *One-tailed test.* A test which is sensitive to departures from the null hypothesis in only one direction.
   (*j*) *Type I error.* The rejection of a true null hypothesis.
   (*k*) *Biased estimator.* A sample value which does not correspond closely to the population value when a large number of samples are averaged.
   (*l*) *Efficient estimator.* A sample value which has a small sampling error.

(*m*) *Confidence coefficient.* A statement of the degree of confidence we wish to have in our whole estimating procedure.
(*n*) *Confidence limits.* A pair of values between which we expect to find the population value.
(*o*) *Confidence interval.* The range of the value between the confidence limits.
(*p*) *Parameter.* A population value.
(*q*) *Estimate.* A sample statistic used to estimate a parameter.

3.

Sum of Values Shown on the Faces	Probability
2	$\frac{1}{36}$
3	$\frac{2}{36}$
4	$\frac{3}{36}$
5	$\frac{4}{36}$
6	$\frac{5}{36}$
7	$\frac{6}{36}$
8	$\frac{5}{36}$
9	$\frac{4}{36}$
10	$\frac{3}{36}$
11	$\frac{2}{36}$
12	$\frac{1}{36}$

(*a*) The sampling distribution for the sum of two dice.
(*b*) Under the assumption that the dice are "fair," and that the outcomes of the two dice are independent of each other.
(*c*) $\frac{8}{36}$.
(*d*) $\frac{6}{36}$.
(*e*) $(\frac{1}{6})^3 = \frac{1}{216}$.
(*f*) $\frac{5}{6}$.

Chapter 13

1. The only hypothesis being examined in this chapter is the null hypothesis that **G** = 0.
3. Yes, it is possible. However, the probability is so small that it rounds to zero in three places.
5. (*a*) No.
   (*b*) No; *N* is too large to permit calculating the sampling distribution with a reasonable amount of effort.
   (*c*) By using the normal distribution.
7. No; previous work with the data suggests that these five cases are not a random sample of anything.

9. *Hypothesis.* There is association between occupation and income.
   Null hypothesis. There is no association between occupation and income.
   Test. We have two ordered variables and $N > 10$; we can use the normal approximation to test the significance of G through z.
   Significance level. Let $\alpha = .01$ for a two-tailed test.
   Sampling distribution. Normal deviates are listed at the bottom of Table E.
   Rejection region. The region of rejection includes all values of G which produce $z \geq 2.576$.
   Decision. $z = 2$. We, therefore, fail to reject H_0.

Chapter 14

1. No. These distributions are both markedly skewed. It is unlikely that either X or Y is sampled from a *normal* population.
3. (*a*) For example,

X	Y
1	1
2	2

   (*b*) For example,

X	Y
1	2
2	1

   (*c*) No. Because two observations are required to fix the line of regression which must pass through both points; consequently there can be no departure from the guessed values and r *must* be $+1$ or -1.
5. (*a*) Reduce α and increase N.
   (*b*) Enlarge α and increase N.
7. Since the tendency to terminate education seems to go by steps (grade school, high school, college), it is unlikely that these variables are really normally distributed.
9. $\hat{\mathbf{r}} = .40$, $\hat{\mathbf{z}} = .42$; at .95 confidence, $\hat{\mathbf{z}}$ falls between .17 and .67.

Chapter 15

1. To test the hypothesis that observed differences among subclass rankings are due to sampling variation from a population where there are no differences.
3. The sampling distribution of U when $N = 5$.
5. (*a*) 0 to $n_1 n_2$.
   (*b*) 0 to 1.
7. Since R for females is less than R for males, we know without computing U that we cannot reject H_0.

Chapter 16

1. F is a test of significance of η; the exact relation is

$$F = \left(\frac{\eta^2}{1 - \eta^2}\right)\left(\frac{N - k}{k - 1}\right)$$

3. Normal distribution and random samples.
5. (*a*)

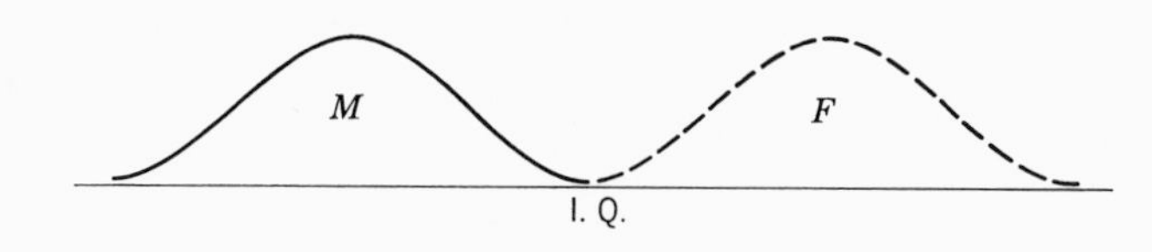

(*b*)

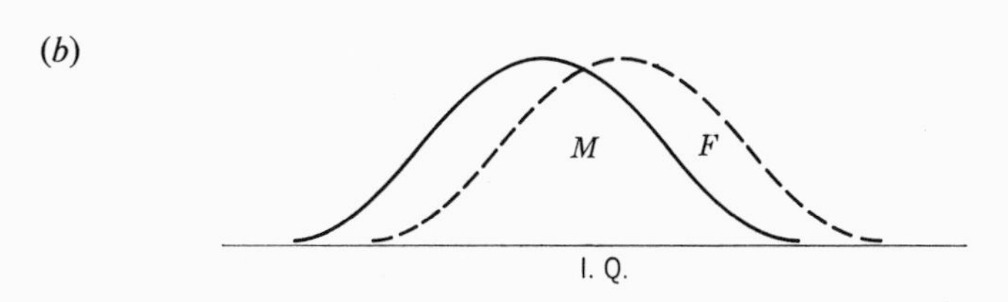

7. An F value of 4.00 is needed to reject H_0 at 1 and 60 degrees of freedom. We have 1 and 78 degrees of freedom and $F = .15$. Therefore we fail to reject H_0.

Chapter 17

1. It is a measure of the Pearson's r we should expect to get if our ordinally scaled variable were measured in an interval scale and if it were normally distributed.
3. (*a*) Increasing travel is found predominantly among those persons with relatively more education.
   (*b*) The two distributions do not have total overlap, that is, their means and ranges seem to be quite different.
5. No, since the size of M is determined not only by the number of degrees of freedom but also by the degree to which it is calculated on a variable that is grouped into broad categories. We should have to have a separate table of M for each possible degree of grouping into broad categories.

Chapter 18

1. It is a test of the hypothesis that the variables under examination are independent in the population from which the sample was drawn.
3. Yes, since it decreases the magnitude of the differences between observed and expected values.
5. (*a*) 1. (*b*) 9. (*c*) 81. (*d*) 99.
7. With $\alpha = .05$ and $df = 2$ we need $\chi^2 \geq 5.99$ to reject H_0. Since χ^2 for this table is .2 we cannot reject H_0.

Index